A
TALE OF A TUB
&c.

 B. Lens delin. J. Sturt sculp.

A

TALE OF A TUB

To which is added

THE BATTLE OF THE BOOKS

and the

MECHANICAL OPERATION OF THE SPIRIT

By *Jonathan Swift*

Together with *The History of Martin*
Wotton's *Observations upon the Tale of a Tub*
Curll's *Complete Key, &c.*

The whole edited with an Introduction and
Notes Historical and Explanatory
By *A. C. Guthkelch* and *D. Nichol Smith*

SECOND EDITION

OXFORD

At the Clarendon Press. MCMLVIII

Oxford University Press, Amen House, London E.C.4

GLASGOW NEW YORK TORONTO MELBOURNE WELLINGTON
BOMBAY CALCUTTA MADRAS KARACHI KUALA LUMPUR
CAPE TOWN IBADAN NAIROBI ACCRA

FIRST EDITION 1920

SECOND EDITION 1958

PRINTED IN GREAT BRITAIN

NOTE TO SECOND EDITION

THIS second edition has been completely reset and the editor has made several substantial alterations to the Introduction, corrected and added to the Notes, and revised the text.

1957

NOTE TO FIRST EDITION

THIS edition has been long in preparation. It was planned and in outline completed by Mr. Guthkelch, who died on June 1, 1916. In the notes which he had written on the text, and in his draft of the introduction, he had embodied the results of many years' study. On his death the editorship was taken over, at the desire of the Delegates of the Clarendon Press, by Mr. Nichol Smith, who has revised and supplemented the introduction and added much new matter to the notes.

Both editors have had the assistance of many friends. As their names cannot now all be given, it is hoped that one general acknowledgement will be taken to cover many and varied obligations. But Captain C. A. Fountaine, R.N., of Narford, must have particular mention. The ready generosity with which he has allowed the original designs for the illustrations to be reproduced has given a unique interest to this edition.

1920

THE CONTENTS

INTRODUCTION

INTRODUCTION

INTRODUCTION

I. PUBLICATION

A Tale of a Tub was published in the spring of 1704, in a volume which contained also *An Account of a Battel between the Antient and Modern Books in St. James's Library* and *A Discourse Concerning the Mechanical Operation of the Spirit*. The volume was anonymous, and no part of it had hitherto been printed.

It is a question how far the author was responsible for the publication of the volume, and for the text as it appeared. From statements in the 'Apology' prefixed to the fifth edition in 1710,[1] in the 'Bookseller to the Reader',[2] and in Swift's letter to Tooke of 29 June 1710[3] we learn that there were three copies of the manuscript of the *Tale*—a 'blotted' or corrected copy which the author had by him, a copy which he had lent to a person 'since dead' and which came to the bookseller's hands in 1698, and a copy of 'some part' which Swift had lent to Thomas Swift, his 'little parson cousin'. The author, we are told, had intended to make another copy,[4] 'with many alterations', but was forestalled by the publication of the copy procured by the bookseller.

The friend to whom the author lent the copy is said to have given it to the bookseller, and to have expunged 'certain Passages where now the Chasms appear under

[1] p. 16.   [2] pp. 28, 29.   [3] p. 349.   [4] p. 16.

the Name of *Desiderata*';[1] and for this 'surreptitious copy' the bookseller is said to have given a good sum of money.[2] In five different places in the 'Apology'[3] the author asserts that his papers were out of his control when the *Tale* was printed. On the other hand there is a passage in the 'Conclusion' of the *Tale*[4] which would suggest that the author dealt directly with the bookseller: 'No Man hath more nicely observed our Climate, than the Bookseller who bought the Copy of this Work. . . . I desired to know, *considering my urgent Necessities*, what he thought might be acceptable this Month.' If we took this literally we should have to hold that the author himself disposed of the copy.[5]

These statements, and other conflicting but not irreconcilable statements about the *Mechanical Operation of the Spirit*, cannot fail to suggest deliberate mystification. On the whole it seems probable that the book was published through the agency of a friend, who may have exercised a certain amount of discretion—probably a very small amount—in seeing it through the press.

It was quite in keeping with Swift's methods on other occasions to provide the printer with a fair copy of the manuscript, and to keep the 'blotted' autograph. When he brought out his *Letter to the October Club* it was a transcript in another hand that he sent to the press, in order that he 'might not be known for author'.[6] A similar course was followed with *Gulliver's Travels*, which

---

[1] p. 21; cf. p. 8.
[2] p. 17.
[3] pp. 4, 8, 10, 12, 16.
[4] pp. 206–7.
[5] The following note appears in Nichols's edition of Swift (1801) vol. ii, p. xxxi: 'it has been asserted that Swift got a sum of money for his first work, The Tale of a Tub; and as a proof of this, it is said, there is still in being an entry made in the books of the first publisher of a certain sum paid for that work. But this entry does not say to whom it was paid.' Nothing else appears to be known of this entry.
[6] *Journal to Stella*, 18 Jan. 1712.

came mysteriously to the publisher from the hands of 'Richard Sympson', and then was altered here and there without Swift's knowledge.

Yet is cannot be proved that the *Tale of a Tub* and the other pieces in the volume did not appear as the author intended. The publisher was John Nutt.[1] Now Benjamin Tooke had published for Swift the third part of Temple's *Miscellanea* in 1701, and it was Tooke with whom Swift corresponded in 1710 about the fifth edition of the *Tale*, which still bore the name of Nutt on the title-page. Similarly Tooke arranged for the publication of Swift's *Miscellanies in Prose and Verse*,[2] which was brought out at the end of February 1711 by John Morphew, Nutt's successor. Swift called Tooke 'my bookseller';[3] and the *Journal to Stella* and the *Letters* show that he helped Swift on occasion in matters of business. He was a man 'for whose honesty', said Swift, 'I will engage'.[4] The publishing and bookselling connexion, the trust and the familiarity that began with Temple's *Miscellanea* continued till Tooke's death; and it was Tooke's successor, Benjamin Motte, who brought out *Gulliver's Travels* in 1726. Why Tooke should not have been Swift's acknowledged publisher is not clear; but that he acted as Swift's literary agent is certain. Was he already his literary agent in 1704? The assistance of a sagacious and trusty friend, himself a publisher, who

---

[1] John Nutt appears to have started publishing in 1698. He had been a printer in the Savoy, and returned to printing about 1708: see Arber's *Term Catalogues*, and Dunton's *Life and Errors*, 1705, p. 298; ed. 1818, p. 220. Nutt was the publisher of Swift's *Contests and Dissensions in Athens and Rome*, 1701.

[2] See p. 350. For the date of the publication of the *Miscellanies* see the advertisement in *The Post Boy* for 24–27 Feb. 1711.

[3] *Journal to Stella*, 16 Jan. 1712.

[4] Ibid. 25 Jan. 1712. Dunton says that 'He's truly Honest, a Man of refin'd Sense . . . and is unblemish'd in his Reputation.' *Life and Errors*, 1705, p. 288; ed. 1818, p. 212.

was given a fair copy of the manuscript and acted in accordance with the author's wishes, while the author himself remained in the background, would provide an explanation of much of the mystery in which the issue of the *Tale* was purposely involved.

II. AUTHORSHIP

There was much speculation about the author of the anonymous *Tale*. Some hinted that Sir William Temple had a hand in it.[1] Sacheverell thought it might be by Smalridge.[2] Atterbury reported that at Oxford it was generally supposed to be by Edmund Smith and John Philips, though he himself suspected Swift.[3] Others claimed it for Lord Somers.[4] Others attributed it, in whole or in part, to Thomas Swift.

Only the claims made for Thomas Swift need to be stated. They were seriously urged, and gave the real author much annoyance; and for this reason the evidence for them is here set down fully:

1. The following passage is printed in John Nichols's *Select Collection of Poems*, 1780, vol. iv, p. *358:

One striking anecdote . . . is so remarkable, that I shall insert it here: it is extracted from a letter of Dr. Charles Davenant,

[1] See the quotation from Wotton's *Observations*, 1705, given below; also p. 295. Deane Swift in his *Essay upon Jonathan Swift*, 1755, p. 60, says that 'every section' of the *Tale* was revised by Temple.

[2] Johnson, *Life of Swift*.

[3] Atterbury's *Correspondence*, 1784, iii. 203, 214, 218. His doubt disposes of the story that the *Battle of the Books* was circulated in manuscript as a reply to Wotton and Bentley. If anyone had seen such a manuscript, it would have been Atterbury. Thomas Hearne's Oxford diary, 22 August 1705, names Swift as the author of the *Tale* (*Collections*, 1885, i. 32).

[4] See p. 22, note 1. Cf. Addison, *The Free-Holder*, No. 39, 4 May 1716: 'this extraordinary Person, out of his natural Aversion to Vain-glory, wrote several Pieces as well as performed several Actions, which he did not assume the Honour of: . . . many Works of this Nature have appeared, which every one has ascribed to him.'

dated Sept. 22, to his son Harry, secretary and chargé d'affairs for
Q. Anne at Francfort. 'I desire you to deliver the inclosed to
Col. Parks (aid-de-camp to the Duke of Marlborough). The
chief subject of it is to bespeak his kindness for *my cousin Swift* to
be his chaplain against he has a regiment. My cousin has gained
immortal honour by *having had the principal hand* in a book
lately published, called *The Tale of a Tub*, which has made as
much noise, and is as full of wit, as any book perhaps that has
come out in these last hundred years.'

Nichols thought that 'my cousin Swift' was Jonathan
Swift; but Davenant evidently meant Thomas Swift,
who was his nephew, the word 'cousin' being used in
the old loose sense of 'relative'.

   2. Wotton refers thus to Thomas Swift in his *Observations upon The Tale of a Tub*:[1]

   The World besides will think it odd, that a Man should in a
Dedication play upon that Great Man [i.e. Somers], to whom he
is more obliged than to any other Man now living; for it was at
Sir *William Temple's* Request, that my Lord *Sommers*, then
Lord-Keeper of the Great-Seal of *England*, gave Mr. Swift[2] a
very good Benefice in one of the most Delicious Parts of one of
the Pleasantest Counties of *England*. It is publicly reported that
he wrote this Book: It is a Story, which you know, Sir, I neither
made, nor spread; for it has been long as public as it can well
be. . . . I acquit him from composing it. The Author, I believe,
is dead, and it is probable that it was writ in the Year 1697,
when it is said to have been written.

Thomas Swift had been presented by Somers to the
Rectory of Puttenham in Surrey. 'The Author' whom
Wotton believes to be dead is Sir William Temple, who
died in January 1699.[3]

---

   [1] See Appendix B, p. 327.
   [2] Wotton thought that Thomas Swift was Jonathan's brother, and distinguishes them as 'Mr. Swift' and 'Dr. Swift' (D.D. Dublin, 1701). In another passage he says that 'a Brother of Dr. *Swift*'s is publicly reported to have been the Editor at least, if not the Author' (p. 316).
   [3] See p. 314.

3. In June 1710, shortly before the fifth edition appeared, Edmund Curll published *A Complete Key to the Tale of a Tub.*[1] The first part of it asserted definitely that Thomas Swift wrote the main portion of the *Tale*, as well as the *Mechanical Operation of the Spirit*, and that Jonathan Swift added the Dedications to Somers and to Posterity, the Preface, and the four Digressions that form Sections iii, v, vii, and ix, as well as the *Battle of the Books*. The main part of the pamphlet, the 'Clavis' proper, annotates more or less fully what is ascribed to Thomas Swift (with the exception of the 'Conclusion'), and leaves unexplained what is ascribed to Jonathan Swift (with the exception of Section ix). The notes are of little value, and some of them are wrong.[2] As a whole the *Complete Key* has two purposes: to claim that a large part of the *Tale* was the work of Thomas Swift, and to explain that part, and that part only. On the first page of a copy preserved in the British Museum,[3] Curll has written the following words: 'Given me by Ralph Noden, Esq; of the Middle Temple. E Curll.' Evidently Noden[4] was either the author of the *Key*, or had acted as intermediary for its publication.

4. In Nichols's edition of Swift's Works, 1808, vol. ii, there is prefixed to the *Tale* an 'Advertisement' consisting of 'Historical Particulars' communicated to

---

[1] Printed in full, pp. 329–48.

[2] e.g. 'exantlation', pp. 67 (47), 333, and 'Lord', pp. 91 (73), 335.

The notes in Sir Walter Scott's edition which are marked 'Bentley' were taken from the *Key*. There is no reason of any kind for attributing any of them to Bentley, but the mistake has been reproduced by many of Swift's editors.

[3] Brit. Mus. C. 28 b 11 (6).

[4] Noden was admitted to the Middle Temple on 7 Mar. 1701. He—or another man of the same uncommon name—had been admitted to the Inner Temple on 13 July 1687. He was the son of Hugh Noden, of London, and matriculated in the University of Oxford as a member of Brasenose College on 20 May 1680, aged 16: see Foster's *Alumni Oxonienses*.

Nichols 'in 1777 by the Rev. Samuel Salter, D.D. then Master of the Charter-house'. One paragraph is as follows:

In March 1766, a copy of the first edition of the 'Tale of a Tub' was sold (for 5s. 6d. only) at an auction of books, by S. Baker:[1] this copy had, it seems, belonged to Sheffield duke of Bucks; with whom Dean Swift does not appear either to have had, or to have wished for, any intimacy. In the first blank leaf the duke (as is believed and there affirmed) had written these words: 'What follows here written, is all by the hand of Mr. Thomas Swift:' or something of this tenour. In the next page Thomas Swift has given the following anecdotes.

[1] This book was in the library of David Mallet and was sold by Samuel Baker on 15 March 1766. The entry in the catalogue is as follows: '828 Tale of a Tub, *with MS. Additions by Tho. Swift, near Relation to the Dean, and shewing what part[s] of the Book were written by the Doctor and himself,* 1704.' A similar but fuller entry appears in the catalogue for the sale of Dr. Charles Chauncy's books, 15 April–1 May 1790: '2408 Swift's Tale of a Tub, *morocco, with large MS. note,* 1704. Note in this Book. *All that is contained here, in writing, was set down by Thomas Swift himself. The above is said to be the Hand-writing of Lady Betty Germain, whose Book this was.* C. Chauncey.' The volume then fetched £3. 3s. (priced catalogue, British Museum Library 7004 cc 10). In a copy of the *Tale* now in the Forster Collection at South Kensington, Forster jotted a note about this sale based on a newspaper paragraph, and ending thus: 'Autograph of Lady Betty Germain at comm[t] of vol. "All that is contained here in writing was set down by Jon. Swift himself." Sold for 3. 3.' Another account appeared in *Notes and Queries* on 4 Aug. 1877: 'Last week at Sotheby and Co.'s a copy of Swift's *Tale of a Tub* was sold, which was said to have belonged to Lady Betty Germain, who has noted in it that it was written by *Jonathan and Thomas Swift,* and that she had got Thomas to write on the margins what each wrote. It confirms the dean's assertion that he did not write the *Tale of a Tub,* but only the *Digressions.* In this copy "Jon. Swift" is written against the preface and the *Digressions,* but Thomas's against each chapter of *The Tale.*' Further information is given in a letter by Sir Harold Williams in *The Times Literary Supplement,* 30 September 1926.

The anecdotes were, as Nichols pointed out, all copied word for word from Curll's *Key*.

This is all the evidence for Thomas Swift's participation in the *Tale*—nothing but rumour and Curll's *Key*.

It is wholly disposed of by the letter[1] which Swift wrote to Benjamin Tooke the publisher on 29 June 1710, when they were making arrangements for the fifth edition of the *Tale*. After referring to the *Key* as 'so perfect a Grub street piece', he proceeds thus:

I cannot but think that little Parson-cousin of mine is at the bottom of this; for, having lent him a copy of some part of, &c. and he shewing it, after I was gone for Ireland, and the thing abroad, he affected to talk suspiciously, as if he had some share in it. If he should happen to be in town, and you light on him, I think you ought to tell him gravely, that, if he be the author, he should set his name to the &c. and railly him a little upon it: and tell him, if he can explain some things, you will, if he pleases, set his name to the next edition. I should be glad to see how far the foolish impudence of a dunce could go.

Swift goes on to say that at the conclusion of the Apology in the new edition he would 'take a little contemptible notice of the thing you sent me'. This he did in the Postscript. It has much in common with the letter. 'The Author', it says, 'asserts that the whole Work is entirely of one Hand, which every Reader of Judgment will easily discover'; and it challenges any person to 'prove his Claim to three Lines in the whole Book'.

The facts are clear. The little parson cousin, who had been resident chaplain to Sir William Temple at Moor Park, had in his possession a copy of part of the *Tale*. He had spoken about it, and had enjoyed sharing its secret. From this the rumour grew that he was the author. Then, after the *Tale* had been out about six years, a 'Grub street piece' definitely claimed some parts of it for him, and purported to give explanations, many

[1] See Appendix D, pp. 349–50.

of which are worthless. We do not know if he contributed to this piece, nor even if it had his approval. That he was incapable of writing any part of the *Tale* is shown by the one publication to which he put his name.[1]

But Swift's authorship of the *Tale* was long questioned. Johnson remained unconvinced. 'I doubt', he said, 'if the *Tale of a Tub* was his: it has so much more thinking, more knowledge, more power, more colour, than any of the works which are indisputably his. If it was his, I shall only say, he was *impar sibi*.' What he had said frequently in conversation he repeated deliberately in his *Life of Swift*: 'His *Tale of a Tub* has little resemblance to his other pieces. It exhibits a vehemence and rapidity of mind, a copiousness of images, and vivacity of diction, such as he afterwards never possessed, or never exerted. It is of a mode so distinct and peculiar, that it must be considered by itself; what is true of that, is not true of any thing else which he has written.' All doubt is now laid to rest. There is Swift's own letter about the *Tale*; there are the recurrent parallelisms in phrase and thought with his acknowledged writings; and there is the overheard muttering of the old man (which goes some way towards justifying Johnson's doubts)—'Good God! what a genius I had when I wrote that book'.[2]

III. THE FIFTH EDITION

The second and third editions of the *Tale* were published in 1704, and the fourth in 1705. They repro-

[1] See *Noah's Dove*, a thanksgiving sermon, 1710; cf. *Correspondence of Swift*, ed. Elrington Ball, vol. i, pp. 387–8.

[2] See Scott, *Works of Swift*, 1824, vol. i, p. 89. Scott got the story from Theophilus Swift. Perhaps another reference is in the *Journal to Stella*, 7 Oct. 1710: 'They may talk of the *you know what*; but, gad, if it had not been for that, I should never have been able to get the access I have had; and if that helps me to succeed, then that *same thing* will be serviceable to the church.'

duced the first edition page for page, but with a few corrections of misprints, and some new misprints. A new edition which was intended to be final was taken in hand some time in 1709. It was to contain a reply to the critics and a substantial series of notes, and was to be adorned with cuts. But the printing was not begun before 1710. The volume appeared late in the same year. No advertisement of its publication has been found in the newspapers.

The Apology. At the end of 1708, probably in October or early in November, Swift is found thinking of an 'Apology for the &c.' It is one of several 'Subjects for a Volume' that he jotted down on the back of a letter addressed to him at Lord Pembroke's in Leicester Fields in October 1708.[1] But he did not proceed with it during his busy winter in London. When it was published it bore the date 'June 3, 1709'. Swift was at Leicester, on what proved to be his final visit to his mother, from 7 May to 14 June,[2] and there the 'Apology' would appear to have been written. We next hear of it a year later, in the letter which he sent to Benjamin Tooke from Dublin on 29 June 1710,[3] when he acknowledged the return of the manuscript. The printing had been put off till Swift sent his final instructions, and now at his request Tooke returned it for revision and completion, after taking a copy in case it should miscarry, and not without showing some impatience at the delay. The short Postscript was probably added about the middle of July 1710 when Swift was in Dublin.

[1] The original appears to be lost. A copy is inserted between pp. 36 and 37 of Lyon's copy of Hawkesworth's *Life of Swift*, now in the Forster Collection at South Kensington: see below, p. xxxv, note 2. The list of subjects is printed in Sheridan's *Life of Swift*, ed. 1784, p. 56, and in Forster's *Life of Swift*, 1875, pp. 257–8; cf. *Correspondence of Swift*, ed. Elrington Ball, 1910, vol. i, p. 111.

[2] *Correspondence*, vol. i, pp. 153 and 158.   [3] p. 349.

His letter to Tooke and Tooke's reply remove all doubt concerning the authorship of the 'Apology'. The manuscript had been returned in order that Swift might 'finish that business'; and there is no reason for supposing that it was not printed exactly as it left his hands. He may have meant to suggest that it was not written by the same person as the *Tale*, for he wrote it in the first person and spoke of 'the Author'. But the writer of the 'Apology' and the author of the *Tale* are identified, perhaps inadvertently, in such a sentence as this: 'The Author cannot conclude this Apology without making this one Reflection . . .'[1] The identification is complete on the title-page, where it is called 'the Author's Apology'.

The heading—'An Apology For the, &c.'—must have been copied from Swift's manuscript. In his letter to Tooke, as in his list of 'Subjects for a Volume', he does not name the *Tale*, but refers to it as '&c.' He was careful to avoid any written statement that could be taken as proof of his authorship, should his correspondence fall into wrong hands; and the same cryptic form of the title was pointlessly left unexpanded by the printers.

The Text. The fifth edition was set up from the fourth. It is stated in the 'Apology' that overtures were made to the bookseller 'for the Author's altering those Passages which he thought might require it'; and the bookseller is represented as unwilling to allow the author to alter the text, on the ground that the alterations 'might spoil the Sale of the Book'.[2] The obvious comment on this is that the author of *A Tale of a Tub* was not the man to care for a bookseller's apprehensions. If he had desired to alter the text, he would have altered it. Further the tenor of the correspondence with Tooke shows that this edition was far from being beyond

[1] p. 18.   [2] p. 18.

Swift's control. Respect for the bookseller's apprehensions must be taken to be only the author's device for explaining why he did not do what he never intended to do. The book was to remain as it was, and the new 'Apology' was to correct the misunderstandings of its purpose. None the less Swift took the opportunity of making a few minor alterations which do not extend beyond a word or a phrase and never affect the sense of a passage.[1] There are other minor alterations which must be attributed to the printer.

The Notes. The volume of 1710 contains two sets of notes—those printed in the margin, and those printed at the foot of the page. The former had appeared in the first four editions; the latter were added in the fifth edition.

Of the notes in the first set, two affect to be by another person than the author of the text—

The Title Page in the Original was so torn, that it was not possible to recover several Titles which the Author here speaks of (p. 71).

Here the whole Scheme of spiritual Mechanism was deduced and explained, with an Appearance of great reading and observation; but it was thought neither safe nor Convenient to Print it (p. 276).

If these notes were not by Swift, he had the opportunity of deleting or altering them in 1710, but he let them remain. They correspond in character with some of the others, such as 'Hiatus in MS.' and 'Hic multa disiderantur', the authorship of which has never been questioned, and was in fact assumed in the notes added in 1710.[2] All these notes must stand or fall together. Some

[1] e.g. pp. 147, l. 6; 165, l. 6; 193, ll. 3, 22; 202, l. 15; 275, l. 18. Most of these alterations have an obvious purpose. The omission on p. 71, l. 5 may also be by the author; it is of a different kind from the omissions on p. 84, l. 10, and p. 89, l. 3.

[2] pp. 62, 170.

of them are nothing less than an integral part of the text, the humour being transferred to the margin from the body of the page.

The second set of notes makes a fairly elaborate comment on the text. The author is said in the 'Apology' never to have seen any of them.[1] Tooke's letter to Swift settles at least the responsibility for them. 'Inclosed', says Tooke,[2] 'I have sent the Key, and think it would be much more proper to add the notes at the bottom of the respective pages they refer to, than printing them at the end by themselves.' This Key is the second set of notes. They must have been written out consecutively and, as Swift apparently intended, might have been printed in a body at the end of the volume as a Key. Tooke had his way and they were printed at the foot of the page as notes. But they were also printed together, along with the 'Apology', in a pamphlet that was issued in the following year and could be bound up with the earlier editions.[3] Some of the notes are unsigned; others bear the name of Wotton.

There is no room for doubt that Swift had a hand in the unsigned notes, if he did not write them all. Their style is often like his, and they say the kind of thing he might have said. There is a striking repetition of one of the explanations, in much the same words, in a private letter that he wrote several years afterwards.[4] And there is the similarity of one of the notes to a passage in the 'Apology'. The passage is as follows:

. . . the Author personates the Style and Manner of other Writers, whom he has a mind to expose. I shall produce one Instance, it is in the *51st Page. Dryden, L'Estrange,* and some others I shall not name, are here levelled at, who having spent their Lives in Faction, and Apostacies, and all manner of Vice, pretended to be Sufferers for Loyalty and Religion. So *Dryden*

[1] p. 20.
[2] p. 350.
[3] See List of Editions, p. xlviii.
[4] See p. 115, note on *Boutade*.

tells us in one of his Prefaces of his Merits and Suffering, thanks God that he *possesses his Soul in Patience.*[1]

The note at the page referred to runs thus:

Here the Author seems to personate *L'Estrange*, *Dryden*, and some others, who after having past their Lives in Vices, Faction and Falshood, have the Impudence to talk of Merit and Innocence and Sufferings.[2]

This note was either written by the author of the 'Apology', or copied from the 'Apology' by some other person. It is inconceivable that Swift would copy into the 'Apology' both the matter and the wording of another man's note on his book; it is very unlikely that any one but Swift, Tooke, and the printer saw the 'Apology' before it was published. We may conclude that the note was written by Swift.

The unsigned notes gain greatly in interest if we consider them—as it appears we must, despite the disclaimer in the 'Apology'—to be a commentary which Swift had at least sanctioned.[3] They have different purposes. In one place there is a rebuke to the author;[4] in another he is corrected in a matter of fact;[5] in another his judgement is not approved.[6] Sometimes they explain why there are chasms in the manuscript;[7] on two occasions they deal with the date at which a passage was written.[8] Usually they profess to explain the author's meaning; they provide some information about books referred to in the text; and for the ease of the reader Latin quotations are given in the English of a standard version, such as Creech's *Lucretius* and Dryden's *Virgil.*[9] But the commentator sometimes says with roguish

[1] p. 7.
[2] p. 70.
[3] Swift approved of Pope's similar device for *The Dunciad*. See his letter of 16 July 1728

(*Correspondence*, vol. iv, pp. 36, 38).   [4] p. 42.   [5] p. 67.
[6] p. 250.   [7] pp. 62, 170.
[8] pp. 86, 208.
[9] pp. 55, 60, 100.

frankness that he cannot understand the author.[1] Such notes are quite in Swift's manner. He enjoyed the difficulty of his book. It was not only his little parson cousin whom he defied to 'explain some things'. So far as they go the notes often give valuable help. But there are still many things to be explained; and this is as Swift intended.

The notes signed 'W. Wotton' are a humorous revenge on the *Tale's* chief critic. In 1705 William Wotton brought out a third edition of his *Reflections upon Ancient and Modern Learning* and added as an appendix *A Defense of the Reflections . . . With Observations upon The Tale of a Tub*. Swift's 'Apology' is largely an answer to these *Observations*. But in the course of his hostile remarks Wotton explained a large number of difficulties in the allegory. These explanations were inserted, word for word, in the new notes, and thus the critic was turned into the 'learned commentator'.[2]

The Illustrations. The eight illustrations which were first included in the fifth edition are likewise referred to in the letters of Swift to Tooke. 'I dare say', wrote Swift, 'you have neither printed the rest, nor finished the cuts'; to which Tooke replied, 'as to the cuts, Sir Andrew Fountaine has had them from the time they were designed, with an intent of altering them. But he is now gone into Norfolk, and will not return till Michaelmas; so that, I think, they must be laid aside; for, unless they are very well done, it is better they were quite let alone.'[3] During the summer and autumn of 1709 Swift had been in active correspondence with Fountaine.[4] Unfortunately none of their letters at this

---

[1] pp. 84, 159, 179, 191, 192; cf. p. 53.

[2] p. 73, note †.

[3] pp. 349–50. Cf. Nichols, *Literary Anecdotes*, vol. v, p. 253.

[4] See Swift's List of Letters Nov. 1708 to Nov. 1709 in *Correspondence of Swift*, ed. Elrington Ball, vol. i, pp. 384–5, and Forster, *Life of Swift*, p. 269.

time have been preserved. It is no rash assumption that they would have supplemented the little that is known about the illustrations, and might have shown that Swift discussed their subjects, and perhaps some of their details, with one of the great art critics and collectors of the day.

But if the letters are lost the original designs to which Tooke refers were preserved at Narford Hall, the seat of the Fountaine family in Norfolk. They were found in a drawer in 1831, and were then inserted in the very fine large-paper copy of the *Tale* which Sir Andrew Fountaine had received in 1710. By the courtesy of Captain C. A. Fountaine, R.N., they are reproduced in the present edition, and at last serve the purpose for which they were intended, side by side with the inferior illustrations which were derived from them.[1]

The eight engravings published with the *Tale* were produced by Bernard Lens and John Sturt, who at this time kept a drawing-school in St. Paul's Churchyard. Only the frontispiece is signed 'B. Lens delin: J. Sturt sculp.' The absence of any name on the other seven plates and the differences in the workmanship cannot be taken to mean that Lens and Sturt were not responsible for all. The engravings had probably been distributed among their draughtsmen or assistants. In books of this period a signature is often found only on the first of a series of cuts.

The engravings as a whole are disappointing. Most of them are flat journeywork. The details in some are

_____

[1] Captain Fountaine had just returned from service with the Grand Fleet in the North Sea when he gave every facility for the reproduction of these designs.

Photographs of them had been made for John Forster when he was writing his *Life of Swift* (1875, p. 258) and are now in the Forster Collection in the South Kensington Museum (Swift Correspondence, Box 44 E).

The reproductions are on the same scale as the originals.

interesting, such as the 'stage itinerant' inset in the Preaching scene; but in others, as in the frontispiece to the *Battle of the Books*, they are not wholly warranted by the text. Even the signed frontispiece to the *Tale* follows a traditional design in the build of the ship, and a conventional dolphin does service as a whale.

The original designs are likewise eight in number, but only five correspond in subject to the engravings. Three of them represent the father on his death-bed giving the will to his sons (p. 73), Peter on his throne blowing off a man's hat (p. 115), and the three brothers at table, Peter with a large goblet of wine in his right hand, and Martin and Jack on either side with crusts on their plates (p. 119). There are no designs for the ship and the whale, the Bedlam scene, or the Lord Mayor on his great horse.

In the five cases where the subject corresponds, the engravings are ultimately derived from the designs; the idea has been taken, but the treatment and details differ. Even in the picture of Martin and Jack 'reforming their vestures into the primitive state' the relationship is clear, though the unfortunate change in the background may disguise it. Were the designs altered by the original artist? Or were the engravers solely responsible for the changes? What is certain is that the designs are markedly superior to the cuts in life and grip and freedom of treatment.

Who drew the designs is not known. The lost correspondence of Swift and Fountaine might have told us. They cannot be ascribed to Bernard Lens; all the specimens of his work in the British Museum are in a harder and more conventional style. There is a tradition that they were by Sir Andrew Fountaine himself. 'In 1709 his judgment and fancy', says Nichols in his *Literary Anecdotes*,[1] 'were exerted in embellishing "The Tale of

[1] Vol. v, p. 253.

a Tub" with designs almost equal to the excellent satire they illustrate', and this statement is repeated in Chalmers's *Biographical Dictionary*. But it may have been based on the sentence about Fountaine in Tooke's letter, which was published in 1765. The sentence is open to different interpretations. It may mean that Fountaine himself made the designs and was not satisfied with them, or had to introduce more detail for the benefit of the engraver; or it may mean that they had been submitted to him as critic and improver. The Fountaine family does not possess any drawings that are attributed to him, and nothing has been discovered to show that he was ever a practising draughtsman. If he drew these illustrations for the *Tale* he was more than a great collector and virtuoso; he was an artist of real talent.

IV. THE TITLE

The phrase 'a tale of a tub' is found frequently in the literature of the sixteenth and seventeenth centuries. Sir Thomas More's use of it in his *Confutacyon of Tyndale* (1532) shows it to have been then a common expression.[1] Cotgrave gives it several times in his Dictionary as synonymous with 'a flimflam', 'idle discourse', 'a tale of a roasted horse'.[2] It has this sense as the title of Ben Jonson's comedy. It was used in the title of a 'book' entered in the Stationers' Registers on 16 January 1638, but otherwise unknown—*A Tale of a Tubb or a Gallamaufrey of Merriment*. A broadsheet issued at the time of the Meal-tub Plot was headed *A Tale of The Tubbs or Romes Master Peice Defeated*.[3]

In adopting the words for his title Swift gave them an additional meaning. 'Sea-men', he explains, 'have

---

[1] 'consyder the placys and his wordes to gyther, and ye shall fynde all hys processe therin a fayre tale of a tubbe' (ed. 1532, p. xxix; ed. 1557, p. 371, col. 2).

[2] s.vv. 'cicogne', 'fariboles', 'riotte'.

[3] Dated 11 Nov. 1679.

a Custom when they meet a *Whale*, to fling him out an empty *Tub*, by way of Amusement, to divert him from laying violent Hands upon the Ship.'[1] He writes a tale of a tub in order that the wits of his age may be diverted from sporting with the commonwealth or ship of state.

Many references to this custom are to be found in sixteenth and seventeenth century literature. In Sir James Mackintosh's *Life of More*[2] it was pointed out, from information supplied by Douce, that the custom is both illustrated and described in Sebastian Münster's *Cosmography* (1544). This work contains a plate entitled, in the Latin version, 'Monstra marina & terrestria, quæ passim in partibus aquilonis inueniuntur', in the top left-hand corner of which sailors are represented throwing out barrels to a whale that is getting too near the ship; and the letterpress gives this explanation— 'Cete grandia ad instar montium prope Islandiam aliquando conspiciuntur, quæ naues euertunt nisi sono tubarum absterreantur, aut missis in mare rotundis & uacuis uasis, quorum lusu delectantur, ludificentur.'[3] The identical plate and similar explanations are found in the German, French, and Italian versions. What is probably the earliest reference to the custom in English occurs in the little volume of extracts published in London in 1572: *A Briefe Collection and compendious extract of straunge and memorable thinges, gathered oute of the Cosmographye of Sebastian Munster.*[4]

At the same time as the custom was being made

---

[1] p. 40.

[2] 1831, p. 107.

[3] Ed. 1554, pp. 852 and 850.

[4] Ed. 1572, fol. 24 v, section 'Of Whales': 'There be great Whales as big as hylles almost nighe vnto Iselande which are sometimes openly seene and those will drowne and ouerthrowe shyps, except they be made a fearde with the sound of trompets, and drums, or except some round & empty vessels be caste vnto them, wherwith they may play and sporte theym, because they are delited in playing with such thinges.'

known throughout Europe by the different versions of
Münster's *Cosmography* it was described also by Olaus
Magnus in his *Historia de Gentibus Septentrionalibus*
(1555); 'Verum malignitati eius remedio occurritur
opportuno, tuba videlicet militari . . . ob asperum
acutumque sonum, quem ferre haud potest: & magnis,
ac immanibus vasis, seu doliis eiectis, cursum beluæ
impedientibus, siue pro lusu ei oppositis'.[1] The custom
was soon well enough known to be given a literary
application in the *Emblems* of Camerarius. In the
*Symbolorum et Emblematum ex Aquatilibus et Reptilibus
Desumptorum Centuria Quarta* (1604) the second plate
represents sailors casting out their cargo to save themselves from an enormous whale; and underneath it are
these lines:

> Vt te ipsum & navim serves, comitesque pericli,
> In pontum cunctas abjice divitias.

How well this method of dealing with whales was
known to English readers in the seventeenth century is
proved by a casual allusion to it in *The Rehearsal Transpros'd*. 'I only threw it out', says Marvell, 'like an empty
Cask to amuze him, knowing that I had a *Whale* to deal
with, and least he should overset me.'[2] Further proof is
provided by Francis Osborne in his *Advice to a Son*: 'in
imitation of Sea-men', he says, 'I may perhaps now
cast out some empty stuffe, to find play for the Whale-
mouth'd gapers after Levity'.[3]

In calling his work 'a tale of a tub' Swift thought
quite as much of the proverbial phrase as of the sea-
men's custom, of which nothing more is heard after the
beginning of the Preface.

---

[1] Lib. xxi, cap. vii, p. 736.
[2] *The Rehearsal Transpros'd:
The Second Part*, 1673, p. 115.
[3] *Advice to a Son*, fourth edition, 1656, 'To the Reader'.

V. THE ALLEGORY[1]

The allegory of the *Tale*—the dispute of the three brothers, Peter, Martin, and Jack—has often been said to have been borrowed. It had certainly been anticipated in part; but that it was consciously copied is questionable. The main sources which have been suggested, and the evidence for Swift's use of them, must be stated.

1. John Sharp's *Sermons*

The suggestion that Swift borrowed the allegory from one of John Sharp's sermons seems to have been made first in a letter signed 'Indagator' which appeared in *The Protestant Advocate* for May 1814,[2] and was reprinted in *The Gentleman's Magazine* for July 1814. The suggestion was repeated in 1893 by Churton Collins, with considerable amplification.[3]

Sharp, afterwards Archbishop of York, was Rector of St. Giles's in the Fields, London, and the sermon in question was delivered in his parish church on 9 May 1686.[4] It was one of a series preached at an anxious time of controversy on the English and Roman Churches. But it is not known to have been printed till 1735,[5] when it was given this heading:

Sermon VI. A discussion of the question which the Roman Catholics much insist upon with the Protestants, *viz.* In which of the different communions in Christendom, the only true church of Christ is to be found?

With a refutation of a certain Popish argument handed about in MS. in 1686.

Towards the end of the Sermon,[6] Sharp quotes the

---

[1] This section and the next are based in part on two articles in the *Modern Language Review* for July and October 1913.

[2] pp. 356–60. The letter is dated 'London, March 24, 1814.'

[3] *Jonathan Swift*, 1893, p. 47.

[4] *Life of John Sharp*, by Thomas Sharp and Thomas Newcome, 1825, vol. i, pp. 70 ff.

[5] Ibid., p. 71; and *The Works of John Sharp*, third ed. 1754, vol. vii, 'To the Reader', pp. vii, viii.

[6] Ed. 1754, p. 106.

argument in 'a little manuscript paper' that had come to his hands, and answers it thus:

The argument is, That if we cannot shew a visible church distinct from the Roman, that hath in all times, from the beginning, oppos'd the doctrines and practices of the present church of Rome, then it will undeniably follow, that the present church of Rome is the only visible church.

Why now, methinks, this is just such an argument as this:

A father bequeaths a large estate among his children, and their children after them. They do for some generations quietly and peaceably enjoy their several shares, without disturbance from each other. At last, one branch of this family (and not of the eldest house neither) starts up, and being of greater power than the rest, and having got some of the same family to join with him, very impudently challengeth the whole estate to himself, and those that adhere to him; and would dispossess all the rest of the descendants, accounting them no better than bastards, though they be far more in number than his own party, and have a far greater share in the inheritance. Upon this they contest their own right against him, alledging their father's will and testament, and their long possession, and that they are lawfully descended from their first common ancestor.

But this gentleman, who would lord it over his brethren, offers this irrefragable argument for the justice of his claim. If, says he, you deny me and my adherents to be the sole proprietors of this estate, then it lies upon you to shew, That ever since the death of our progenitor, who left us this estate, there hath appeared some of the family who have always opposed my claim to this estate. But *that* you cannot shew; and therefore I have an undoubted title to the whole estate: I am lord of the whole inheritance.

I do appeal to any man living, whether this plea would pass in any court of judicature; nay, whether any private man, tho' never so unlearned, can believe that this insolent pretender doth offer any fair reason for the disseising the coheirs of their inheritance. And yet this is just the argument with which those learned gentlemen would persuade us to give up our birthright, to depart from that share of the inheritance we have in the catholic church.

Well, but what will the coheirs that are concerned say to this argument? Why there are three things so obvious to be said to it, that if the persons concerned have not the wit to hit upon them, they are fit to come under the custody and guardianship of this pretended heir-general. May they not say to this gentleman that makes so universal a claim,—Sir, your claim was not so early as the death of our forefather, who left us this joint-inheritance. Your ancestors and ours lived a great while peaceably together, without any clashing about this estate; and we were suffered for some ages to enjoy our own right, without any molestation from you or those you derive from: And the case being so, there was no need of opposing your pretences, because you made none. But then, (which is the second thing) when you did set up for this principality, and wheedled some of our family, and forced others to join with you, you know you were presently opposed by others of our family, who would not so easily part from their rights. You know, that as soon as ever you made your claim, there were some that stoutly declared against it, tho' they had not power, and strength, and interest enough in the world to stem the torrent of your ambition.

But then thirdly, may they say; supposing it was not so; supposing you had met with no rub in your pretences (which yet you know you did); supposing our family were not so suddenly aware of the mischief that would come upon them from those your usurpations, as to make a present opposition; doth now it follow, that because no opposition was just then made to your pretences, that therefore your pretensions to the whole estate are justifiable? No, we can prove they are not so; for it is plain by the Testament, by the settlement of our common father, that we have as much a right to our parts in this estate as you have, or as your ancestors ever had. Tell not us, that you were not at first, or that you were not always, opposed in your claim: But tell us by what right or justice you can pretend to be the sole lord of this inheritance. Let the will of our common parent be produced, and that will plainly shew, that we have as much a share in this estate as you have.[1]

The allegory is so pat to our business, and the application of it

---

[1] Dryden replied to this argument in *The Hind and the Panther* (ii, ll. 373 ff.), published in April 1687. Cf. *Religio Laici*, 1682, ll. 388–93.

so easy to our present case, that I think I should injure the most
vulgar understanding, if I should suspect his ability to make that
use of it which I intend.

'Indagator' was satisfied with pointing out the similarity between this allegory and the allegory in the *Tale*.
Churton Collins went further: 'The sermon referred
to', he said, 'is one of fourteen[1] which are devoted to an
elaborate exposure of the errors and corruptions of the
Church of Rome, furnishing indeed, even to minute
details, the whole text for Swift's satire, which follows
Sharp's commentary step by step.' He made no attempt
to illustrate his statement. The sermon was apparently
not printed until thirty-one years after the *Tale* was published. It is most unlikely that Swift could have obtained
such accurate reports of it as to be able to follow it
'step by step' and 'in minute details'. In May 1686 he
was in Ireland, and the sermon was preached in London.
But the sermon was well known. It was brought to the
notice of James II, who instructed the Bishop of
London, Henry Compton, to suspend Sharp from further preaching. Compton refused, and the dispute
roused much public interest.[2]

The view that Swift was indebted to Sharp may seem
to gain some support from a passage in Deane Swift's
*Essay upon the Life, Writings, and Character, of Dr. Jona-
than Swift* (1755):

Mr. WARREN, the *chamber fellow* of DR. SWIFT in the university of *Dublin*, and a gentleman of undoubted veracity, (whose
sister had made some very considerable impressions upon the
Doctor's heart in the days of his youth) assured a relation of mine,
whom he courted for a wife about eight or nine and forty years
ago, that he saw *The Tale of a Tub* in the hand-writing of DR.
SWIFT, when the Doctor was but nineteen years old; but what

[1] There are fifteen sermons in the series.

[2] See Macaulay's *History of England*, chap. vi.

corrections or improvements it might have received before its publication in the year 1697, he could by no means declare.[1]

Deane Swift is not always a trustworthy authority, and this statement is full of blunders: he gets Waring's name wrong, calls him a 'chamber fellow' when in fact he did not enter Trinity College till three years after Swift had left, and gives the date of publication of the *Tale* as 1697, whereas it was not published till 1704. But the main point of his statement is supported by the annotations made by the Rev. John Lyon, who had charge of Swift in his last illness, in his copy of Hawkesworth's *Life of Swift*.[2] Hawkesworth had paraphrased the statement in a footnote, and in continuation of the words 'declared that he then saw a copy of the *Tale of a Tub* in Swift's own hand writing' Lyon wrote in the margin: 'So did other persons'. Later on Hawkesworth says that when Swift was with Sir William Temple at

[1] p. 31, where there is this footnote: 'Wessendra Warren, esq; a gentleman of fortune in the neighbourhood of *Belfast* in the north of *Ireland*.' 'Warren' is a mistake for 'Waring'. When Swift was at Trinity College (1681–8) there were two undergraduates named Waring—William, who matriculated in June 1681, and Richard, who matriculated in April 1684. But they were cousins of the Jane Waring who 'made some very considerable impressions upon the Doctor's heart'. Her brother Westenra did not enter Trinity till June 1691. See Dr. Elrington Ball's note in *The Correspondence of Swift*, 1910, vol. i, p. 16.

[2] This volume (Dublin, 1755) is now in the Forster Collection in the South Kensington Museum. It has had a distinguished pedigree, having been in the possession of Monck Mason, John Nichols, Malone, Haslewood, and Mitford before it was procured by Forster. It may have been owned also by Farmer, as it contains a MS. note by him. The notes quoted above are on pp. 15 and 24.

There is the following note on Lyon (1702–90) in Mason's hand: '. . . the Rev. John Lyon, sometime Curate of St. Bride's, and after, a præb. of St. Patrick's —he was the Compiler of the Novum Registrum in Christ Church, the Catalogue of the College MSS. and other important works.' There is an account of him in the *Dictionary of National Biography*.

Moor Park he 'corrected and improved his *Tale of a Tub*', and again Lyon wrote in the margin 'which he had begun in the College'.

There is, further, a remarkable coincidence in dates. The *Tale* is said to have existed in manuscript when Swift was nineteen years old—that is in 1686. Sharp's sermon was preached in 1686.

A comparison of the two allegories shows that the resemblance is slight. In Swift's the heirs are three, in Sharp's their number is not stated; in Swift's they are sons, in Sharp's they are descendants removed by 'some generations'; in Swift's the main part of the allegory concerns the coats which the father gives his sons, in Sharp's there is nothing corresponding; and on the other hand in Swift's there is nothing corresponding to the argument of Sharp's 'insolent pretender'. In fact there is nothing in common but the ancestor, the descendants, and the will. So much of Sharp's sermon might have reached Swift, and might have remained in his mind for years before he used it.[1] But it is plain enough that Swift might have thought of the father, the sons, and the will for himself. The allegory is much older than Sharp's sermon. It had been used by Dryden in his *Religio Laici*;[2] and it is found in other supposed 'sources' of the *Tale*.

2. *The Story of the Three Rings*

The story of the three rings exists in several forms. In general, a father gives or bequeaths a ring to each of his three sons, and leads each of them to understand that his ring alone is genuine. The owner of the genuine ring is to be the heir to his father's estate, but the rings

---

[1] By a strange coincidence Sharp is supposed to have been instrumental in debarring Swift from a bishopric on account of the *Tale*: see p. 6, note 1.

[2] ll. 388 ff.

are so similar that they cannot be distinguished. In some forms of the story, as in Boccaccio's *Decameron*,[1] the sons are never able to decide which is the genuine ring; in others, as in the *Gesta Romanorum*,[2] the true ring is known by its power to heal the sick, or by some other virtue. In either case the father is God, and the three rings represent the Jewish, Christian, and Mohammedan religions.[3]

The likeness of the story to the allegory in the *Tale* was first noticed in a French adaptation, *Les Trois Justaucorps*, which was published, professedly at Dublin, in 1721, and has been ascribed to René Macé. It begins as follows:

Il y eut jadis, dans un certain coin de l'Empire Romain, un bon Père de Famille qui avoit trois Garçons, que sa Femme lui avoit mis au Monde d'une seule couche. Ils étoient si ressemblans, que la sage Femme ne put certainement dire lequel étoit l'Aîné. Cette question se trouva aussi difficile à décider que celle des *trois aneaux*, que le Juif *Melchisédech* proposa autrefois à *Saladin*, Soudan de Babilone, lesquels étoient si semblables que les experts n'en purent faire la diférence.

A poem entitled *Les Trois Anneaux* was printed at the end of the little volume, and was thus referred to in the *Avertissement*: 'On a ajouté *les trois Anneaux*, qui y sont citez dès la première page. C'est une Nouvelle tirée de

---

[1] Day I, Tale 3. This form was translated in Painter's *Palace of Pleasure* (ed. Jacobs, vol. i, pp. 116–18).

[2] Tale lxxxix in Swan's translation.

[3] See A. C. Lee, *The Decameron: its Sources and Analogues*, pp. 6–13; Gaston Paris, *La Poésie du Moyen-Age*, ii, pp. 131–63 (this contains abstracts of the stories); Marcus Landau, *Die Quellen des Dekameron*, pp. 183–8; and *Gesta Romanorum*, ed. Oesterley, p. 726 (Oesterley cites the parallel in Plutarch, *Numa*, 13). Further references will be found in Traversari, *Bibliografia Boccaccesca*, under *Anelli, Novella de' Tre*; Painter's *Palace of Pleasure*, ed. Jacobs, vol. i, p. lxxi; Gaston Paris, *La Légende de Saladin*, pp. 13 ff.; and Lessing, *Nathan der Weise*, ed. J. G. Robertson, pp. xxi–xxv.

Bocace, qu'on ne sera point fâché de trouver à la suite de ce Conte.'

The likeness was again pointed out in Voltaire's *Lettres Philosophiques*, xxii, 'Sur Mr Pope et quelques autres Poëtes fameux': 'Ce fameux *Conte du Tonneau* est une imitation de l'ancien Conte des trois Anneaux indiscernables qu'un père légua à ses trois enfans. Ces trois Anneaux étaient la Religion Juive, la Chrétienne & la Mahométane.'[1]

Both the story and the allegory in the *Tale* deal with three conflicting forms of religion, and both employ the imagery of a father giving or leaving to each of three sons objects which were exactly alike. But in the allegory the likeness of the coats causes no dispute, because nothing is made to depend upon distinguishing them, and there is this further difference that the allegory proceeds with the history of the three sons and their treatment of their father's gifts from the point at which the story ends. A testament is mentioned in some versions of the story, but all that is said of it is that the father left instructions how the true heir was to be recognized. The interpretation of the will is a main part of the allegory of the *Tale*.

3. Fontenelle's *Histoire de Mréo et de Eénegu*

The passage from the *Lettres Philosophiques* quoted above is continued as follows:

C'est encor une imitation de l'*Histoire de Méro et d'Enégu*, par Fontenelle. Méro était l'anagramme de Rome, & Enégu de Genéve. Ce sont deux sœurs qui prétendent à la succession du Royaume de leur père. Méro règne la première. Fontenelle la

---

[1] This passage is not in the original edition of the *Lettres Philosophiques* but is found in the *Collection complète des œuvres de M. de Voltaire* published in 1756. See Gustave Lanson's edition (Société des Textes Français Modernes, 1909), vol. ii, p. 136. Cf. *Œuvres*, 1879, vol. xxii, p. 175, and vol. xxvi, p. 489.

représente comme une Sorciére qui escamotait le pain, & qui faisait des conjurations avec des cadavres. C'est-là précisément le milord Pierre de Swift.

Fontenelle's *Histoire de Mréo et d'Eénegu* purports to be an extract from a letter written from 'Batavia dans les Indes Orientales, le 27 Novembre 1684', and was published in Bayle's *Nouvelles de la République des Lettres* in January 1686.[1] It tells of the disputes between two rival queens of Borneo. Mliséo,[2] queen of Borneo, had died, and was succeeded by her daughter Mréo (i.e. Rome) who introduced several vexatious regulations,—all her ministers were made eunuchs *d'une certaine façon*; the public feasts were retrenched; the price of bread was raised by the machinations of certain magicians; there was a *salle des cadavres* in the palace, and homage had to be paid to the embalmed bodies of the royal favourites; and so forth. The people of Borneo were angered by these things, and a new queen Eénegu (i.e. Genève) arose who said that she was the real daughter of Mliséo, and alleged her likeness in proof. She abolished all the innovations. Civil war at once spread throughout the whole island. When the letter was written the issue was said to be still undecided.

The chief points in favour of Voltaire's assertion are that Fontenelle and Swift both deal with the Roman and Calvinistic Churches, speak of them as children of a common ancestor, and make one introduce novelties which the other abolishes. Beyond this the likeness is not striking. The *Histoire* caused a good deal of interest when it was published, and it appeared in a volume which Swift might well have seen in Temple's library. It will be noticed that it was published in 1686, the year in which Sharp preached his sermons on the Roman

[1] Article x, pp. 87–90. Cf. Louis Maigron, *Fontenelle*, 1906, p. 40.

[2] Mliséo is an anagram of Solime, i.e. Solyma (Jerusalem).

Catholic controversy, and the year in which the *Tale*
was seen by Westenra Waring and others—if we are
to believe Deane Swift and Dr. Lyon.[1]

4. Optatus: *De Chismate Donatistarum*

In *Notes and Queries* for 4 July 1863 (3rd ser., vol. iv,
p. 5), it was suggested that Swift derived the allegory
in the *Tale* from a passage in St. Optatus, at the beginning of the Fifth Book of his *De Chismate* (or *Scismate*)
Donatistarum.[2] Optatus is speaking of rebaptism, and
remarks that it is difficult to find impartial judges of the
question at issue. He continues thus:

Quærendi sunt iudices: Si Christiani, de vtraque parte dari
non possunt: quia studiis veritas impeditur. De foris quærendus
est iudex: Si paganus, non potest nosse Christiana secreta. Si
Iudæus, inimicus est Christiani baptismatis: Ergo in terris de
hac re nullum poterit reperiri iudicium, de cœlo quærendus est
iudex. Sed vt quid pulsamus ad cœlum, cum habeamus hic in
Euangelio testamentum? Quia hoc loco rectè possunt terrena
cœlestibus comparari: tale est, quod quiuis hominum habens
numerosos filios. His, quamdiu pater præsens est, ipse imperat
singulis: non est adhuc necessarium testamentum. Sic & Christus,
quamdiu præsens in terris fuit (quamuis nec modo desit) pro
tempore quicquid necessarium erat, Apostolis imperauit. Sed quo
modo terrenus pater, cum se in confinio senserit mortis, timens
ne post mortem suam, rupta pace, litigent fratres, adhibitis testi-
bus, voluntatem suam de pectore morituro transfert in tabulas
diu duraturas. Et si fuerit inter fratres contentio nata, non itur
ad tumultum, sed quæritur testamentum: Et qui in tumulo
quiescit, tacitus de tabulis loquitur: viuus, is, cuius est testa-

---

[1] A newspaper cutting pasted
in at the end of Douce's copy of
the fifth edition (Bodleian, Douce
SS 292), after referring to Fontenelle's allegorical tale, concludes
by suggesting that Swift might
have seen Ferranti Palavicino's *Il
Divortio Celeste* (1643), a satire
against the abuses of the Popish
power. An English translation,
The Heavenly Divorce, was published in 1679. Swift may well
have known the work, but he took
nothing from it.

[2] *Sancti Optati Milevitani Opera*
(Paris, 1631), pp. 84–85.

mentum, in cœlo est. Ergo voluntas eius, velut in testamento, sic in Euangelio inquiratur.

In this passage we have the father, the sons, and the will. In view of the extent of Swift's reading, we cannot safely say that he was not likely to have known it. But there was little in it for him to borrow.[1]

5. Buckingham's *Letter to Mr. Clifford* and *Conference with an Irish Priest*

Towards the conclusion of his *Observations on The Tale of a Tub*, published in 1705, William Wotton said that the author of the *Tale* was indebted to two pieces by George Villiers, second Duke of Buckingham: 'The *Actors* in his *Farce*, *Peter*, *Martin*, and *Jack*, are by name borrowed from a Letter written by the late Witty D. of *Buckingham*, concerning Mr. *Clifford's Human Reason*: And *Peter's* Banter upon *Transubstantiation*, is taken from the same D. of *Buckingham's Conference with an Irish Priest*.'[2]

The passage in Buckingham's letter 'To Mr. Clifford, on his Humane-Reason' is as follows:

For when the First heat once was over, and considering Men began to reflect, that the Reformation offer'd nothing but Words, that it gave no intire Freedom to Consciences and Enquiries, they saw no satisfactory Motive of quitting their old *Mumsimus* for a new *Sumsimus*, and cou'd find no real Advantage in withdrawing from Father *Peter*, to Father *Martin*, and Father *John*, since tho' these disclaim'd the *Infallibility*, the other usurpt, yet

---

[1] It was also suggested in *Notes and Queries* for 30 Nov. 1867 (3rd ser., xii, p. 451) that the following passage in Selden's *Table Talk* (published 1689) might have been a source of the allegory: 'Religion is like the Fashion, one Man wears his Doublet slash'd, another lac'd, another plain; but every Man has a Doublet: So every Man has his Religion. We differ about Trimming' (ed. Arber, p. 102). In this there is nothing like the *Tale* except the use of the simile from clothing.

[2] p. 323.

they still, without that Guard, demanded our Belief of their Doctrines, tho' not less absurd and ridiculous.[1]

The dialogue entitled *An Account of a Conference between His Grace George, late Duke of Buckingham, and Father Fitzgerald an Irish Priest*[2] recounts how the priest was sent by James II to convert the Duke to Roman Catholicism. The Duke receives the priest, and calls for a bottle of wine, which the priest shares with him. He tells the priest that the cork of the bottle is a horse. The priest thinks him disordered in his senses, and contradicts him. The Duke accepts the contradiction, but when the priest proceeds to speak of Transubstantiation the Duke recalls the argument about the cork.

These two pieces were both printed in the second volume of Buckingham's *Miscellaneous Works* collected and prepared for the press by 'the Late Ingenious Mr. Tho. Brown' and published in 1705. In his reply to Wotton Swift expresses the opinion that the *Conference* was first published then,[3] that is in the year after the appearance of the *Tale*. No earlier edition is now known. Similarly he states that he had not heard of the letter to Martin Clifford till Wotton mentioned it in his *Observations*. Buckingham had died in 1687, and it is doubtful if Wotton would have mentioned these works as he did in 1705 if they had been kept private till then. On the other hand, Swift's statement that he was ignorant of them cannot be rejected.

It would appear that while the *Tale* was still a new work, Wotton was the only man who said that 'this Author's Wit is not his own in many Places', and it was therefore to Wotton that Swift replied in his 'Apology'. His reply has a wider application, and covers the other

---

[1] *Miscellaneous Works*, 1705, vol. ii, p. 67.
[2] Ibid., pp. 33–57. Cf. 'The Calendar Reform'd' (by Sir Fleetwood Sheppard, 1687) in vol. i, 1704, p. 219.   [3] pp. 13, 14.

possible sources that have subsequently been pointed out. There is every reason for believing that the author wrote the *Tale* 'without enquiring what other People had writ'. Yet it is not improbable that Swift was unconsciously indebted for the rough idea of the allegory to one or more of the books that have been cited. His 'Apology' was written about twelve years after the date which he assigns to the main body of the *Tale*; and in the interval he may have forgotten how he came to begin it. Every writer borrows more than he is aware. Ideas pass into the mind, and grow and transform themselves without our knowledge.

VI. DATE OF COMPOSITION

Swift's statements place the composition of the *Tale* in 1696 and 1697.[1] It is difficult to see why he should have given these dates if the book was not written then. He wanted it to be thought of as the work of a young man, in order that excuse might be found for some of its levities. As he said in the 'Apology', he had given 'a Liberty to his Pen which might not suit with maturer Years or graver Characters'. But, had he been choosing a date, he might have put most of the book much earlier. He might, for instance, have ascribed the allegory of Peter, Martin, and Jack to some time before 1694, when he took orders. As he did not foresee the harm that the book was to do him, he had no obvious motive to give a date that was wrong. In the main, therefore, we must accept Swift's statements, and there is nothing to show that they are not substantially correct.

He admits that the book was not written all at one time. 'This Discourse', he says, 'is the Product of the Study, the Observation, and the Invention of several Years'; and he describes himself as having been 'at the

[1] See, e.g., pp. 4, 38, 44, and cf. p. 86, note †, p. 208, note*.

Pains to insert one or two Remarks'.[1] References to persons and events are therefore uncertain evidence. They may give the date of revision rather than the date of composition. But, in default of better evidence, we have to consider what such references suggest.

Dedication to Somers. The 'late Reign' (p. 26) is the reign of William III, who died on 8 March 1702.

The Bookseller to the Reader. The first paragraph shows that this section was written in 1704.

Dedication to Prince Posterity. This is dated at the conclusion 'Decemb. 1697', but two passages are to be noted, one of which is certainly later:

(*a*) ... our Corporation of *Poets*, from whom I am preparing a Petition to *Your Highness*, to be subscribed with the Names of one hundred thirty six of the first Rate, but whose immortal Productions are never likely to reach your eyes, tho' each of them is now an humble and an earnest Appellant for the Laurel (p. 33).

On the death of the sovereign the office of Laureate became vacant. The 'one hundred thirty six' poets would be appellants for the laurel on the death of William III. Nahum Tate, who succeeded Shadwell as Laureate in 1692, was at once reappointed by Queen Anne in 1702. But this passage might have been written in prospect of a vacancy.

(*b*) There is a Person styl'd Dr. *B–tl–y*, who has written near a thousand Pages of immense Erudition, *giving a full and true Account* of the certain *Squable* of wonderful Importance between himself and a Bookseller (p. 37).

The reference is clearly not to Bentley's first *Dissertation*, which is an appendix to Wotton's *Reflections*, but to his second *Dissertation*, published in February 1699, which forms a substantial volume by itself, and begins with a full account of his relations with Thomas Bennet, the bookseller.

[1] pp. 10, 12.

The Preface. There is a reference to 'this present Month of *August*, 1697' (p. 44), and there appears to be no reason for doubting this date. Three passages are to be noted: (*a*) the 'long Peace' (p. 39) must be the Peace that was expected as a result of the Conference at Ryswick, which began on 7 May 1697. Peace was concluded in September 1697; (*b*) the reference to 'the following Treatise' (p. 42) implies that the Preface was written after the body of the book; (*c*) 'The Tax upon Paper' (p. 45) was imposed in 1696.

The Introduction. Three passages give 1697 as the earliest limit.

(*a*) a famous Writer † now living
    † Viz *in the Year* 1698 (p. 69).

The first three editions read '*in the Year* 1697'.

(*b*) The *Wise Men of* Gotham, *cum Appendice*. This is a Treatise of immense Erudition, being the great Original and Fountain of those Arguments, bandied about both in *France* and *England*, for a just Defence of the *Modern* Learning and Wit (p. 69).

This is an allusion to the second edition of Wotton's *Reflections*, published in June 1697, with Bentley's first *Dissertation* as an Appendix.

(*c*) Our famous *Dryden* has ventured to proceed a Point farther, endeavouring to introduce also a Multiplicity of *Godfathers* (p. 72).

A marginal note explains this as an allusion to Dryden's *Virgil*. It was published in July 1697.

Section II. The footnote of 1710 which speaks of 'about fourteen Years since' (p. 86) would give the date about 1696.

Sections III, V, VII. The allusions to Bentley cannot be earlier than June 1697.

Section IX. The passage on Sir Edward Seymour and other 'Patriots' (p. 175) does not give a clear date, as they were leading Tories from 1696 to 1702. 'Flanders' (p. 176, l. 23) might point to the war of the Spanish succession which began in May 1702, but a subsequent note (p. 208) gives a date before the Peace of Ryswick in September 1697.

Section X. 'His Majesty' (p. 181) is William III, died March 1702. The reference to Bentley's first *Dissertation*, June 1697, gives the earlier limit (pp. 183–4).

Section XI. A footnote of 1710 (p. 204) points out the allusion to Sir Humphrey Edwin, who was elected Lord Mayor of London in September 1697.

The Conclusion. Four passages bear on the date: (a) The *Histoire de M. Constance* (cited on p. 206 was read by Swift in 1697; (b) the reference to Bentley (p. 207) cannot be earlier than June 1697; (c) the sentence about 'Times so turbulent and unquiet as these' (p. 208) is said in a footnote of 1710 to have been written before the Peace of Ryswick. (d) the conversation with the bookseller gives a date just before publication.

On the above evidence Swift was engaged on the *Tale* in the latter part of 1697. In 1700 he edited the *Letters* of Sir William Temple and in 1701 brought out his *Contests and Dissensions in Athens and Rome,* and there is no evidence of any work on the *Tale* during these years. He might have written the 'Dedication to Somers' in 1702, but a more likely time is on the eve of publication, when he wrote 'The Bookseller to the Reader' and at least part of the 'Conclusion'. The sections most difficult to date contain the allegory, and it is probable that Swift had them in mind when he said that the greatest part was finished in 1696. The critical digressions belong to the latter half of 1697 at the earliest. The addition of the 'abuses in Learning' to the 'abuses in Religion' was an afterthought.

The circumstances of Swift's life point to the same dates. He lived with Temple at Moor Park from 1689 to 1690, from 1691 to 1694, and from the summer of 1696 till Temple's death in January 1699. During the interval from 1694 to 1696 he was in Ireland. He was ordained Deacon in October 1694, and Priest in January 1695, and a fortnight later was presented to the small Prebend of Kilroot near Belfast.[1] There his ancestral prejudices against the Nonconformists were likely to be confirmed. When he returned to Temple's house in 1696, he was well equipped to draw the character of Jack. Possibly he had begun the *Tale* at Kilroot, for if there is any truth in the story that Westenra Waring had seen some part of it in manuscript, he is most likely to have seen it there.[2] Then in the third and final period of residence with Temple he had the leisure, and the stimulus, for completing his book. Thereafter he could revise and add to it. Yet the allegory, which there is every reason for considering the original part, may long have been in his mind before it was given its final form; and it is not impossible that the first rough sketch of it was made while he was still an undergraduate at Trinity College, Dublin.

VII. THE BATTLE OF THE BOOKS[3]

The *Battle of the Books* must have been written shortly after the publication of Bentley's first *Dissertation upon the Epistles of Phalaris* in June 1697. If it was begun before that date, it was seriously altered. The references to Boyle, which are confined to the latter part, suggest that it was completed about the time when Boyle's *Examination* of Bentley's *Dissertation* was published, early in March 1698. The 'Bookseller to the Reader' gives the date as 1697.

---

[1] See *Correspondence*, ed. Elrington Ball, vol. i, p. 15.
[2] Cf. above, p. xxxiv, and Forster, *Life of Swift*, p. 84.

[3] Edited separately by A. C. Guthkelch in 1908 (Chatto and Windus).

A letter written by Sir William Temple about Boyle's *Examination* on 30 March 1698 may explain why the *Battle* was not published when it was written. It shows, at least, that whereas the *Examination* drew a distinction between the manners of Bentley and Wotton, Swift followed Temple in thinking them equally guilty of misapplied learning and 'foul-mouthed railing'.[1] The letter does no credit to Temple's judgement, nor to his temper; but it indicates the kind of conversation that must have largely inspired Swift's work:

Moor-Park, *March 30. 98.*

I think there can be no Exception to any thing in it [*Mr Boyle's Book*] besides His Partiality to me; which perhaps will be less forgiven him by the Dr, than any other Fault. For the rest, the Compass and Application of so much Learning, the Strength and Pertinence of Arguments, the Candour of his Relations, in Return to such Foulmouth'd Railing, the pleasant Turns of Wit, and the Easiness of Style, are, in my Opinion, as extraordinary, as the contrary of these all appear to be, in what the Dr and his Friend have written. So that I have as much reason to be pleased with finding my self in Mr *Boyle's* good Opinion, as I should be sorry to be in Theirs.

You needed no Excuse for any thing in your former Letter, nor Mr —— for giving you the Occasion for it. What he saw, was written to a Friend—who had undertaken—without my Knowledge: Which I afterwards diverted, having no mind to Enter the List, with such a Mean, Dull, Unmannerly PEDANT.[2]

The blanks cannot now be filled with any certainty, and we do not know what it was that Temple 'diverted'. It may have been the *Battle of the Books*. But even if Temple referred to another work, the letter serves to show that in postponing publication Swift acted in harmony with Temple's wishes.

---

[1] See p. 11, note 2.

[2] Printed at the end of the Appendix to *A Short Account of Dr Bentley's Humanity and Justice,* 1699, p. 140.

Hawkesworth described the *Battle* as 'an allegorical representation of Sir William Temple's *Essay*'.[1] Several points of resemblance have been noted by Sir Walter Scott and other editors.[2] Not the least striking is that Swift's choice of combatants to represent the Ancients corresponds to Temple's. Had Swift been taxed with the omission of the ancient dramatists and orators, he might have replied that their deeds were recorded in those parts of the manuscript which perished 'by the Injury of Fortune or Weather'. But as Temple had omitted them all except Cicero, it is simpler to suppose that Swift merely followed the lead of his patron. Their lists of the Moderns are not so similar, because Temple had mentioned many of the Moderns with praise, but Swift was careful to include nearly all whom Temple had disparaged.

In his *Observations upon The Tale of a Tub* Wotton said he had been assured that the *Battle* was '*mutatis mutandis* taken out of a French book', entitled, he thought, *Combat des Livres*.[3] This book must be the *Histoire Poëtique de la Guerre nouvellement declarée entre les Anciens et les Modernes*, written in prose by François de Callières, and published anonymously in 1688. In it all the main kinds of Ancient and Modern literature are ranged in order of battle against each other; and in the combats which ensue the author produced what the English translator in 1714 called a just piece of general criticism.[4] The parallelisms in Swift's work are not

[1] p. 250, note 2.

[2] See notes, pp. 220, 226, 231, 234, 240, 241, 245.

[3] pp. 14, 328.

[4] *Characters and Criticisms upon the Ancient and Modern Orators, Poets,* [&c.] *Written Originally in French by the Archbishop of Cam-* *bray, and made English by J. G.,* London, 1714. The running title is 'A Poetical Account of the War between the Ancients and Moderns'. The attribution of the work to Fénelon is erroneous, but indicates the translator's opinion of its excellence.

striking,[1] and may well have been fortuitous. Swift denied that he was obliged to it, or any other book, for the smallest hint.[2] At a time when the claims of the Ancients and the Moderns were debated with so much vigour in France and in England, the setting of a battle would naturally present itself to anyone.

Another French book, to which the *Histoire Poëtique* itself might have been indebted,[3] has also been stated to be a 'source' of Swift's work. Abel Boyer said in his *Memoirs of Sir William Temple* (1714) that the hint for the *Battle* was taken from 'an allegorical novel by Monsieur de Furetière', which is explained in a footnote to be the *Nouvelle Allegorique, ou Histoire des Derniers Troubles arrivez au Royaume d'Eloquence*, published at Paris in 1658.[4] It describes a civil war in the kingdom of Eloquence, the rule of 'la reine Rhétorique' having been challenged by 'le prince Galimatias'. The troops that are marshalled in defence of the former are the chief literary forms, such as Dramas, Epics, Histories, Romances, and Speeches; and the army of the latter is composed of the figures of speech, such as Hyperboles, Antitheses, Allusions, Allegories, and Puns. The leaders on both sides are well-known writers. It would be remarkable if no points of similarity could be discovered between this book and Swift's.[5] But again it has to be

[1] See, e.g., p. 215, note 2. In both works the Ancients and Moderns each occupy one peak of Parnassus. The parallelisms are of this kind.

[2] 'Apology', pp. 14, 15.

[3] In both there are plates giving the plans of battle. The plate in the *Histoire Poëtique* is reproduced, and Englished, in the translation of 1714; the other is given as a frontispiece to J. E. Spingarn's

Critical Essays of the Seventeenth Century, vol. i.

[4] An English adaptation, *The Rebellion, or an Account of the late Civil-War in the Kingdom of Eloquence*, appeared in 1704, and was republished in 1705 as *The Tale of a Tub, revers'd*. It was described by A. C. Guthkelch in *The Library* for July 1913.

[5] Perhaps the most striking is the satire on Indexes and Com-

said that the general idea of a battle is the main thing they have in common.[1]

Though written at the time when the *Tale* was taking shape, the *Battle of the Books* does not show the same maturity. Its lower power must be accounted for by the comparative narrowness of its subject. The structure could not allow the full display of Swift's peculiar talents. It was an interlude, not unwillingly abandoned, in the composition of the greater work.

VIII. THE MECHANICAL OPERATION OF THE SPIRIT

In the 'Apology' Swift disclaimed responsibility for the *Discourse Concerning the Mechanical Operation of the Spirit* in the form in which it was published.[2] He had lent to a gentleman, he says, ' a most imperfect Sketch with the addition of a few loose Hints', all being but 'the Ground-work of a much larger Discourse'. Without his knowledge, it had been 'pieced up together,

mon-place Books, two Lieutenant-Generals in the army of Galimatias: l'un se nommoit *Index*, qui au contraire des autres Chefs marchoit toûjours à la queuë, afin de rallier ses Troupes, fort sujettes à se débander. L'autre appellé *Polyanthéa*, marchoit a la teste' (p. 24). *Polyanthéa* is explained in a note to be 'le titre d'un gros Dictionnaire, ou Recueil de lieux communs, où sont ramassez par ordre alphabétique les passages de plusieurs autheurs sur toutes sortes de matières'. There is no possible question of borrowing here. The 'source' of Swift's satire on indexes and commonplace-books, which plays so large a part in the critical digres-

sions of the *Tale*, was not another man's book, but his own observation, mainly of Bentley.

[1] A note on Swift's debt to French 'sources' will be found in Rigault's *Histoire de la querelle des anciens et des modernes*, 1861, p. 345: 'En remontant plus haut que le XVIIe siècle, on verrait que l'idée première de la *Bataille des livres* est empruntée peut-être à un vieux fabliau, où se trouve raconté un combat de ce genre entre l'Université de Paris et celle d'Orléans. (Voir le recueil de Barbazan et de Méon.) Ce qui est sûr, c'est que l'idée de Swift est d'origine française.'

[2] p. 17.

wholly out of the Method and Scheme he had intended', and published with the *Tale* and the *Battle*. But in the Bookseller's Advertisement,[1] which there is reason to attribute to Swift himself, the Bookseller is made to say that the Discourse came into his hands 'perfect and entire', and that 'several Things in it, which the present Age could not very well bear' were cut out by the advice and assistance of a judicious friend. Again in a note added in 1710,[2] and probably also written by Swift himself, it is said that 'this Discourse is not altogether equal to the two Former, the best Parts of it being omitted; whether the Bookseller's Account be true, that he durst not print the rest, I know not'. These discrepancies are evidently part of the general scheme of mystification. It is not rash to assume that the *Discourse* appeared exactly as Swift meant it to appear, though he may at one time have thought of writing a larger treatise which he refrained from completing, finding it easier to call asterisks to his aid. The marginal note[3] explaining why the kernel of the whole *Discourse* had to be omitted is exactly in Swift's manner. We assume that it had never been written.

There are no passages to fix the date of the *Discourse*. The 'Literati of Tobinambou'[4] was suggested by one of Boileau's epigrams, which was quoted in full in Sir William Temple's *Thoughts upon Reviewing the Essay of Ancient and Modern Learning*. This had been published under Swift's supervision in 1701, in the Third Part of Temple's *Miscellanea*. But the epigram had been written in 1687, and Swift may have come to know it at Moor Park any time before Temple's death in 1699. The allusion to Sir Humphrey Edwin[5] points to a date after September 1697.

The general character of the *Discourse* is the best

[1] p. 260. [3] p. 276. [4] p. 263.
[2] p. 261. [5] p. 279.

evidence of its date. There is every sign that it is later than the *Battle*. But the reader is not conscious of any marked change on passing to it from the later sections of the *Tale*. It is the product of the same mind, and in the same phase, that gave us the greater but not stronger 'Digression concerning Madness' and the section on the Æolists. The editor of the edition of 1720 had some reason for printing it before the *Battle* and calling it 'A Fragment of The Tale of a Tub'.[1]

IX. SWIFT'S READING

Swift liked to think of the difficulties his readers would find in the *Tale*. He too was a 'mysterious writer', quite as mysterious as any of the writers he satirized. 'It were much to be wisht', he says, 'and I do here humbly propose for an Experiment, that every Prince in *Christendom* will take seven of the *deepest Scholars* in his Dominions, and shut them up close for *seven* Years, in *seven* Chambers, with a Command to write *seven* ample Commentaries on this comprehensive Discourse. I shall venture to affirm, that whatever Difference may be found in their several Conjectures, they will be all, without the least Distortion, manifestly deduceable from the Text.'[2] Some of the deductions were more serious for him than he had suspected; they barred his way to high office in the Church, and they induced him to write an Apology. But in the glow of composition he found new zest in imagining his readers wondering what he could mean. He would have been pleased had he heard Bishop Burnet declaring that for his part he could find out neither head nor tail.[3] To us nowadays the main drift of the book is clear and unmistakable. It is a satire

---

[1] See p. lxx.
[2] p. 185.
[3] *Letters of Thomas Burnet to* *George Duckett*, ed. D. Nichol Smith (Roxburghe Club), 1914, p. 11.

on the abuses in religion, with satires on the abuses in
learning introduced by way of digressions. After two
centuries of annotation it still has its puzzles in plenty.
In not a few passages the more knowing readers in
Swift's own day may have found the meaning and purpose that we miss. But the wealth of detailed allusion
must always have been baffling; and Swift meant it to
be so. 'I believe one of the Author's Designs', he makes
his annotator say, 'was to set curious Men a hunting
thro' Indexes, and enquiring for Books out of the
common Road.'[1] He issued a solemn warning to 'those
whom the *Learned* among Posterity will appoint for
Commentators upon this elaborate Treatise';[2] and they
dare never forget that he may be playing a game with
them. The modern editor must always be conscious of
the shade of Swift finding amused pleasure in the false
surmises that send him searching on the wrong track,
and when the hunt is successful, as often by luck as by
skill, in the explanations that sometimes come perilously
near pedantry.

Swift's reading was remarkably wide. In his younger
days he was a hard student, and he had the use of a
good library when he lived with Sir William Temple
at Moor Park. During the third and most important
period of his residence there, from May 1696 till
Temple's death in January 1699, he employed his
leisured independence in varied and constant study. The
Tale was written, mainly if not wholly, at this time. He
wrote it from a full mind. He speaks humorously of his
'indefatigable reading'.[3] The humour of the passage
cannot conceal its sober truth.

His references to his commonplace-books are likewise not to be dismissed as mere satire. He finds, he
says, that his commonplace-book fills much slower than
he had reason to expect;[4] he has 'a laborious Collection

[1] p. 187.   [2] p. 114.   [3] p. 189.   [4] p. 54.

of Seven Hundred Thirty Eight *Flowers*, and *shining Hints* of the best *Modern* Authors', disgested with great reading into a book of common-places;[1] he lays his memorandums before him and inserts them 'with a wonderful facility of application'.[2] The satire here is so obvious that we are apt to see nothing but satire. Moreover, these passages are of a piece with many others in the *Tale*. One of its many recurring themes is that learning is abused by excessive reliance on commonplace-books, as on indexes, epitomes, and other devices that save the trouble of reading and thinking. He never spares the 'judicious Collectors of *bright Parts*, and *Flowers*, and *Observanda's*'. What though the head be empty, he asks, provided the commonplace-book be full?[3] We may therefore not suspect how assiduous he was in making abstracts of the authors that he read. The real difference between him and the 'judicious collectors' was that his head and his commonplace-book were both full at the same time. Deane Swift and Hawkesworth tell us that copious extracts from Cyprian, Irenaeus, Sleidan's Commentaries, and Sarpi's history of the Council of Trent were found among his papers, and that they appeared from memorandums in his own writing to have been made while he lived with Temple. To this list Dr. John Lyon added Tertullian, Epiphanius, Diodorus Siculus, and Thucydides.[4] Swift had his own commonplace-books, and epitomes, and abstracts. He made them in the process of filling and exercising his mind, about the very time when he was engaged on the *Tale*.

Fortunately we have a list of books read by Swift in 1697 and at the beginning of 1698, apparently one of the memorandums to which Deane Swift and

[1] p. 209.
[2] p. 266. [3] p. 148.
[4] In the margins of his copy of Hawkesworth's *Life of Swift*, Dublin, 1755, p. 20; see above, p. xxxv.

Hawkesworth refer. It survives in a transcript made by John Lyon, and bound in at the beginning of Lyon's annotated copy of Hawkesworth's *Life of Swift*:[1]

While he was at *Moor park*, he kept an Acc^t one Year of the Books he read in the following manner—

From Jan: 7. 169$\frac{6}{7}$.

Lord Herbert's Harry 8. f^{ol}
Sleidan's Coment: abstracted f^{ol}
Council of *Trent* abstr: f^{ol}
Virgil, bis
Horace, 9. volumes
Sr *W. Temple*'s Memoirs
—— Introduction
Camden's Elisabeth
Prince *Arthur*
Histoire de *Chypre*
Voyage de *Syam*
Voiture
Memoires de *Maurier*
Lucius Florus, ter
Collier's Essays 2 volumes
Count *Gabalis*
Sr *John Davis* of the Soul
Conformité de Religion, &c
Dialogues de Morts, 2 Vol:
Lucretius, ter
Histoire de Mr *Constance*
Histoire d'*Æthiopie*
Historie de *Cotes* de &c
Diodorus Siculus, abstr: f^o
Cyprian & *Irenæus* abstr: f^o
Voyage de *Maroc* &c
Ælian, 1st Vol:
Homer, Iliad & Odyss.
Cicero's Epistles

[1] The list was printed in Sheridan's *Life of Swift*, 1784, p. 25. Sheridan writes as if he followed the original; he describes Swift's list as 'preserved in his own handwriting'.

Bernier's Grand Mogol 2 Vol:
Burnet's Hist: of Reform: fº
Petronius Arbiter
Oevres Melées 5 Vol:

From Jan: 7ᵗʰ 169⁷⁄₈

Thucydides by *Hobbes* fºl abstracted
Theophrasti Characteres.
Vossius de Sybillinis

No farther Accᵗ remains of his Studys at this time.

This list contains two of the small number of modern books that Swift cited in his marginal notes, the *Histoire de M. Constance* by the Père d'Orléans,[1] and Bernier's *Grand Mogol*.[2] Neither of the citations can be dated before the middle of 1697. About the same time he read the passage from Irenæus that he gave on his title-page.[3] The quotations from Lucretius must likewise have been suggested by his three recent readings. Other books on the list supplied him with allusions. He appears, for instance, sometimes to have remembered Jeremy Collier's *Essays upon Several Moral Subjects*;[4] he certainly remembered Blackmore's *Prince Arthur*. The annotator who had the energy to work his way through all the books in Swift's list would probably be able to overburden his notes with a large number of parallel passages. But the list has a much wider interest. It admits us, as it were, to a secret view of Swift's habits of mind when he was gaining his full powers, and Swift

---

[1] p. 206. [2] p. 271.
[3] Deane Swift saw the 'book of extracts from St. *Cyprian* and St. *Irenæus*, taken by Swift in the year 1697', and has given us the exact dates: 'He has not marked in this book when he began to read St. *Cyprian*; but the day, on which he compleated his extract, was *Nov.* 19, 1697. And the day following he began to read St. *Irenæus*, and finished his extract from that early father, *Dec.* 12, 1697.'—*Essay upon Swift*, 1755, p. 276.
[4] pp. 52, 79, 84.

never wrote anything that gives a greater sense of sheer
power than some of the later sections of the *Tale*.

The list gives only a fraction of the reading that went
to the making of the *Tale*. His constant allusions to the
classics are drawn from a very large number of authors,
not merely from the authors that he read in 1697, but
even from Pausanias, Photius, and Hippocrates. His
knowledge of rosicrucian and alchemical literature
ranged far beyond the *Comte de Gabalis*; he had found
prolonged amusement in the 'dark authors', and notably
in Paracelsus and Thomas Vaughan. As a churchman he
knew the Fathers, and the controversial literature of the
seventeenth century. In the household of Temple he
was familiar with every detail of the controversy on the
letters of Phalaris, and the wider controversy on the
Ancients and Moderns. He could speak with authority
on current criticism and the productions of Grub Street.
He was equally at home in Rabelais[1] and Cervantes.
And already he had long been preparing himself for
Gulliver's Travels. The list includes accounts of travels
and descriptions of far-away countries such as the
Voyage de Syam, the *Histoire d'Æthiopie*, and the *Voyage
de Maroc*, and they are among its most interesting entries.
The *Tale* itself shows that he knew Heylyn's *Cosmo-
graphy*, Guagninus's *Sarmatiae Descriptio*, and Hall's
Mundus Alter et Idem.

All this multifarious reading is placed under contribu-
tion. At one time it is Hippocrates or the Schoolmen,
Bentley or Scaliger, Cervantes or the Apocrypha; at
another Dick Whittington and his Cat somehow get
into the same sentence with Jehuda Hannasi and the
Jerusalem Mishna. Yet the *Tale* remains one of the most
original books ever written. 'The author's wit was en-

---

[1] 'Among the Dean's books,
sold by auction, 1745, was an edition of Rabelais' works, with remarks and annotations in his own
hand.' Scott, *Works of Swift*,
1824, vol. i, p. 83 n.

tirely his own.' The ingredients of a dozen *Tales* lie ready to hand for any writer who has the wit to make another. Though the book is a tissue of allusions, Swift could well insist upon it, that throughout it all he had not borrowed one single hint from any writer in the world. Many years afterwards he made the same proud boast in his verses 'On the Death of Dr. Swift':

> To steal a hint was never known,
> But what he writ was all his own.

Two other books must be mentioned, both of which Swift knew much better than might be suspected. The first is Sir Thomas Browne's *Vulgar Errors*. It appears to have suggested not only the use of some uncommon words like 'exantlation', 'atramentous', and 'fuliginous', but also the passages about the orientation of man's body,[1] the description of Moses,[2] the white powder that kills without report,[3] the belief that by slitting the ear of a stag the defect may be spread through a whole herd,[4] and the story of the Macrocephali.[5] Swift might have been directly indebted to the same sources as Browne, but, taken together, these points of contact are satisfactory evidence that the *Vulgar Errors* was one of his favourite volumes. The other book is Marvell's *Rehearsal Transpros'd*. There he met with the whale and the tub and could learn that a straight line if continued far enough will become a circle.[6] He also found the familiar story about the same food appearing again and again at table in different guises. In Italian it is 'tutta fava'; in French 'toujours perdrix'. Swift has 'it is all *Pork*', and cites Plutarch in the margin.[7] He might also have cited Marvell. He refers to the *Rehearsal Transpros'd* in his 'Apology' as a book that we still read 'with pleasure'.[8] The style of Swift is Swift

[1] pp. 152, 358. [3] p. 236. [5] p. 268. [7] p. 50.
[2] p. 177. [4] p. 201. [6] p. 158. [8] p. 10, l. 2.

himself, a style which has never been imitated successfully, and could not be formed by imitation. But when we read Marvell after reading Swift we feel the kinship in the muscular strength, the simplicity that is fraught with meaning, and the seemingly careless ease that comes from perfect confidence.[1]

X. THE HISTORY OF MARTIN

A Tale of a Tub was included in the collection of Swift's writings issued in 1720 under the title *Miscellaneous Works, Comical & Diverting*. It was there furnished with 'explanatory Notes, never before printed'; and there were 'considerable Additions', the most important of which was the Abstract of 'The History of Martin'.

This collection was printed in Holland and was one of a series of English books published by T. Johnson at The Hague. Nichols calls it 'the Dutch edition'. There is no evidence that Swift knew about it.

The volume opens with 'The Bookseller's Advertisement' which consists almost entirely of an extract from a letter by 'an ingenious gentleman' explaining how the new matter came to his hands. He claims to have seen a manuscript of the *Tale* 'which contains a great deal more than what is printed'. Not being allowed to take a copy, he had to trust to his memory, and wrote down 'as near as I can now remember' the heads of the most material parts, and afterwards extended them 'as near as I can remember in the Author's own words'. The authenticity of the 'History of Martin' is therefore made

---

[1] See Pierre Legouis, 'Marvell et Swift', *Revue Anglo-Américaine*, 1924, p. 24. On Swift's knowledge of Pascal see Emile Pons, 'Swift et Pascal', *Langues Modernes*, 1951, p. 135, and *Études Anglaises*, 1952, p. 319.

to depend on the word of an anonymous bookseller quoting an anonymous ingenious gentleman who professed to have seen a manuscript which is not even said to have been written by the author of the *Tale*, and of which he had made a summary from memory.

The manuscript version is described as differing from the printed version after Section X. Here are said to have come—

The History of Martin;[1]
A Digression on Wars and Quarels;
The History of Martin (continued);
A Discourse concerning the Mechanical Operation of the Spirit;
A Project, for the universal benefit of Mankind.

But 'prudential considerations' necessitated another ending. 'Some things', we are told, 'seem to have been written since to fill up the place of what was not thought convenient then to print.'[2] We are asked to believe that Section XI as we know it was patched up as an afterthought.

It will at once be recognized that if the sections containing 'The History of Martin' ever existed in more than abstract, they must have been an awkward sequel to the main part of the *Tale*. They satirize the Church of England. The objects of Swift's satire were the abuses in Roman Catholicism and Calvinism. As he said explicitly in the 'Apology', the *Tale* 'celebrates the Church of England as the most perfect of all others in Discipline and Doctrine, it advances no Opinion they reject, nor condemns any they receive'.[3] The purpose of the *Tale* did not require an account of Martin corresponding in scheme to the accounts of Peter and Jack. There was no occasion to deal with the Church of England during the period from the Reformation to the reign of

---

[1] pp. 302 ff.   [2] pp. 294, 307.   [3] p. 5.

James II, and the rest of the story was dismissed in a few sentences.

'The History of Martin' must be attributed to an imitator of Swift who was hostile to the Church of England. He seized the opportunity to supply what a prejudiced and careless reader of the *Tale* might think was an omission. It was suggested to him, not merely by what at first may seem to be the claims of symmetry, but also by a passage of the *Tale* itself:

> I can only assure thee, Courteous Reader, for both our Comforts, that my Concern is altogether equal to thine, for my Unhappiness in losing, or mislaying among my Papers the remaining Part of these Memoirs; which consisted of Accidents, Turns, and Adventures, both New, Agreeable, and Surprizing.[1]

From the continuation of this passage he borrowed the device of writing down 'the Heads', and beginning his sentences with the word 'How'. The two sections on Martin as he sketched them differ from Swift's work in scale of treatment as well as in manner. Moreover, he had to describe Swift as 'embarassed for having introduced into his History a new Sect'. Martin had come to represent both the Lutherans and the Church of England, and Swift, we are told, was therefore obliged 'to drop the former *Martin*, and to substitute in his place Lady *Besses* Institution, which is to pass under the name of *Martin* in the sequel'.[2]

Swift had warned the reader against continuations of the *Tale*. The paltry scribbler who 'deals in a pernicious Kind of Writings, called *Second Parts*' was abroad in this famous island of Britain. 'I easily foresee', he says, 'that as soon as I lay down my Pen, this nimble *Operator* will have stole it'; and he therefore appeals to Dr. Bentley, the great Modern who claimed to distinguish the spurious from the genuine in ancient literature, to

[1] p. 203. [2] p. 304.

come to his assistance. If a continuation of the *Tale* is
for his sins to be clapped upon his back, let Bentley
lighten him of this burden, and take charge of it till the
'true Beast' thinks fit to call for it.[1] But the 'true Beast'
remains unknown.

The first writer to cast doubt on the authenticity of
this continuation was Justus van Effen. His version of
the *Tale* as *Le Conte du Tonneau* was based on the edition of 1720, and so included the summary of the new
sections. But he expressed his doubts with no hesita-
tion: 'Pour moi je crois plûtôt, que l'Abregé que nous
venons de voir est un extrait en l'air et que l'Auteur du
reste de l'Ouvrage, n'a jamais fait un discours dont ce
que nous venons de voir puisse être le Sommaire.'[2] He
also introduced his work with a striking exposition of
the purpose of the *Tale*, which he had found could be
too easily misunderstood. 'Si jamais livre a eu besoin
d'une Préface, j'ose dire que c'est celui-ci', he begins;
and he works up to this passage:

Tous les Chefs des Sectes ont été des hommes; il est naturel
que la vanité, le dépit, & l'esprit de contradiction les aïent jettez
dans quelque égarement, & qu'un homme qui se trouve dans une
assiette calme & Philosophique, s'en apperçoive sans peine.

J'ose promettre à tous ceux, qui sont capables de sentir cette
verité, qu'ils ne trouveront rien ici, qui ait le moindre air de
libertinage, & d'Irreligion; l'Auteur ne touche jamais à aucun de
ces Dogmes, que toutes les Sectes Chrêtiennes regardent comme
fondamentaux. Il turlupine dans l'Eglise Romaine, ce qu'il con-
sidere, comme des Doctrines inventées, pour asservir la raison à
l'autorité humaine, & à une stupide credulité; & par raport aux
differentes branches de la Religion Protestante, il tourne en ridicule cet Esprit d'Enthousiasme & de fanatisme, qui rend la pieté
incompatible avec le Sens commun. Je m'imagine que toutes
les personnes sensées en seront obligées à l'Auteur.

This was written in 1721, a year after the appearance

[1] pp. 183-4.   [2] ed. 1721, i, pp. 249-50.

of 'The History of Martin', and it is the earliest judicial statement of Swift's purpose.

XI. THE 'PATE MS.'

In the reissue of Nichols's edition of Swift's *Works* published in 1808, a number of notes marked '*MS. Pate*' are given at the foot of the page, and the following explanation is added to the first of them: 'This note is copied from one by Mr. Pate, whom Swift styles "the learned woollen draper"; and who had this and a few others, which will be found distinguished by his name, from the Dean's own mouth.'[1] The notes appear to have been taken from a volume which had been in the possession of Dr. Charles Chauncy, and is thus entered in the catalogue for the sale of his library in April 1790:

304 Swift's Tale of a Tub, cuts, MS. Notes, which are taken from a copy of Mr. Pate's, who had them from the Dean's own Mouth.[2]

An examination of the notes is not reassuring. Some of them are doubtful or wrong;[3] and though most are right, they are often such as any intelligent reader might have written. Many might have been copied from the notes in the fifth edition. But they give at least one explanation that is valuable.[4]

Swift was on very friendly terms with Pate.[5] In his letter of 12 January 1709 to Robert Hunter, he says 'Mr. Addison and I often drink your health, and this

---

[1] Vol. ii, p. 164.

[2] The volume then fetched 14s.; see the priced catalogue in the British Museum, 7004 cc 10. It has not been traced.

[3] e.g. p. 106.

[4] p. 41. Pate's notes (fifty-one in all, of which six are on the *Battle* and one on the *Mechanical Operation*) are included in this edi-tion, but a few are omitted that are verbally identical with notes in the fifth edition.

[5] He was Sheriff of London in 1734. See the account of him in the *Dictionary of National Biography*. He is supposed to be the woollen-draper 'remarkable for his Learning and Good-nature' in Steele's *Guardian*, No. 141.

day I did it with Will Pate, a certain adorer of yours, who is both a *bel esprit* and a woollen-draper'; and in the *Journal to Stella* he makes the entry on 17 September 1710, 'To-day I dined six miles out of town, with Will Pate the learned woollen-draper'. The *Tale of a Tub* may well have been at some time the subject of their conversation, and Swift could easily have suggested explanations without committing himself to be its author. He might have hazarded the suggestion that the mysterious number 'nine thousand seven hundred forty and three' was the number of livings in England, just as he might have put his friend on the wrong track by interpreting the purchase of 'a Large Continent lately said to have been discovered in *Terra Australis incognita*' as a reference to 'the West Indies, sold by the Pope to the King of Spain'. Pate may have entered these explanations in the margins of his copy, and added others of his own.[1] That Swift dictated these notes is inconceivable; and it is highly improbable that he had any part in more than a few of them.

XII. LIST OF EDITIONS
1704–1755

1. A Tale of a Tub. . . . MDCCIV. 8vo.
See the reproduction, p. lxvii.
Collation: Treatises writ by the same Author p. [ii]; title p. [iii]; blank p. [iv]; Dedication pp. [v] (A 3)–[x]; The Bookseller to the Reader pp. [xi–xii]; Epistle Dedicatory pp. 1 (B 1)–11; blank p. [12]; Preface pp. 13–31; blank p. [32]; A Tale of a Tub pp. 33 (D 1)–221 (P 7); blank p. [222]; title of 'The Battel' p. [223]; blank p. [224]; The Bookseller to the Reader pp. [225] (Q 1)–[226]; Preface pp. [227–8]; The Battel pp. 229 (Q 3)–278 (T 3 v); title of 'A Discourse'

---

1 Or some may have been added by another hand. Chauncy's volume was not Pate's; the notes had been transcribed. It must have been a fifth or later edition as it contained cuts.

p. [279]; blank p. [280]; The Bookseller's Advertisement p. [281]; blank p. [282]; A Discourse pp. 283 (T 6)–322 (Y 1 v).

Published May 1704. Price 4s. See *Term Catalogues*.

2. A Tale of a Tub. . . . The Second Edition Corrected. London: Printed for John Nutt, near Stationers-Hall. MDCCIV. 8vo.

This follows ed. 1 page for page, and generally line for line, but the type has been reset.

In the Bodleian copy the first sheet is so folded that the 'Treatises writ by the same Author' faces the Epistle Dedicatory, and is thus p. [xii], the title being p. [i].

3. A Tale of a Tub. . . . The Third Edition Corrected. London: Printed for John Nutt, near Stationers-Hall. MDCCIV. 8vo.

This follows ed. 2 line for line. Only partly reset. In the Bodleian copies of ed. 2 and ed. 3 sheets H, for example, are from the same type; and sheet N shows slight alterations in type that had been kept standing.

Published June 1704.

4. A Tale of a Tub: . . . The Fourth Edition Corrected. London: Printed for John Nutt, near Stationers Hall. MDCCV. 8vo.

This follows ed. 3 line for line. The type has been reset.

Published May 1705.

5. A Tale of a Tub: . . . The Fourth Edition Corrected. Dublin, Re-Printed; and are to be Sold only at Dick's and Lloyd's Coffee-Houses, and at the Printing-Press in Fishamble-street. 1705. 8vo. Pp. x, 182.

Set from ed. 3.

6. A Tale of a Tub . . . The Fifth Edition . . . MDCCX. 8vo.

See the reproduction before the text.

Collation: Title p. [i]; Treatises wrote by the same Author p. [ii]; An Apology For the, &c. pp. [iii] (A 2)–[xxiv] (a 4 v); Dedication pp. [xxv–xxx]; The Bookseller to the Reader pp. [xxxi–ii]; Epistle Dedicatory pp. 1 (B 1)–12; Preface pp. 13–31; blank p. 32; A Tale of a Tub pp. 33 (D 1)–241 (R 1); blank p. [242]; title of 'The Battel'

A

TALE

OF A

TUB.

Written for the Univerſal Improve
ment of Mankind.

Diu multumque deſideratum

To which is added,

An ACCOUNT of a

BATTEL

BETWEEN THE

Antient and Modern BOOKS
in St. *James's* Library.

Baſima eacabaſa eanaa irrauriſta, diarba da caeotaba fobor camelanthi. *Iren. Lib* 1 C. 18.

——— *Juvatque novos decerpere flores,*
Inſignemque meo capiti petere inde coronam,
Unde prius nulli velarunt tempora Muſæ Lucret.

LONDON.

Printed for *John Nutt,* near *Stationers-Hall.*
MDCCIV.

p. 243; blank p. [244]; The Bookseller to the Reader pp. [245–6];
Preface pp. [247–8]; The Battel pp. 249 (R 5)–299 (U 6); blank p.
[300]; title of 'A Discourse' p. [301]; blank p. [302]; The Bookseller's Advertisement p. [303]; blank p. [304]; A Discourse pp. 305
(x 1)–344 (z 4v).

This edition is the first to contain the 'Apology', and the footnotes,
and the plates. The text was set from ed. 4, but there are alterations
and omissions.

Frontispiece to the 'Tale' (signed B. Lens delin: J. Sturt sculp.) and
to the 'Battel', and six other plates facing pp. 35, 56, 121, 138, 192,
and 233. In the copy in the Forster Collection they are subscribed to
face pp. 35, 55, 111, 127, 178, and 214—the corresponding pages in
edd. 1–4. They would appear to have been engraved before the new
notes were distributed throughout ed. 5 as footnotes (see below, No. 7).

The Fountaine large-paper copy measures 8¾ by 5¼ in.

[The authoritative texts are those of the first and
fifth editions. The intervening 'corrected' editions are
reprints which introduce errors and by being in the
direct line of descent of the fifth edition account for
some of its readings.

The present text is reprinted from the fifth edition,
which contains alterations that were made by Swift,
but errors were allowed to stand, and new errors were
introduced by the printer. Several of the readings of the
first edition have now been restored. Variants are recorded in the notes. A few misprints of no significance
have been silently corrected.]

7. An Apology for the Tale of a Tub. With Explanatory Notes . . . London; Printed for John Morphew
near Stationers-Hall. MDCCXI.

See reproduction, p. lxix.

Collation: Title p. [1]; blank p. [2]; An Apology For the, &c. pp. [3]
(A 3)–24 (C 4 v); Explanatory Notes to the Tale of a Tub pp. 25 (D 1)–
51 (G 2); blank p. [52].

The 'Apology' is an offprint from ed. 5 with page numbers added.
The 'Explanatory Notes' are the footnotes in ed. 5, but are printed in
a body in the same type as the text of edd. 1–5. Neither set of notes
was printed from the other; their variants show that both were printed
from the manuscript. The most important will be found on pp. 86 and
192.

AN
APOLOGY
FOR THE
𝕮ale of a'𝕮ub.

WITH
EXPLANATORY
NOTES
BY
W. W-tt-n, B. D.
And others.

LONDON;
Printed for J O H N M O R P H E W near
Stationers-Hall. MDCCXI.

The notes appear to have been set up in a body before Tooke urged Swift to have them printed at the foot of the page to which they refer (see p. xxiii; also p. 350). When Tooke said 'I have sent the Key' he may be taken to have sent a proof. The explanation of the date 1711 may be that the type had been kept standing in order to form along with an offprint of the 'Apology' a supplement to the earlier editions of the *Tale*.

8. A Tale of a Tub. . . . Anno M.DCC.XI. 12mo. Pp. 310.

This was set from ed. 3 and contains neither the 'Apology' nor footnotes. Dr. H. Teerink points out in his *Bibliography*, 1937, pp. 154–5, that there were four issues of this edition, all of different settings, but identical in pagination and lineation. Plates (reduced from those of 1710) are in some of the issues. No name of publisher, but Curll's *Complete Key*, third edition 1714, is bound in at the end of some copies.

The mention of the coming 'Newest Edition' in *The Flying Post* (and *Medley*) of 2–4 October 1712 is a jest.

9. Miscellaneous Works, Comical & Diverting: By T. R. D. J. S. D. O. P. I. I. In Two Parts. 1. The Tale of a Tub; . . . London, Printed by Order of the Society de propagando, &c. M.DCC.XX. 8vo.

See reproduction, p. 291. T.R.D.J.S.D.O.P.I.I. stands for 'The Reverend Dr. Jonathan Swift Dean of Patrick's in Ireland'. 'Printed by Order', &c., is a jest on the 'Congregatio de propaganda fide'.

This book was printed in Holland and published by T. Johnson, bookseller in The Hague. It does not contain the 'Apology'. On the other hand it contains a new Bookseller's Advertisement (see pp. iii–ix), notes which are independent of the notes in ed. 5, and a 'Table, or Index, or Key' incorporating the earliest text of the apocryphal 'History of Martin' (pp. 253–261). The *Mechanical Operation* is printed immediately after the *Tale*, and has the running title 'A Fragment of|The Tale of a Tub'.

The *Tale* is said in its title-page to be 'By a Member of the Illustrious Fraternity of Grubstreet', and the Miscellanies that form the Second Part are said to be 'By a certain paultry Scribler, commonly called, The Author of the first'.

10. A Tale of a Tub. . . . The Sixth Edition: With the Author's Apology and Explanatory Notes. . . . London: Printed for S. Tooke and B. Motte, at the

Middle Temple Gate, Fleet-street, 1724. 12mo. Pp. lvi, 273. Plates.

The sixth edition issued by Swift's publishers, but actually the ninth. Frontispiece signed 'G. Clark sculp'.

11. A Tale of a Tub. . . . The Seventh Edition. . . . Dublin: Printed by A. Rhames for W. Smith at the Hercules in Dame-street, 1726. 12mo. Pp. xlix, 226.

The second Dublin edition.

12. A Tale of a Tub. . . . The Seventh Edition. . . . London: Printed for Benj. Motte, at the Middle-Temple Gate, in Fleet-Street. M.DCC.XXVII. 12mo. Pp. xxiv, 220. Plates.

13. A Tale of a Tub. . . . The Eighth Edition. . . . London: Printed for Benj. Motte, at the Middle-Temple Gate, in Fleetstreet. MDCCXXXIII. 12mo. Pp. xxiv, 220. Plates.

Follows ed. 7 page for page, but reset.

14. A Tale of a Tub: . . . A new Edition . . . London. M.DCC.XXXIV. 8vo. Pp. iv, 292.

No name of publisher. Probably printed in Holland. Set largely from ed. 1720, but with a new 'Bookseller's Advertisement' pp. [iii–iv], and some new notes supplementing the notes of 1720. The *Mechanical Operation* is printed before the *Battle*, which is followed by the 'Apology'. The 'History of Martin' is here printed for the second time.

15. A Tale of a Tub. . . . The Ninth Edition . . . London: Printed for Charles Bathurst, at the Middle-Temple-Gate, in Fleet-Street. M.DCC.XXXIX. 12mo. Pp. [xxiv], 220. Plates.

The first edition by Bathurst. Plates signed 'J. Mynde sculp'.

16. A Tale of a Tub. . . . The Eighth Edition . . . Dublin: Printed by S. Powell, For W. Smith at the Hercules in Dame-street, and G. Faulkner in Essex-street. M DCC XLI. 12mo. Pp. xlvii, 49–264. Plates.

The third Dublin edition.

17. A Tale of a Tub. . . . The Tenth Edition . . . London: Printed for Charles Bathurst, at the Cross-Keys in Fleet-Street. M.DCC.XLIII. 8vo. Pp. i–xvi, 6 pages unnumbered, 220. Plates.

18. . . . The Eleventh Edition . . . Bathurst . . . MDCCXLVII.

19. . . . The Twelfth Edition . . . Bathurst . . . MDCCLI.

20. The Works of Swift, vol. 1 (12mo) . . . Bathurst . . . MDCCLI.

21. A Tale of a Tub. . . . The Twelfth Edition. Edinburgh: Printed by W. Sands, A. Murray, and J. Cochran. For William Gray junior. Sold by G. Crawfurd, W. Gordon, and J. Brown, Edinburgh; J. Barry, Glasgow; and T. Glas, Dundee. MDCCL.

22. A Tale of a Tub. . . . The Thirteenth Edition. Edinburgh: Printed for G. Hamilton & J. Balfour, and L. Hunter, at Edinburgh; and A. Stalker, at Glasgow; and sold by them and other Booksellers. M,DCC,LII.

23. A Tale of a Tub. . . . The Thirteenth Edition. Glasgow: Printed by R. Urie. MDCCLIII.

24, 25. The Works of Jonathan Swift, D.D. Dean of St. Patrick's, Dublin. Accurately revised in Six Volumes, Adorned with Copper-Plates; With Some Account of the Author's Life, And Notes Historical and Explanatory, By John Hawkesworth. London, Printed for C. Bathurst, C. Davis, C. Hitch and L. Hayes, J. Hodges, R. and J. Dodsley, and W. Bowyer. MDCCLV. 4to.
    . . . In Twelve Volumes. M DCC LV. 8vo.
    In both the quarto and octavo editions, vol. 1, the title-page of the

Tale has the imprint 'London: Printed for Charles Bathurst, at the Cross-Keys in Fleetstreet. MDCCLIV.' There is a new set of plates, 'J. S. Müller inv: del: et sc.'

In the preface to the whole edition Hawkesworth says: 'The *Tale of a Tub*, the *Battle of the Books*, and the *Fragment* were first published together in 1704, and the apology, and the notes from *Wotton* were added in 1710; this edition the Dean revised a short time before his understanding was impaired, and his corrections will be found in this impression.' A footnote states that 'the corrected Copy is now in the hands of Mr. Dean Swift'. Deane Swift referred to it in his letter to John Nichols of 25 April 1778 (*Literary Illustrations*, vol. v, p. 378), 'I have besides the Tale of a Tub, corrected by himself.' The copy passed into the possession of his son, Theophilus Swift, who showed it to Sir Walter Scott. From a note in Scott's edition, 1824, vol. i, p. 90, we learn that it bore the inscription 'To Mrs. Martha Whiteway, a present on her birth-day, May 29, 1735, from her affectionate cousin, Jonath. Swift.'

The nature of Swift's revision is thus described by Scott: 'The Dean had corrected, with his pen, all the abbreviations and elisions which were ordinary in the beginning of the century, by replacing *it is* for '*tis, the end* for *th' end*, and the like, but without any other alterations.'

Apart from mere changes in spelling, or such expansions as ''Tis' into 'It is' or 'B——tly' into 'Bentley', Hawkesworth's text contains about 140 variants. Most of them are negligible, such as 'elude' for 'delude' (34.14), 'class' for 'Classis' (63.14), 'evomitation' for 'evomition' (108. 12), 'thither' for 'there' (130.24), 'criticize' for 'Critick' (209.16), 'politics' for 'the Politicks' (218.8 and 277.29), 'New-England' for 'New Holland' (261.9). The best of them are given in the notes to this edition.

The History of Martin

[First published in *Miscellaneous Works*, 1720, and reprinted in the 1734 edition of the *Tale*. See pp. 302–7.]

The History of Martin. Being A Proper Sequel to The Tale of a Tub. With A Digression concerning the Nature, Usefulness, and Necessity of Wars and Quarrels. By the Rev. D—n S—t. Not sparing his own Clergy Cloth, But eats into it like a Moth. To which is added, A Dialogue between A— P—e, Esq; and Mr. C—s C—ffe, Poets, in St. James's Park. London:

Printed for T. Taylor, at the Rose, in Exeter-Exchange.
MDCCXLII.

Title p. [3]; blank p. [iv]; The History of Martin pp. [5]–12; A Dialogue pp. 13–24.

The Bodleian copy (Godwin Pamph. 1911) has the half-title 'The History of Martin. Price Sixpence'. On the verso of the half-title, under the heading 'Just Published', the second item is 'A Tale of a Tub moralized and bottled off. Price 6d'.

The text derives from the text of 1720, but the series of headings is converted into continuous narrative by the omission of 'How' at the beginning of a sentence and by similar changes, e.g. 'Of several efforts *Jack* made' becomes '*Jack* made several efforts'. The 'N.B.' at the conclusion (see p. 306) is omitted, and its place is taken by the following note:—'Here the Author being seized with a Fit of Dulness (to which he is very subject) after having read a poetical Epistle address'd to * * * it entirely composed his Senses, so that he has not writ a Line since.'

The History of Martin. Giving An Account of his Departure from Jack, and their setting up for themselves, . . . With many other extraordinary Adventures of the said Martin in several Places with many considerable Persons. With A Digression concerning the Nature, Usefulness, and Necessity of Wars and Quarrels. By the Rev. D—n S—t. To which is added, A Dialogue between A— P—e, Esq; and Mr. C—s C—ffe, Poets, in St. James's Park. London: Printed for J. Temple, near St. Dunstan's Church, Fleet-[Street. MDCCXLIV.]

In the copies in the British Museum (1080. i. 25(6)), and the Bodleian (Godwin Pamph. 1999) the date has been cut off. The year 1744 is given in Quaritch's catalogue No. 372, October 1922, p. 26.

This is a reissue of the sheets of the 1742 edition with a new title-page.

Translations

Le Conte Du Tonneau Contenant tout ce que les Arts, & les Sciences Ont de plus Sublime, Et de plus Mysterieux. Avec plusieurs autres Piéces très-curieuses. Par le fameux Dr. Swift. Traduit de l'Anglois. Tome

Premier (Second). A La Haye, Chez Henri Scheurleer, M.DCC.XXI. 12mo.

Vol. i, pp. xxiv, 312; vol. ii, pp. xiv, 296.
Translated by Justus van Effen, and based on the edition of 1720. Vol. i contains the 'Conte du Tonneau', with a 'Table des Matieres' at the end, and the 'Histoire de Martin' and the 'Abregé d'une digression sur la nature, l'utilité, & la necessité des Guerres, et des Querelles' inserted in the body of the text after Section IX. Vol. ii contains the 'Dissertation sur l'Operation Mechanique de l'Esprit', the 'Bataille des Livres', and translations of prose pieces in Part II of the 1720 volume. Each volume contains a 'Préface du Traducteur'.
Other editions, La Haye 1732, 1741, and 1757, Lausanne et Genève 1756.

Les Trois Justaucorps, Conte Bleu, Tiré de l'Anglois du Révérend Mr. Jonathan Swif, Ministre de l'Eglise Anglicane, Docteur en Théologie & Doïen de la Cathédrale de St. Patrice de Dublin. Avec Les Trois Anneaux, Nouvelle tirée de Bocace. A Dublin. M.DCC.XXI. sm. 8vo.

Title p. [i]; Avertissement pp. [iii–iv]; Les Trois Justaucorps pp. [1]–79; Les Trois Anneaux pp. 80–88.
This is an adaptation. 'Le Conte, qu'on donne ici, est proprement le Conte d'un Conte Anglois. En effet, ce n'est point une traduction à la lettre, ce n'est point non plus une simple imitation, c'est le Conte même. . . . Le Conteur François, pour s'accommoder au langage & au génie de sa Nation, a choisi Paris pour le Théatre de leurs Avantures.'
Probably printed and published in Holland. The British Museum copy has in pencil on the title-page 'par René Macé'.

Des berühmten Herrn D. Schwifts Måhrgen Von der Tonne, Zum allgemeinen Nutzen des menschlichen Geschlechts abgefasset, Nebst einem vollståndigen Begriffe einer allgemeinen Gelehrsamkeit, Aus dem Englischen ins Teutsche übersetzet. 1 Theil. . . . Altona. 1729. Anderer Theil. 1729. 8vo.

Translated from the edition of 1720.
Other German translations Hamburg and Leipzig 1758, and Zürich 1787.

Vertelsel van de Ton, Behelzende het Merg van alle Kunsten en Weetenschappen. Geschreeven Tot Algemeen Nut Des Menschelyken Geslachts. Mitsgaders een Verhaal van den Strydt der Boeken In de Boekzaal van St. James. Door den beroemden Dr. Swift. Uit het Engelsch vertaalt door P. le Clercq. t'Amsterdam, Voor Rekening van de Compagnie. M.D.CC.XXXV.

Derivative Titles

The Tale of a Tub, Revers'd, for the Universal Improvement of Mankind. Diu Multumque desideratum. With a Character of the Author. Nemo me impune Lacessit. London, Printed and Sold by A. Baldwin in Warwick-Lane, M DCC V. 8vo.

The title-page is a cancel. Apart from A1 and B1 the book is a reissue of 'The Rebellion: or, An Account of the Late Civil-War in the Kingdom of Eloquence . . . London, Printed in the Year, 1704' (published November 1704).

The Preface alludes to 'that Reverend Person, who has lately Publish'd a compleat System of Divinity, commonly called, or known by the Name of a *Tale of a Tub*, . . . a most admirable Treatise, wherein the Authors good Breeding and Piety and Good-humour, and Christian Charity and Aversion to Satyr, and incomprehensible Learning most manifestly appear' . . .

A Morning's Discourse of a Bottomless Tubb, Introducing the Historical Fable of the Oak and her Three Provinces; or, Transactions in Government among Trees: Being Historical and Satyrical Remarks on Passages in some late Reigns; mix'd with Comical Dialogues in the Jargon or Brogue of several Nations, viz. French, Irish, Scotch, Welsh, &c. Written by a Lover of the Loyal, Honest, and Moderate Party. London: Printed for John Morphew near Stationer's Hall. 1712. 8vo.

The introductory 'Morning's Discourse' (pp. 1–26) is an attack on the *Tale* and 'Dr. Digression'.

A Second Tale of a Tub: or, The History of Robert Powel the Puppet-Show-Man. . . . London: Printed for J. Roberts near the Oxford Arms in Warwick-lane. 1715. 8vo.

By Thomas Burnet and George Duckett. See *The Letters of Thomas Burnet to George Duckett*, 1712–1722, edited by D. Nichol Smith, Roxburghe Club, 1914, p. 306.

A Tale and No Tale: That is to say, A Tale, and No Tale of a Tub. . . . London: Printed for J. Roberts, near the Oxford-Arms in Warwick-Lane. 1715. 8vo.

Verse; a political sketch of English history from Elizabeth to George I.

A Tale of a Bottomless Tub. . . . London: Printed for J. Roberts at the Oxford-Arms in Warwick-Lane. 1723. [Price 6d. Folio.

Verse; Venus and Cupid on 'Which Sex does merit most Applause'.

Tale of a Tub Bottled off and Moraliz'd. Or, An Heroi-Comick Oration. With A Touch upon the Times. . . . London; Printed for J. Roberts, near the Oxford-Arms in Warwick-Lane. M.DCC.XXXVI. (Price 6d.) Folio.

Verse; an 'Oration To a Glass-Bottle Congregation' in praise of bottles, satirizing those who are 'against all Church-Establishment.'

A Tale of Two Tubs: or, the B. . . . . .rs in Querpo. Being A Humorous and Satirical Description of some principal Characters that have long shone, in this Hemisphere, like Stars of the first Magnitude; . . . London: Printed in the Year, 1749.

Verse; on the brothers the Duke of Newcastle and Henry Pelham.

A TALE

OF A

TUB.

Written for the Univerſal Improvement of Mankınd.

Diu multumque deſideratum

To which is added,

An ACCOUNT of a

BATTEL

BETWEEN THE

Antient and Modern BOOKS in St. *James*'s Library.

Baſima eacabaſa eanaa irrauriſta, diarba da caeotaba fobor camelanthi. *Iren. Lib.* 1. *C.* 18.

———— *Juvatque novos deceɪpere flores,*
Inſignemque meo capiti petere inde coronam,
Unde prius nulli velarunt tempora Muſæ. Lucret.

The Fifth EDITION: With the Author's Apology and Explanatory Notes. By *W. W--tt--n*, B. D. and others.

LONDON: Printed for *John Nutt*, near *Stationers-Hall.* MDCCX.

Treatises[1] wrote by the same Author, most of them mentioned in the following Discourses; which will be speedily published.

A *Character of the present Set of* Wits *in this Island.*

A Panegyrical Essay upon the Number T H R E E.

A Dissertation upon the principal Productions of Grubstreet.

Lectures upon a Dissection of Human Nature.

A Panegyrick upon the World.

An Analytical Discourse upon Zeal, Histori-theo-physi-logically *considered.*

A general History of Ears.

A modest Defence of the Proceedings of the Rabble *in all Ages.*

A Description of the Kingdom of Absurdities.

A Voyage into England, *by a Person of Quality in* Terra Australis incognita, *translated from the Original.*

A Critical Essay upon the Art of Canting, *Philosophically, Physically, and Musically considered.*

[1] This list faces the title-page in the first four editions. They all read 'Treatises writ'. See p. 351.

AN
APOLOGY
For the, &c.

IF good and ill Nature equally operated upon Mankind, I might have saved my self the Trouble of this Apology; for it is manifest by the Reception the following Discourse hath met with, that those who approve it, are a great Majority among the Men of Tast; yet there have been two or three Treatises written expressly against it,[1] besides many others that have flirted at it[2] occasionally, without one Syllable having been ever published in its Defence, or even Quotation to its Advantage, that I can remember, except by the Polite Author of a late Discourse between a Deist and a Socinian.[3]

Therefore, since the Book seems calculated to live at least as long as our Language, and our Tast admit no great Alterations, I am content to convey some Apology along with it.

---

[1] (1) William King's *Remarks on the Tale of a Tub* (1704). (2) William Wotton's *Observations upon the Tale of a Tub* (1705). See Appendix B; and cf. p. 10.

[2] (1) *The Tale of a Tub, revers'd* (1705). (2) Durfey, *An Essay towards the Theory of the Intelligible World* (see p. 36), (3) *The Golden Spy* (1709), 'The Epistle Nuncupatory, to the Author of A Tale of a Tub'.

[3] Swift refers to *The Principles of Deism Truly represented and set in a clear Light, in Two Dialogues between a Sceptick and a Deist* (London, 1708). At p. 54 occurs the following passage:

'*Scep.* No; there's no Subject so Entertaining as this [i.e. Profanity]; no sort of Wit that has so high a Relish: Obscenity does pretty well; but, as an Ingenious Author has lately observ'd, it's so beaten and so exhausted a Topick, that it will never do alone; unless the Scene be now and then relieved with Prophaneness, it goes but heavily off.' *Tale of a Tub*

The work is attributed to Francis Gastrell, to whom there are several references in the *Journal to Stella*.

The greatest Part of that Book was finished above thirteen Years since, 1696, which is eight Years before it was published. The Author was then young, his Invention at the Height, and his Reading fresh in his Head. By the Assistance of some Thinking, and much Conversation, he had endeavour'd to Strip himself of as many real Prejudices as he could; I say real ones, because under the Notion of Prejudices, he knew to what dangerous Heights some Men have proceeded. Thus prepared, he thought the numerous and gross Corruptions in Religion and Learning might furnish Matter for a Satyr, that would be useful and diverting: He resolved to proceed in a manner, that should be altogether new, the World having been already too long nauseated with endless Repetitions upon every Subject. The Abuses in Religion he proposed to set forth in the Allegory of the Coats, and the three Brothers, which was to make up the Body of the Discourse. Those in Learning he chose to introduce by way of Digressions. He was then a young Gentleman much in the World, and wrote to the Tast of those who were like himself; therefore in order to allure them, he gave a Liberty to his Pen, which might not suit with maturer Years, or graver Characters,[1] and which he could have easily corrected with a very few Blots, had he been Master of his Papers for a Year or two before their Publication.

Not that he would have governed his Judgment by the ill-placed Cavils of the Sour, the Envious, the Stupid, and the Tastless, which he mentions with disdain. He acknowledges there are several youthful Sallies, which from the Grave and the Wise may deserve a Rebuke. But he desires to be answerable no farther than he is guilty, and that his Faults may not be multiply'd by the ignorant, the unnatural, and uncharitable Applications of those who have neither

---

[1] This may be taken to suggest that Swift was not in Holy Orders when he wrote *A Tale of a Tub*; but he was ordained in 1694, and he says here that he wrote most of the book in 1696. Cf. 'graver Character', p. 11, l. 13.

Candor to suppose good Meanings, nor Palate to distinguish true Ones. After which, he will forfeit his Life, if any one Opinion can be fairly deduced from that Book, which is contrary to Religion or Morality.

Why should any Clergyman of our Church be angry to see the Follies of Fanaticism and Superstition exposed, tho' in the most ridiculous Manner? since that is perhaps the most probable way to cure them, or at least to hinder them from farther spreading. Besides, tho' it was not intended for their Perusal; it raillies nothing but what they preach against. It contains nothing to provoke them by the least Scurillity upon their Persons or their Functions. It Celebrates the Church of England *as the most perfect of all others in Discipline and Doctrine, it advances no Opinion they reject, nor condemns any they receive. If the Clergy's Resentments lay upon their Hands, in my humble Opinion, they might have found more proper Objects to employ them on:* Nondum tibi defuit Hostis;[1] *I mean those heavy, illiterate Scriblers, prostitute in their Reputations, vicious in their Lives, and ruin'd in their Fortunes, who to the shame of good Sense as well as Piety, are greedily read, meerly upon the Strength of bold, false, impious Assertions, mixt with unmannerly Reflections upon the Priesthood, and openly intended against all Religion; in short, full of such Principles as are kindly received, because they are levell'd to remove those Terrors that Religion tells Men will be the Consequence of immoral Lives. Nothing like which is to be met with in this Discourse, tho' some of them are pleased so freely to censure it. And I wish, there were no other Instance of what I have too frequently observed, that many of that Reverend Body are not always very nice in distinguishing between their Enemies and their Friends.*

Had the Author's Intentions met with a more candid Interpretation from some whom out of Respect he forbears to

---

[1] Lucan, *De bello civili*, i. 23.

name, he might have been encouraged to an Examination of Books written by some of those Authors above-described, whose Errors, Ignorance, Dullness and Villany, he thinks he could have detected and exposed in such a Manner, that the Persons who are most conceived to be infected by them, would soon lay them aside and be ashamed: But he has now given over those Thoughts, since the weightiest *Men in the* weightiest *Stations*[1] *are pleased to think it a more dangerous Point to laugh at those Corruptions in Religion, which they themselves must disapprove, than to endeavour pulling up those very Foundations, wherein all Christians have agreed.*

He thinks it no fair Proceeding, that any Person should offer determinately to fix a name upon the Author of this Discourse, who hath all along concealed himself from most of his nearest Friends: Yet several have gone a

Letter of Enthusiasm.[2]

farther Step, and pronounced another Book to have been the Work of the same Hand with this; which the Author directly affirms to be a thorough mistake; he having yet never so much as read that Discourse, a plain Instance how little Truth, there often is in general Surmises, or in Conjectures drawn from a Similitude of Style, or way of thinking.

Had the Author writ a Book to expose the Abuses in Law,

[1] Alluding to Dr. *Sharp* the archbishop of *York*'s representation of the author [Hawkesworth]. 'Archbishop Sharpe and the Duchess of Somerset, by shewing it [*A Tale of a Tub*] to the Queen, debarred him from a bishoprick' (Johnson, *Lives of the Poets*, ed. Birkbeck Hill, vol. iii, p. 10).

[2] *A Letter concerning Enthusiasm to My Lord * * * * * * [Somers]*, published 1708. It was by Shaftesbury, and was included in his *Characteristicks* in 1711.

Cf. Swift's letter to Ambrose Philips, 14 Sept. 1708 (*Correspondence*, ed. Ball, i. 111): 'There has been an essay of Enthusiasm lately published, that has run mightily, and is very well writ. All my friends will have me to be the author, *sed ego non credulus illis*. By the free Whiggish thinking I should rather take it to be yours; but mine it is not.' Swift attributed it also to Colonel Robert Hunter (ibid. 113, 136). Cf. p. 261, note 2.

or in *Physick*, he believes the *Learned Professors* in either *Faculty*, would have been so far from resenting it, as to have given him *Thanks for his Pains*, especially if he had made an honourable *Reservation* for the true *Practice* of either *Science*: But *Religion* they tell us ought not to be ridiculed, and they tell us *Truth*, yet surely the *Corruptions* in it may; for we are taught by the tritest *Maxim* in the *World*,[1] that *Religion* being the best of *Things*, its *Corruptions* are likely to be the worst.

There is one *Thing* which the judicious *Reader* cannot but have observed, that some of those *Passages* in this *Discourse*, which appear most liable to *Objection* are what they call *Parodies*, where the *Author* personates the *Style* and *Manner* of other *Writers*, whom he has a mind to expose. *I shall produce one Instance, it is in the* 51st Page.[2] Dryden, L'Estrange, *and some others I shall not name, are here levelled at, who having spent their Lives in Faction, and Apostacies, and all manner of Vice, pretended to be Sufferers for Loyalty and Religion. So* Dryden *tells us in one of his Prefaces*[3] *of his Merits and Suffering, thanks God that he* possesses *his Soul in Patience*: In other Places he talks at the same Rate, and L'Estrange *often uses the like Style,*[4] *and I believe the Reader may find more Persons to give that Passage an Application: But this is enough to direct those who may have over-look'd the Authors Intention.*

---

[1] *Corruptio optimi pessima*, a maxim of uncertain origin, though the idea is as old as Aristotle.

[2] p. 70 in this edition.

[3] Swift refers to Dryden's *Discourse concerning Satire* prefixed to his translation of Juvenal. See *Essays of John Dryden*, ed. W. P. Ker, vol. ii, pp. 38 and 80: 'I have patiently suffered the ruin of my small fortune, and the loss of that poor subsistence which I had from two kings'; and 'I have seldom answered any scurrilous lampoon . . . and, being naturally vindicative, have suffered in silence, and possessed my soul in quiet'.

Cf. footnote*, p. 70.

[4] Examples of such language will be found in L'Estrange's later writings, as in the Preface to the collected numbers of *The Observator*.

There are three or four other Passages which prejudiced or ignorant Readers have drawn by great Force to hint at ill Meanings, as if they glanced at some Tenets in Religion;[1] in answer to all which, the Author solemnly protests he is entirely Innocent, and never had it once in his Thoughts that any thing he said would in the least be capable of such Interpretations, which he will engage to deduce full as fairly from the most innocent Book in the World. And it will be obvious to every Reader, that this was not any part of his Scheme or Design, the Abuses he notes being such as all Church of England Men agree in, nor was it proper for his Subject to meddle with other Points, than such as have been perpetually controverted since the Reformation.

To instance only in that Passage about the three wooden Machines mentioned in the Introduction: In the Original Manuscript there was a description of a Fourth, which those who had the Papers in their Power, blotted out, as having something in it of Satyr, that I suppose they thought was too particular, and therefore they were forced to change it to the Number Three, *from whence some have endeavour'd to squeeze out a dangerous Meaning that was never thought on. And indeed the Conceit was half spoiled by changing the Numbers; that of* Four *being much more Cabalistick,[2] and therefore better exposing the pretended Virtue of Numbers, a Superstition there intended to be ridicul'd.*

Another Thing to be observed is, that there generally runs an Irony through the Thread of the whole Book, which the Men of Tast will observe and distinguish, and which will render some Objections that have been made, very weak and insignificant.

[1] 'Meanings; ... Religion', ed. 1710.

[2] It is difficult to form a guess what the fourth machine may have been, by which the quaternion was completed, and the author saved from the accusation of intending to ridicule one of the most solemn parts of our creed. But the fancies of mystical authors, in favour of particular numbers, were as capricious as those of the fancies of lucky numbers in the lottery [Scott]. See p. 354.

This Apology being chiefly intended for the Satisfaction of future Readers, it may be thought unnecessary to take any notice of such Treatises as have been writ against this ensuing Discourse, which are already sunk into waste Paper and Oblivion; after the usual Fate of common Answerers to Books, which are allowed to have any Merit: They are indeed like Annuals that grow about a young Tree, and seem to vye with it for a Summer, but fall and die with the Leaves in Autumn, and are never heard of any more. When Dr. Eachard writ his Book about the Contempt of the Clergy,[1] numbers of those Answerers immediately started up, whose Memory if he had not kept alive by his Replies, it would now be utterly unknown that he were ever answered at all.[2] There is indeed an Exception, when any great Genius thinks

[1] John Eachard (1636?–1697) published in 1670 *The Grounds & Occasions of the Contempt of the Clergy and Religion Enquired into. In a Letter written to R.L.* The book was attacked in (1) *An Answer to A Letter of Enquiry into the Grounds*, &c. (1671). (2) Barnabas Oley's preface to George Herbert's *Country Parson* (1671). (3) John Owen's preface to *Seven Sermons* by W. Bridge (1671). (4) *Hieragonisticon, or Corah's Doom, being an Answer to Two Letters of Enquiry*, by D.T. (1672). (5) *A Vindication of the Clergy from the Contempt imposed upon them by the Author of The Grounds and Occasions of the Contempt of the Clergy* (1672). (6) *An Answer to Two Letters of T.B.* [i.e. Eachard]. *By the Author of the Vindication of the Clergy* (1673). Eachard replied to the first of these in *Some Observations upon the Answer to an Enquiry into the Grounds, &c. In a Second Letter to R.L.* (1671).

The following occurs in Swift's *Thoughts on Various Subjects*: 'I have known men happy enough at ridicule, who upon grave subjects were perfectly stupid; of which Dr Eachard of Cambridge, who writ "The Contempt of the Clergy", was a great instance.

[2] Cf. *Thoughts on Various Subjects*: 'If the men of wit and genius would resolve never to complain in their works of critics and detractors, the next age would not know that they ever had any'; and Swift's letter to Pope, 26 Nov. 1725 (*Correspondence*, iii. 293): 'Take care the bad poets do not outwit you, as they have served the good ones in every age, whom they have provoked to transmit their names to posterity. Maevius is as well known as Virgil, and Gildon will be as well known as you, if his name gets into your verses.'

it worth his while to expose a foolish Piece; so we still read Marvel's *Answer to* Parker[1] *with Pleasure, tho' the Book it answers be sunk long[2] ago; so the Earl of* Orrery's *Remarks[3] will be read with Delight, when the Dissertation he exposes will neither be sought nor found; but these are no Enterprises for common Hands, nor to be hoped for above once or twice in an Age. Men would be more cautious of losing their Time in such an Undertaking, if they did but consider, that to answer a Book effectually, requires more Pains and Skill, more Wit, Learning, and Judgment than were employ'd in the Writing it. And the Author assures those Gentlemen who have given themselves that Trouble with him, that his Discourse is the Product of the Study, the Observation, and the Invention of several Years, that he often blotted out much more than he left, and if his Papers had not been a long time out of his Possession, they must have still undergone more severe Corrections; and do they think such a Building is to be battered with Dirt-Pellets however envenom'd the Mouths may be that discharge them. He hath seen the Productions but of two Answerers, One of which first appear'd as from an unknown hand,[4] but since avowed*

---

[1] In 1670 Samuel Parker (afterwards Bishop of Oxford) published *A Discourse of Ecclesiastical Politie: wherein The Authority of the Civil Magistrate over the Consciences of Subjects in Matters of Religion is Asserted; The Mischiefs and Inconveniences of Toleration are Represented, and all Pretences pleaded in behalf of Liberty of Conscience are fully Answered.* Marvell's reply to this and two subsequent attacks on the nonconformists was *The Rehearsal Transpros'd* (two parts, 1672–3).

[2] 'along' ed. 1710.

[3] *Dr. Bentley's Dissertations on the Epistles of Phalaris, and the Fables of Æsop, examin'd by the Honourable Charles Boyle, Esq.* (1698). Boyle succeeded his brother as fourth Earl of Orrery in 1703.

[4] King's *Remarks* appeared in 1704 with the following title: *Some Remarks on the Tale of a Tub. . . . By the Author of the Journey to London.*

Swift was now on terms of friendship with King, who was the first editor of *The Examiner*; and in December 1711 he helped 'poor Dr. King' to be appointed Gazetteer.

by a Person, who upon some Occasions hath discover'd no ill
Vein of Humor. 'Tis a Pity any Occasions should put him
under a necessity of being so hasty in his Productions, which
otherwise might often be entertaining. But there were other
Reasons obvious enough for his Miscarriage in this; he writ
against the Conviction of his Talent, and enter'd upon one of
the wrongest Attempts in Nature, to turn into ridicule by a
Weeks Labour, a Work which had cost so much time, and
met with so much Success in ridiculing others, the manner
how he has handled his Subject, I have now forgot, having
just look'd it over when it first came out, as others did, meerly
for the sake of the Title.

The other Answer is from a Person of a graver Character,[1] and is made up of half Invective, and half Annotation.
In the latter of which he hath generally succeeded well
enough. And the Project at that time was not amiss, to draw
in Readers to his Pamphlet, several having appear'd desirous that there might be some Explication of the more difficult
Passages. Neither can he be altogether blamed for offering
at the Invective Part, because it is agreed on all hands that
the Author had given him sufficient Provocation. The great
Objection is against his manner of treating it, very unsuitable to one of his Function. It was determined by a fair
Majority, that this Answerer had in a way not to be pardon'd, drawn his Pen against a certain great Man then
alive,[2] and universally reverenced for every good Quality
that could possibly enter into the Composition of the most
accomplish'd Person; it was observed, how he was pleased
and affected to have that noble Writer call'd his Adversary,

[1] William Wotton was Rector
of Middleton Keynes, Bucking-
hamshire, from 1693 till his death
in 1726. He was Chaplain to the
Earl of Nottingham, to whom he
dedicated the Reflections.

[2] Cf. pp. 37, 38. The charge
is questionable. In Boyle's Examination, pp. 23–25, it is admitted
that Wotton, in his treatment of
Sir William Temple, 'is modest
and decent, speaks generally with
respect of those he differs from';
but he had been 'prevail'd upon
to allow a place to the ill Manners
of another man', i.e. Bentley.

and it was a Point of Satyr well directed, for I have been told, Sir W. T. was sufficiently mortify'd at the Term. All the Men of Wit and Politeness were immediately up in Arms, through Indignation, which prevailed over their Contempt, by the Consequences they apprehended from such an Example, and it grew to be Porsenna's *Case*; Idem trecenti juravimus.[1] *In short, things were ripe for a general Insurrection, till my Lord* Orrery *had a little laid the Spirit, and settled the Ferment. But his Lordship being principally engaged with another Antagonist,[2] it was thought necessary in order to quiet the Minds of Men, that this Opposer should receive a Reprimand, which partly occasioned that Discourse of the Battle of the Books, and the Author was farther at the Pains to insert one or two Remarks on him in the Body of the Book.*

This Answerer has been pleased to find Fault with about a dozen Passages, which the Author will not be at the Trouble of defending, farther than by assuring the Reader, that for the greater Part the Reflector is entirely mistaken, and forces Interpretations which never once entered into the Writers' Head, nor will he is sure into that of any Reader of Tast and Candor; he allows two or three at most there produced to have been deliver'd unwarily, for which he desires to plead the Excuse offered already, of his Youth, and Franckness of Speech, and his Papers being out of his Power at the Time they were published.

But this Answerer insists, and says, what he chiefly dislikes, is the Design; *what that was I have already told, and I believe there is not a Person in* England *who can understand that Book, that ever imagined it to have been any thing else, but to expose the Abuses and Corruptions in Learning and Religion.*

But it would be good to know what Design *this Reflecter was serving, when he concludes his Pamphlet with a*

[1] Florus, *Epitoma*, i. 10. 6.   [2] Bentley.
Swift read Florus thrice in 1697.

*Caution to Readers, to beware of thinking the Authors Wit
was entirely his own, surely this must have had some Allay of
Personal Animosity, at least mixt with the* Design *of serving the Publick by so useful a Discovery; and it indeed touches
the Author in a very tender Point, who insists upon it, that
through the whole Book he has not borrowed one single Hint
from any Writer in the World; and he thought, of all
Criticisms, that would never have been one. He conceived it
was never disputed to be an Original, whatever Faults it
might have. However this Answerer produces three Instances to prove* this Author's Wit is not his own in many
Places.[1] *The first is, that the Names of* Peter, Martin *and*
Jack *are borrowed from a Letter of the late Duke of* Buckingham.[2] *Whatever Wit is contained in those three Names,
the Author is content to give it up, and desires his Readers
will substract as much as they placed upon that Account; at
the same time protesting solemnly that he never once heard
of that Letter, except in this Passage of the Answerer: So
that the Names were not borrowed as he affirms, tho' they
should happen to be the same, which however is odd enough,
and what he hardly believes; that of* Jack, *being not quite so
obvious as the other two. The second Instance to shew* the
Author's Wit is not his own, *is* Peter's Banter[3] (*as he
calls it in his* Alsatia Phrase[4]) *upon Transubstantiation,
which is taken from the same Duke's Conference with an*
Irish *Priest, where a Cork is turned into a Horse. This the*

---

[1] Wotton's *Observations*, p. 68
(or 540); see Appendix B, p. 327.

[2] Buckingham's letter 'To Mr.
Clifford, on his Humane-Reason',
—*Works*, ed. Tho. Brown, vol. ii
(1705), p. 67.

[3] About the same time, in *The
Tatler*, No. 230, Swift wrote: 'I
have done my utmost for some
Years past to stop the Progress of
Mobb and *Banter*, but have been
plainly born down by Numbers,
and betrayed by those who promised to assist me.'

According to Anthony Wood,
bantering 'came up at Oxon' in
1676 (*Life and Times of A. Wood*,
ed. A. Clark, vol. ii, pp. 334,
419). See also his account of John
Birkenhead in *Athenæ Oxonienses*.
Cf. p. 19, l. 8.

[4] See p. 19, note 1.

Author confesses to have seen, about ten Years after his Book was writ, and a Year or two after it was published. Nay, the Answerer overthrows this himself; for he allows the Tale was writ in 1697; *and I think that Pamphlet was not printed in many Years after.*[1] *It was necessary, that Corruption should have some Allegory as well as the rest; and the Author invented the properest he could, without enquiring what other People had writ, and the commonest Reader will find, there is not the least Resemblance between the two Stories. The third Instance is in these Words:* I have been assured, that the Battle in St. James's Library, is *mutatis mutandis,* taken out of a *French* Book, entituled, *Combat des livres,*[2] if I misremember not. *In which Passage there are two Clauses observable:* I have been assured; *and,* if I misremember not. *I desire first to know, whether if that Conjecture proves an utter falshood, those two Clauses will be a sufficient Excuse for this worthy Critick. The Matter is a Trifle; but, would he venture to pronounce at this Rate upon one of greater Moment? I know nothing more contemptible in a Writer than the Character of a Plagiary; which he here fixes at a venture, and this, not for a Passage, but a whole Discourse, taken out from another Book only* mutatis mutandis. *The Author is as much in the dark about this as the Answerer; and will imitate him by an Affirmation at Random; that if there be a word of Truth in this Reflection, he is a paultry, imitating Pedant, and the Answerer is a Person of Wit, Manners and Truth. He takes his Boldness, from never having seen any such Treatise in his Life nor heard of it before; and he is sure it is impossible for two Writers of different Times and Countries to agree in their*

[1] The 'Conference' appears to have been first printed in 1705 in Brown's edition of Buckingham's *Works,* vol. ii, pp. 33–57. This is the issue here referred to, 'pamphlet' being used in a sense that does not imply separate publication. The 'Conference' was published by itself in 1714, and then described as 'the second edition'.

[2] Presumably *Histoire Poëtique de la Guerre nouvellement declarée entre les Anciens et les Modernes* (1688), by François de Callières.

Thoughts after such a Manner, that two continued Discourses shall be the same only mutatis mutandis. *Neither will he insist upon the mistake of the Title, but let the Answerer and his Friend*[1] *produce any Book they please, he defies them to shew one single Particular, where the judicious Reader will affirm he has been obliged for the smallest Hint; giving only Allowance for the accidental encountring of a single Thought, which he knows may sometimes happen; tho' he has never yet found it in that Discourse, not has heard it objected by any body else.*

So that if ever any design was unfortunately executed, it must be that of this Answerer, who when he would have it observed that the Author's Wit is not his own, is able to produce but three Instances, two of them meer Trifles, and all three manifestly false. If this be the way these Gentlemen deal with the World in those Criticisms, where we have not Leisure to defeat them,[2] *their Readers had need be cautious how they rely upon their Credit; and whether this Proceeding can be reconciled to Humanity or Truth, let those who think it worth their while, determine.*

It is agreed, this Answerer would have succeeded much better, if he had stuck wholly to his Business as a Commentator upon the Tale of a Tub, *wherein it cannot be deny'd that he hath been of some Service to the Publick, and has given very fair Conjectures towards clearing up some difficult Passages; but, it is the frequent Error of those Men (otherwise very commendable for their Labors) to make Excursions beyond their Talent and their Office, by pretending to point out the Beauties and the Faults; which is no part of their Trade, which they always fail in, which the World never expected from them, nor gave them any thanks for endeavouring at. The Part of* Minellius,[3] *or* Farnaby[4]

---

[1] Bentley.
[2] i.e. the Phalaris controversy.
[3] Jean Minell (1625–83), a Dutch classical scholar, who edited many Latin classics for schools, e.g. Virgil, Sallust, Horace, Ovid, Terence, &c.

[4] Thomas Farnaby (1575?–

would have fallen in with his Genius, and might have been serviceable to many Readers who cannot enter into the abstruser Parts of that Discourse; but Optat ephippia bos piger.[1] *The dull, unwieldy, ill-shaped Ox would needs put on the Furniture of a Horse, not considering he was born to Labour, to plow the Ground for the Sake of superior Beings, and that he has neither the Shape, Mettle nor Speed of that nobler Animal he would affect to personate.*

It is another Pattern of this Answerer's fair dealing, to give us Hints that the Author is dead,[2] and yet to lay the Suspicion upon somebody, I know not who, in the Country; to which can be only returned, that he is absolutely mistaken in all his Conjectures; and surely Conjectures are at best too light a Pretence to allow a Man to assign a Name in Publick. He condemns a Book, and consequently the Author, of whom he is utterly ignorant, yet at the same time fixes in Print, what he thinks a disadvantageous Character upon those who never deserved it. A Man who receives a Buffet in the Dark may be allowed to be vexed; but it is an odd kind of Revenge to go to Cuffs in broad day with the first he meets with, and lay the last Nights Injury at his Door. And thus much for this discreet, candid, pious, *and* ingenious *Answerer.*

How the Author came to be without his Papers, is a Story not proper to be told, and of very little use, being a private Fact of which the Reader would believe as little or as much as he thought good. He had however a blotted Copy by him, which he intended to have writ over, with many Alterations, and this the Publishers[3] were well aware of,

1647), thus described in Wood's *Athenæ Oxonienses* (vol. ii, 1692, col. 54): 'He was the chief Grammarian, Rhetorician, Poet, Latinist and Grecian of his time, and his School was so much frequented, that more Churchmen and Statesmen issued thence, than from any School taught by one Man in England.'

[1] Horace, *Ep.* i. xiv. 43.

[2] *Observations*, p. 67 (or 539); see Appendix B, p. 327.

[3] The editors. Cf. Swift's Preface to the third volume of Temple's *Letters* (1703): 'If I could

having put it into the Booksellers Preface,[1] that they appre-
hended a surreptitious Copy, which was to be altered, &c.
This though not regarded by Readers, was a real Truth, only
the surreptitious Copy was rather that which was printed,
and they made all hast they could, which indeed was need-
less; the Author not being at all prepared; but he has been
told, the Bookseller was in much Pain, having given a good
Sum of Money for the Copy.

In the Authors Original Copy there were not so many
Chasms as appear in the Book; and why some of them were
left he knows not; had the Publication been trusted to him,
he should have made several Corrections of Passages against
which nothing hath been ever objected. He should like-
wise have altered a few of those that seem with any Reason
to be excepted against, but to deal freely, the greatest Num-
ber he should have left untouch'd, as never suspecting
it possible any wrong Interpretations could be made of
them.

The Author observes, at the End of the Book there is a
Discourse called A Fragment; *which he more wondered to*
see in Print than all the rest. Having been a most imperfect
Sketch with the Addition of a few loose Hints, which he once
lent a Gentleman who had designed a Discourse of some-
what the same Subject; he never thought of it afterwards,
and it was a sufficient Surprize to see it pieced up together,
wholly out of the Method and Scheme he had intended, for it

have been prevailed with by the *Rhetorick of Booksellers* ... I might easily, instead of Retrenching, have made very considerable Additions. ... But, if the Press must needs be loaded, I had rather it should not be by my means. And there-fore I may hope to be allowed one Word in the Style of a *Publisher* (an Office lyable to much Censure, without the least Pretension to Merit or to Praise), that ... the Reader will hardly find one *Letter* in this Collection unworthy of the Author.' Cf. also *Gulliver's Travels*, 'The Publisher to the Reader'. The use of 'publisher' in the modern sense of 'editor', and of 'book-seller' in the sense of 'publisher', was regular till the latter half of the eighteenth century.

[1] See p. 29, l. 3.

was the Ground-work of a much larger Discourse, and he was sorry to observe the Materials so foolishly employ'd.

There is one farther Objection[1] made by those who have answered this Book, as well as by some others, that Peter *is frequently made to repeat Oaths and Curses. Every Reader observes it was necessary to know that* Peter *did Swear and Curse. The Oaths are not printed out, but only supposed, and the Idea of an Oath is not immoral, like the Idea of a Prophane or Immodest Speech. A Man may laugh at the Popish Folly of cursing People to Hell, and imagine them swearing, without any crime; but lewd Words, or dangerous Opinions though printed by halves, fill the Readers Mind with ill Idea's; and of these the Author cannot be accused. For the judicious Reader will find that the severest Stroaks of Satyr in his Book are levelled against the modern Custom of Employing Wit upon those Topicks, of which there is a remarkable Instance in the* 153d. *Page,[2] as well as in several others, tho' perhaps once or twice exprest in too free a manner, excusable only for the Reasons already alledged. Some Overtures have been made by a third Hand to the Bookseller for the Author's altering those Passages which he thought might require it. But it seems the Bookseller will not hear of any such Thing, being apprehensive it might spoil the Sale of the Book.*

The Author cannot conclude this Apology, without making this one Reflection; that, as Wit is the noblest and most useful Gift of humane Nature, so Humor is the most agreeable, and where these two enter far into the Composition of any Work, they will render it always acceptable to the World. Now,

---

[1] 'The Second [aim] is to show how great a Proficient he is, at Hectoring and Bullying, at Ranting and Roaring, and especially at Cursing and Swearing. He makes his Persons of all Characters full of their Oaths and Imprecations; nay, his very Spider has his share, and as far as in the Author lies, he would transmit his Impiety to things that are Irrational.' (King's *Remarks on the Tale of a Tub* (1704), p. 9—*Works* (1776), vol. i, p. 215.)

[2] p. 147 in this edition.

the great Part of those who have no Share or Tast of either,
but by their Pride, Pedantry and Ill Manners, lay themselves
bare to the Lashes of Both, think the Blow is weak, because
they are insensible, and where Wit hath any mixture of
Raillery; 'Tis but calling it Banter, *and the work is done.*
This Polite Word of theirs was first borrowed from the Bul-
lies in White-Fryars,[1] *then fell among the Footmen, and at*
last retired to the Pedants,[2] by whom it is applied as properly
to the Productions of Wit, as if I should apply it to Sir Isaac
Newton's *Mathematicks, but if this* Bantring *as they call it,*
be so despisable a Thing, whence comes it to pass they have
such a perpetual Itch towards it themselves? To instance
only in the Answerer already mentioned; it is grievous to see
him in some of his Writings at every turn going out of his
way to be waggish, to tell us of a Cow *that* prickt up her
Tail, *and in his answer to this Discourse, he says* it is all a
Farce and a Ladle:[3] *With other Passages equally shining.*
One may say of these Impedimenta Literarum, *that Wit*
ows them a Shame; and they cannot take wiser Counsel than
to keep out of harms way, or at least not to come till they are
sure they are called.[4]

[1] 'A precinct or liberty between Fleet Street and the Thames, the Temple walls and Water Lane ... The privileges of sanctuary, continued to this precinct after the Dissolution, were confirmed and enlarged in 1608 by royal charter.' (Cunningham and Wheatley, *London Past and Present*, s.v.) See Macaulay's *History*, chap. iii. The privilege was abolished in 1697. *Alsatia* was a part of Whitefriars. See Shadwell's *Squire of Alsatia* (1688). [2] See p. 13, note 3. [3] Wotton's *Reflections* (1694), p. 101, and *Observations* (1705), p. 57 (or 529). [4] In the *Examination* (1698),

p. 285, Bentley is given the same advice by Boyle: '... the first piece of Advice that I will venture to give the Dr is, that he would know his own Talent; and resolve for the future not to venture upon any way of writing that Nature never design'd him for. Wit, and Ridicule, are either the most Diverting, or the most Insipid things in the World. I have the Opinion of good Judges, that he has no true Taste of either of these, and performs very untowardly in 'em. He would do wisely therefore to forbear 'em.'

The authors of the *Examination* thought that 'nothing is so

To conclude; with those Allowances above-required, this Book should be read, after which the Author conceives, few things will remain which may not be excused in a young Writer. He wrote only to the Men of Wit and Tast, and he thinks he is not mistaken in his Accounts, when he says they have been all of his side, enough to give him the vanity of telling his Name, wherein the World with all its wise Conjectures, is yet very much in the dark, which Circumstance is no disagreeable Amusement either to the Publick or himself.

The Author is informed, that the Bookseller has prevailed on several Gentlemen, to write some explanatory Notes,[1] for the goodness of which he is not to answer, having never seen any of them, nor intends it, till they appear in Print, when it is not unlikely he may have the Pleasure to find twenty Meanings, which never enter'd into his Imagination.

June 3, 1709.

POSTSCRIPT

*S**Ince** the writing of this which was about a Year ago; a Prostitute Bookseller[2] hath publish'd a foolish Paper, under the Name of Notes on the* Tale of a Tub, *with some Account of the Author, and with an Insolence which I suppose is punishable by Law, hath presumed to assign certain Names. It will be enough for the Author to assure the World, that the Writer of that Paper is utterly wrong in all his Conjectures upon that Affair. The Author farther asserts that the whole Work is entirely of one Hand, which every Reader*

Divertive, or raises Laughter so much as Deformity, especially when Wit goes along with it' (p. 272).

Cf. Marvell on clerical wit in *Mr. Smirke, or the Divine in Mode* (1676), pp. 1–3.

[1] Swift certainly saw the 'explanatory Notes' before they were published. They were sent to him on 10 July 1710: see Tooke's letter, Appendix D, p. 350. On the authorship of the Notes see the Introduction.

[2] Edmund Curll. The 'foolish Paper' is reprinted in full as Appendix C, pp. 329–48.

of Judgment will easily discover. The Gentleman who gave the Copy to the Bookseller, being a Friend of the Author, and using no other Liberties besides that of expunging certain Passages where now the Chasms appear under the Name of Desiderata. *But if any Person will prove his Claim to three Lines in the whole Book, let him step forth and tell his Name and Titles, upon which the Bookseller shall have Orders to prefix them to the next Edition, and the Claimant shall from henceforward be acknowledged the undisputed Author.*

TO

The Right Honourable
JOHN
Lord S O M M E R S.[1]

My LORD,

THO' the Author has written a large Dedication, yet That being address'd to a Prince, whom I am never likely to have the Honour of being known to; A Person, besides, as far as I can observe, not at all regarded, or thought on by any of our present Writers; And, being[2] wholly free from the Slavery, which Booksellers usually lie under, to the Caprices of Authors; I think it a wise Piece of Presumption, to inscribe these Papers to your Lordship, and to implore your Lordship's Protection of them. God and your Lordship

---

[1] John Lord Somers, Chancelor of England in 1697, was one of the greatest men of his Age and Nation, and a great Patron of Learning, which induced many Learned men to dedicate their Works to him, and this Author in particular who had great obligations to him [1720].

Somers was well known for his generosity to men of letters. The following works (among many others) were dedicated to him: Addison's *Remarks on Italy* (1705), Shaftesbury's *Letter concerning Enthusiasm* (1708), and the first volume of the collected edition of *The Spectator* (1712).

It was a family tradition that Somers had written the *Tale of a Tub* in his youth, in company with Lord Shrewsbury, and that his papers 'after many years lying by, and passing through the hands of Lord Shaftesbury and Sir William Temple', were given to the world by Swift. See Richard Cooksey's *Essay on the Life and Character of John Lord Somers* (1791), pp. 17 ff.

[2] 'And, I being' edd. 1–4.

know their Faults, and their Merits; for as to my own Particular, I am altogether a Stranger to the Matter; And, tho' every Body else should be equally ignorant, I do not fear the Sale of the Book, at all the worse, upon that Score. Your Lordship's Name on the Front, in Capital Letters, will at any time get off one Edition: Neither would I desire any other Help, to grow an Alderman, than a Patent for the sole Priviledge of Dedicating to your Lordship.

I should now, in right of a Dedicator, give your Lordship a List of your own Virtues, and at the same time, be very unwilling to offend your Modesty; But, chiefly, I should celebrate your Liberality towards Men of great Parts and small Fortunes, and give you broad Hints, that I mean my self. And, I was just going on in the usual Method, to peruse a hundred or two of Dedications, and transcribe an Abstract, to be applied to your Lordship; But, I was diverted by a certain Accident. For, upon the Covers of these Papers, I casually observed written in large Letters, the two following Words, *DETUR DIGNISSIMO*;[1] which, for ought I knew, might contain some important Meaning. But, it unluckily fell out, that none of the Authors I employ, understood *Latin* (tho' I have them often in pay, to translate out of that Language) I was therefore compelled to have recourse to the Curate of our Parish, who Englished it thus, *Let it be given to the Worthiest;* And his Comment was, that the Author meant, his Work should be dedicated to the sublimest Genius of the Age, for Wit, Learning, Judgment, Eloquence and Wisdom.

---

[1] Perhaps Swift has in mind one of the versions of Alexander the Great's words on his death-bed, e.g. Justinus, *Hist.* xii. 15: 'Cum deficere eum amici viderent, quaerunt quem imperii faciat here-dem. Respondit, Dignissimum.'

The phrase may be a modification of the common *detur digniori*; or of the motto on the apple which Paris gave to Venus—*detur pulchriori*.

I call'd at a Poet's Chamber (who works for my Shop) in an Alley hard by, shewed him the Translation, and desired his Opinion, who it was that the Author could mean; He told me, after some Consideration, that Vanity was a Thing he abhorr'd; but by the Description, he thought Himself to be the Person aimed at; And, at the same time, he very kindly offer'd his own Assistance *gratis*, towards penning a Dedication to Himself. I desired him, however, to give a second Guess; Why then, said he, It must be I, or my Lord *Sommers*. From thence I went to several other Wits of my Acquaintance, with no small Hazard and Weariness to my Person, from a prodigious Number of dark, winding Stairs;[1] But found them all in the same Story, both of your Lordship and themselves. Now, your Lordship is to understand, that this Proceeding was not of my own Invention; For, I have somewhere heard, it is a Maxim, that those, to whom every Body allows the second Place, have an undoubted Title to the First.[2]

THIS infallibly convinced me, that your Lordship was the Person intended by the Author. But, being very unacquainted in the Style and Form of Dedications, I employ'd those Wits aforesaid, to furnish me with Hints and Materials, towards a Panegyrick upon your Lordship's Virtues.

IN two Days, they brought me ten Sheets of Paper, fill'd up on every Side. They swore to me, that they had ransack'd whatever could be found in the Characters of *Socrates, Aristides, Epaminondas, Cato, Tully, Atticus*, and other hard Names, which I cannot now recollect. However, I have Reason to believe, they imposed upon my Ignorance, because, when I came to read over their Collections, there was not a Syllable there, but what I and every body else knew as well as themselves: There-

[1] Poor Authors generally lodge in Garrets [1720].
[2] Herodotus, viii. 123–4.

fore, I grievously suspect a Cheat; and, that these Authors of mine, stole and transcribed every Word, from the universal Report of Mankind. So that I look upon my self, as fifty Shillings out of Pocket, to no manner of Purpose.

IF, by altering the Title, I could make the same Materials serve for another Dedication[1] (as my Betters have done) it would help to make up my Loss: But, I have made several Persons, dip here and there in those Papers, and before they read three Lines, they have all assured me, plainly, that they cannot possibly be applied to any Person besides your Lordship.

I expected, indeed, to have heard of your Lordship's Bravery, at the Head of an Army;[2] Of your undaunted Courage, in mounting a Breach, or scaling a Wall; Or, to have had your Pedigree trac'd in a Lineal Descent from the House of *Austria*; Or, of your wonderful Talent at Dress and Dancing; Or, your Profound Knowledge in *Algebra*, *Metaphysicks*, and the Oriental Tongues. But to ply the World with an old beaten Story of your Wit, and Eloquence, and Learning, and Wisdom, and Justice, and Politeness, and Candor, and Evenness of Temper[3] in all Scenes of Life; Of that

[1] Cf. Swift's *On Poetry* (1733):
Your Garland in the following Reign,
Change but their Names, will do again.

[2] 'Tis a ridiculous custom of most Authors in their Dedications, to praise their Patrons for many qualitys they have not, and oftimes need not to have [1720].

[3] 'His good temper and his good breeding never failed. His gesture, his look, his tones were expressive of benevolence. His humanity was the more remark-able, because he had received from nature a body such as is generally found united with a peevish and irritable mind. . . . Yet his enemies could not pretend that he had ever once, during a long and troubled public life, been goaded, even by sudden provocation, into vehemence inconsistent with the mild dignity of his character.' (Macaulay, *History of England*, chap. xx, ed. C. H. Firth, vol. v, pp. 2394–6.)

A remarkable contemporary portrait will be found in *The*

great Discernment in Discovering, and Readiness in Favouring deserving Men; with forty other common Topicks: I confess, I have neither Conscience, nor Countenance to do it. Because, there is no Virtue, either of a Publick or Private Life, which some Circumstances of your own, have not often produced upon the Stage of the World; And those few, which for want of Occasions to exert them, might otherwise have pass'd unseen or unobserved by your *Friends*, your *Enemies* have at length brought to Light.[1]

'TIS true, I should be very loth, the Bright Example of your Lordship's Virtues should be lost to After-Ages, both for their sake and your own; but chiefly, because they will be so very necessary to adorn the History of a *late Reign*;[2] And That is another Reason, why I would forbear to make a Recital of them here; Because, I have been told by Wise Men, that as Dedications have run for some Years past, a good Historian will not be apt to have Recourse thither, in search of Characters.

THERE is one Point, wherein I think we Dedicators would do well to change our Measures; I mean, instead of running on so far, upon the Praise of our Patron's *Liberality*, to spend a Word or two, in admiring their *Patience*. I can put no greater Compliment on your Lordship's, than by giving you so ample an Occasion to exercise it at present. Tho', perhaps, I shall not be apt to reckon much Merit to your Lordship upon that

---

Free-Holder, No. 39 (4 May 1716). It was written by Addison on Somers's death.

[1] In 1701 lord *Sommers* was impeached by the commons, who either finding their proofs defective, or for other reasons, delay'd coming to a trial, and the lords thereupon proceeded to the trial without them, and acquitted him [Hawkesworth].

[2] That of K. *WILLIAM*, who had a great value for this Lord and took much of his advice [1720].

K. *William*'s; whose memory he defended in the H. of Lords against some invidious reflexions of the E. of *Nottingham* [Hawkesworth].

Score, who having been formerly used to tedious Harangues, and sometimes to as little Purpose,[1] will be the readier to pardon this, especially, when it is offered by one, who is with all Respect and Veneration,

My LORD,

Your Lordship's most Obedient,

and most Faithful Servant,

The Bookseller.

[1] As member of Parliament, Solicitor-General, Attorney-General, and Lord Chancellor.

THE
BOOKSELLER
TO THE
READER.[1]

*I*T is now *Six Years* since these *Papers came first to my Hands*,[2] *which seems to have been about a Twelvemonth after they were writ; For, the Author tells us*[3] *in his Preface to the first Treatise, that he hath calculated it for the Year* 1697, *and in several Passages of that Discourse, as well as the second*,[4] *it appears, they were written about that Time.*

As to the Author, I can give no manner of Satisfaction; However, I am credibly informed that this Publication is without his Knowledge; for he concludes the Copy is lost, having lent it to a Person, since dead, and being never in Possession of it after: So that, whether the Work received his last Hand, or, whether he intended to fill up the defective Places, is like to remain a Secret.

If I should go about to tell the Reader, by what Accident, I became Master of these Papers, it would, in this unbelieving Age, pass for little more than the Cant, or Jargon of the Trade. I, therefore, gladly spare both him and my self so unnecessary a Trouble. There yet remains a difficult Question, why I publish'd them no sooner. I forbore upon two Accounts: First, because I thought I had better Work upon my Hands; and Secondly, because I was not without some

[1] In the 'Apology' (pp. 16, 17) this notice is said to have been written by the 'publishers'. Style and content point clearly to Swift.

[2] 'Hands' edd. 1, 2; 'Hand' edd. 3–5. Cf. p. 289.

[3] See p. 44, l. 9.

[4] The *Battle of the Books*.

Hope of hearing from the Author, and receiving his Direc-
tions. But I have been lately alarm'd with Intelligence of a
surreptitious Copy, which a certain great Wit had new
polish'd and refin'd, or as our present Writers express them-
selves, fitted to the Humor of the Age; *as they have*
already done, with great Felicity, to Don Quixot, Boccalini,
la Bruyere *and other Authors.*[1] *However, I thought it*
fairer Dealing, to offer the whole Work in its Naturals. If
any Gentleman will please to furnish me with a Key, in
order to explain the more difficult Parts, I shall very grate-
fully acknowledge the Favour, and print it by it self.

[1] For example (1) *The History Of the most Renowned Don Quixote . . . Now made English according to the Humour of our Modern Language. By J[ohn] P[hillips].* (1687); (2) *Advertisements from Parnassus. Written originally in Italian. By the Famous Trajano Boccalini. Newly Done into English, and adapted to the Present Times. . . . By N. N.* 3 vols. (1704); (3) *The Characters, or the Manners of the Age. By Monsieur De La Bruyere . . . Made English by* several hands (1699); (4) *The English Theophrastus: or, the Manners of the Age. Being the Modern Characters of the Court, the Town, and the City* (1702); (5) *The Visions of Dom Francisco de Quevedo Villegas . . . Made English by R[oger] L['Estrange].* (1667; tenth edition 1708); (6) *Il Decamerone. . . . Written by John Boccacio. . . . Now done into English, and accommodated to the Gust of the present Age* (1702).

THE

Epistle Dedicatory,

TO

His Royal Highness

PRINCE POSTERITY.

SIR,

I HERE present *Your Highness* with the Fruits of a very few leisure Hours, stollen from the short Intervals of a World of Business, and of an Employment quite alien from such Amusements as this:[1] The poor Production of that Refuse of Time which has lain heavy upon my Hands, during a long Prorogation of Parliament, a great Dearth of Forein News, and a tedious Fit of rainy Weather: For which, and other Reasons, it cannot chuse extremely to deserve such a Patronage as that of *Your Highness*, whose numberless

The Citation out of Irenæus *in the* Title-Page, *which seems to be all* Gibberish, *is a Form of Initiation used antiently by the* Marcosian *Hereticks.* W. Wotton.[2]

It is the usual Style of decry'd Writers to appeal to Posterity, *who is here represented*[3] *as a Prince in his Nonage, and* Time *as his Governour, and the Author begins in a way very frequent with him, by personating other Writers, who sometimes offer such Reasons and Excuses for publishing their Works as they ought chiefly to conceal and be asham'd of.*

[1] Cf. p. 182, note 2.

[2] The footnotes were added in 1710 and issued as 'Explanatory Notes' with the 'Apology' in 1711.

[3] 'represented here' *Notes* 1711.

Virtues in so few Years, make the World look upon
You as the future Example to all Princes: For altho'
Your Highness is hardly got clear of Infancy, yet has the
universal learned World already resolv'd upon appeal-
ing to Your future Dictates with the lowest and most
resigned Submission: Fate having decreed You sole
Arbiter of the Productions of human Wit, in this polite
and most accomplish'd Age. Methinks, the Number of
Appellants were enough to shock and startle any Judge
of a Genius less unlimited than Yours: But in order to
prevent such glorious Tryals, the *Person*[1] (it seems) to
whose Care the Education of *Your Highness* is committed, has resolved (as I am told) to keep you in almost
an universal Ignorance of our Studies, which it is Your
inherent Birth-right to inspect.

I T is amazing to me, that this *Person* should have
Assurance in the face of the Sun, to go about persuading
Your Highness, that our Age is almost wholly illiterate,
and has hardly produc'd one Writer upon any Subject.
I know very well, that when *Your Highness* shall come
to riper Years, and have gone through the Learning of
Antiquity, you will be too curious to neglect inquiring
into the Authors of the very age before You: And to
think that this *Insolent*, in the Account he is preparing
for Your View, designs to reduce them to a Number so
insignificant as I am asham'd to mention; it moves my
Zeal and my Spleen for the Honor and Interest of our
vast flourishing Body, as well as of my self, for whom
I know by long Experience, he has profess'd, and still
continues a peculiar Malice.[2]

'T I S not unlikely, that when *Your Highness* will one
day peruse what I am now writing, You may be ready

[1] Time [1720].
   Time, allegorically described as
the tutor of Posterity [Scott].
[2] Cf. p. 70, ll. 15–17: 'Fourscore and eleven Pamphlets have
I written under three Reigns, and
for the Service of six and thirty
Factions.'

to expostulate with Your *Governour* upon the Credit of what I here affirm, and command Him to shew You some of our Productions. To which he will answer, (for I am well informed of his Designs) by asking *Your Highness*, where they are? and what is become of them? and pretend it a Demonstration that there never were any, because they are not then to be found: Not to be found! Who has mislaid them? Are they sunk in the Abyss of Things? 'Tis certain, that in their own Nature they were *light* enough to swim upon the Surface for all Eternity. Therefore the Fault is in Him, who tied Weights so heavy to their Heels, as to depress them to the Center.[1] Is their very Essence destroyed? Who has annihilated them? Were they drowned by *Purges* or martyred by *Pipes*? Who administered them to the Posteriors of ———? But that it may no longer be a Doubt with *Your Highness*, who is to be the Author of this universal Ruin; I beseech You to observe that large and terrible *Scythe* which your *Governour* affects to bear continually about him. Be pleased to remark the Length and Strength, the Sharpness and Hardness of his *Nails* and *Teeth*: Consider his baneful abominable *Breath*, Enemy to Life and Matter, infectious and corrupting: And then reflect whether it be possible for any mortal Ink and Paper of this Generation to make a suitable Resistance. Oh, that *Your Highness* would one day resolve to disarm this Usurping* *Maitre du Palais*,[2]

* *Comptroller.*

[1] The centre of the earth, as in *Hamlet*, ii. ii. 159. Cf. Bacon, *Novum Organum*, i. 104: 'hominum Intellectui non plumae addendae, sed plumbum potius, et pondera'; and i. 71: 'Tempore (ut fluvio) leviora et magis inflata ad nos devehente.'

[2] This should be *maire du palais*, 'intendant en chef de la maison du roi, au temps des derniers Mérovingiens, qui devint bientôt un ministre tout-puissant' (Hatzfeld et Darmesteter, s.v.). The phrase is given correctly in the *Miscellaneous Works* of 1720. The first four editions have *Maitre de Palais* and *hors du Page*.

of his furious Engins, and bring Your Empire* *hors de Page.*[1]

IT were endless to recount the several Methods of Tyranny and Destruction, which Your *Governour* is pleased to practise upon this Occasion. His inveterate Malice is such to the Writings of our Age, that of several Thousands produced yearly from this renowned City, before the next Revolution of the Sun, there is not one to be heard of: Unhappy Infants, many of them barbarously destroyed, before they have so much as learnt their *Mother-Tongue* to beg for Pity. Some he stifles in their Cradles, others he frights into Convulsions, whereof they suddenly die; Some he flays alive, others he tears Limb from Limb. Great Numbers are offered to *Moloch,*[2] and the rest tainted by his Breath, die of a languishing Consumption.

BUT the Concern I have most at Heart, is for our Corporation of *Poets*, from whom I am preparing a Petition to *Your Highness*, to be subscribed with the Names of one hundred thirty six of the first Rate, but whose immortal Productions are never likely to reach your Eyes, tho' each of them is now an humble and an earnest Appellant for the Laurel,[3] and has large comely Volumes ready to shew for a Support to his Pretensions. The *never-dying* Works of these illustrious Persons, Your *Governour*, Sir, has devoted to unavoidable Death, and *Your Highness* is to be made believe, that our Age has never arrived at the Honor to produce one single Poet.

* *Out of Guardianship.*

[1] Cf. Algernon Sidney, *Discourses concerning Government* (1698), p. 233.

[2] Cf. Jeremiah xxxii. 35.

[3] The appointment as Poet-Laureate lapsed on the death of the sovereign. Does this sentence refer to the vacancy on the accession of Anne (in which case it is an insertion, the dedication being dated 'Decemb. 1697'); or is its application general? Cf. p. 36, note 2, and p. xliv.

WE confess *Immortality* to be a great and powerful Goddess, but in vain we offer up to her our Devotions and our Sacrifices, if *Your Highness's Governour*, who has usurped the *Priesthood*, must by an unparallel'd Ambition and Avarice, wholly intercept and devour them.

TO affirm that our Age is altogether Unlearned, and devoid of Writers in any kind, seems to be an Assertion so bold and so false, that I have been sometime thinking, the contrary may almost be proved by uncontroulable Demonstration.[1] 'Tis true indeed, that altho' their Numbers be vast, and their Productions numerous in proportion, yet are they hurryed so hastily off the Scene, that they escape our Memory, and delude our Sight. When I first thought of this Address, I had prepared a copious List of *Titles* to present *Your Highness* as an undisputed Argument for what I affirm. The Originals were posted fresh upon all Gates and Corners of Streets;[2] but returning in a very few Hours to take a Review, they were all torn down, and fresh ones in their Places: I enquired after them among Readers and Booksellers, but I enquired in vain, the *Memorial of them was lost*

[1] Irrefutable proof. Cf. Swift's *Maxims Controlled in Ireland*: 'It hath likewise been a maxim among politicians "That the great increase of buildings in the metropolis argues a flourishing state". But this, I confess, hath been *controlled* from the example of London.'

[2]   Mediocribus esse poetis Non homines, non Dî, non concessêre columnæ. Hor. *de Arte Poeticâ*, ver. 372 [*MS. Pate*]. The following passage occurs in King's *Remarks on the Tale of a Tub*, pp. 4, 5: 'as I was returning from my *Nightly* Vocation . . . I saw a Fellow pasting up the Title-Pages of Books at the Corners of the Streets; and there, among others, I saw one called *The Tale of a Tub*'.

Cf. also Marvell, *The Rehearsal Transpros'd* (1672), pp. 67, 68; the *Battle of the Books*, p. 222: 'fixed up in all Publick Places, either by themselves or their* Representa- tives, for Passen- gers to gaze at'; and Pope, *Epistle to Dr. Arbuthnot*, ll. 215–16.

*Their Title-Pages

among Men, their Place was no more to be found:[1] and I
was laughed to scorn, for a *Clown* and a *Pedant*, without[2]
all Taste and Refinement, little versed in the Course of
present Affairs, and that knew nothing of what had
pass'd in the best Companies of Court and Town. So
that I can only avow in general to *Your Highness*, that
we do[3] abound in Learning and Wit; but to fix upon
Particulars, is a Task too slippery for my slender Abilities. If I should venture in a windy Day,[4] to affirm to
Your Highness, that there is a large[5] Cloud near the
Horizon in the Form of a *Bear*, another in the *Zenith*
with the Head of an *Ass*, a third to the Westward with
Claws like a *Dragon*; and *Your Highness* should in a few
Minutes think fit to examine the Truth, 'tis certain,
they would all be changed in Figure and Position, new
ones would arise, and all we could agree upon would be,
that Clouds there were, but that I was grossly mistaken
in the *Zoography* and *Topography* of them.

BUT Your *Governour*, perhaps, may still insist, and
put the Question: What is then become of those immense Bales of Paper, which must needs have been
employ'd in such Numbers of Books? Can these also be
wholly annihilate, and so of a sudden as I pretend?
What shall I say in return of so invidious an Objection?
It ill befits the Distance between *Your Highness* and Me,

---

[1] These sentences are reminis-
cences of Biblical phrases, e.g.
Deut. xxxii. 26; Zech. x. 10;
Rev. xii. 8, xx. 11; 1 Mac. xii. 53.

[2] '*Pedant*, devoid of all' edd.
1–4.

[3] 'do' in italics edd. 1–4.

[4] Cf. *Antony and Cleopatra*
(Act IV, sc. xii):
  Ant. Sometime we see a cloud
    that's dragonish;
A vapour sometime, like a bear,
  or lion,

A tower'd citadel, a pendent rock,
A forked mountain, or blue pro-
  montory
With trees upon't, that nod unto
  the world,
And mock our eyes with air: thou
  hast seen these signs;
They are black vesper's pageants.
  Eros.   Ay, my lord.
  Ant. That which is now a
    horse, even with a thought
The rack dislimns.

[5] 'huge' ed. 1; 'large' edd. 2–5.

to send You for ocular Conviction to a *Jakes*, or an *Oven*; to the Windows of a *Bawdy-house*, or to a sordid *Lanthorn*. Books, like Men their Authors, have no more than one Way of coming into the World, but there are ten Thousand to go out of it, and return no more.

I profess to *Your Highness*, in the Integrity of my Heart, that what I am going to say is literally true this Minute I am writing: What Revolutions may happen before it shall be ready for your Perusal, I can by no means warrant: However I beg You, to accept it as a Specimen of our Learning, our Politeness and our Wit. I do therefore affirm upon the Word of a sincere Man, that there is now actually in being, a certain Poet called *John Dryden*, whose Translation of *Virgil* was lately printed[1] in a large Folio, well bound, and if diligent search were made, for ought I know, is yet to be seen. There is another call'd *Nahum Tate*,[2] who is ready to make Oath that he has caused many Rheams of Verse to be published, whereof both himself and his Book-seller (if lawfully required) can still produce authentick Copies, and therefore wonders why the World is pleased to make such a Secret of it. There is a Third, known by the Name of *Tom Durfey*,[3] a Poet of a vast Comprehen-

---

[1] Published in July 1697. It was 'seen' by the writer of the notes of 1710; see p. 55, note 2.

[2] Nahum Tate was Poet-Laureate; he succeeded Shadwell in 1692, and was reappointed by Anne.

[3] Among the works of Tom Durfey is a burlesque of John Norris's *Theory of the Intelligible World* (1700–4), entitled 'An Essay Towards the Theory of the Intelligible World. Intuitively Considered. Designed for Forty-nine Parts. Part III. Consisting of a Preface, a Post-script, and a little something between. By Gabriel John. Enriched with a Faithful Account of his Ideal Voyage, and Illustrated with Poems by several Hands, as likewise with other strange things not insufferably Clever, nor furiously to the Purpose. The Archetypally Second Edition.

θέλω, θέλω μανῆναι. *Why Should all Mankind be mad but I?*

sion, an universal Genius, and most profound Learning. There are also one Mr. *Rymer*, and one Mr. *Dennis*, most profound Cricks. There is a Person styl'd Dr. *B--tl-y*, who has written near a thousand Pages of immense Erudition,[1] *giving a full and true Account*[2] of a certain *Squable* of wonderful Importance between himself and a Bookseller: He is a Writer of infinite Wit and Humour: no Man raillyes with a better Grace, and in more sprightly Turns. Farther, I avow to *Your Highness*, that with these Eyes I have beheld the Person of *William W--tt--n*, B.D. who has written a good sizeable volume[3] against a *Friend of Your Governor*,[4] (from whom, alas! he must therefore look for little Favour) in a most gentlemanly Style, adorned with utmost Politeness and Civility; replete with Discoveries equally valuable for their Novelty and Use: and embellish'd

You that are wisest tell me why.
Tribues HIS temporis quantum
      poteris,
Poteris autem quantum voles.
            Tully's Offices.
Printed in the Year One Thousand Seven Hundred, &c.'

The exact date is not known. The title is given in Arber's *Term Catalogues* (iii. 595) under the year 1708. The *Tale of a Tub* is alluded to in the following passage (p. 149): 'The *Ideal* Hoops, or Circles, are not without their Cylinder, or Ideal *Tub*; but this Vessel is now become a very empty and dry Subject, having lately been exhausted, *as it were*, in the Telling of a *merry Tale*.' The fantastic arrangement of the book, and its use of 'chasms', are partly imitated from the *Tale*.

[1] Bentley's Pieces concerning Phalaris' Epistles, &c. [1720].
The reference is not to Bentley's 'Pieces' in general, but to the long preface to the *Dissertation* of 1699. The 'Bookseller' was Thomas Bennet, the publisher of Boyle's *Examination*.
[2] Cf. the title-page of the *Battle of the Books*.
[3] *Reflexions on ancient and modern Learning* [1720].
The second edition of Wotton's *Reflexions*, with Bentley's *Dissertation*, contains over 600 pages. It contrasted in size with Temple's 'essay'.
[4] Antiquity [1720]. Swift refers to Temple, the champion of the ancients, and therefore the friend of Time.

with *Traits* of Wit so poignant and so apposite, that he is a worthy Yokemate to his foremention'd *Friend*.

WHY should I go upon farther Particulars, which might fill a Volume with the just Elogies[1] of my cotemporary[2] Brethren? I shall bequeath this Piece of Justice to a larger Work: wherein I intend to write a Character of the present Set of *Wits*[3] in our Nation: Their Persons I shall describe particularly, and at Length, their Genius and Understandings in *Mignature*.

IN the mean time, I do here make bold to present *Your Highness* with a faithful Abstract drawn from the Universal Body of all Arts and Sciences, intended wholly for your Service and Instruction:[4] Nor do I doubt in the least, but *Your Highness* will peruse it as carefully, and make as considerable Improvements, as *other* young *Princes* have already done by the many Volumes of late Years written for a Help to their Studies.[5]

THAT *Your Highness* may advance in Wisdom and Virtue, as well as Years, and at last out-shine all Your Royal Ancestors, shall be the daily Prayer of,

SIR,

Decemb.
   1697.

Your Highness's

Most devoted, &c.

---

[1] 'Elogy' (*elogium*) came to be confused with 'eulogy'; cf. French *éloge*. But Swift uses it here in the strict sense of 'characterization'.

[2] The form 'cotemporary' was described by Bentley as 'a downright barbarism' (*Dissertation* (1699), p. lxxxvi). Ed. 7 (1727) first prints 'contemporary'.

[3] See the Catalogue before the title-page [1720].

[4] 'Instruction:' edd. 1 and 3; 'Instruction;' ed. 4; 'Instruction?' edd. 2 and 5. Further points of interrogation in ed. 5 instead of colons will not be recorded.

[5] The Dauphin and Princes of France have had a great many Authors commented, and Treatises written for their use and instruction [1720].

THE
PREFACE.

THE Wits of the present Age being so very numerous and penetrating, it seems, the Grandees of *Church* and *State* begin to fall under horrible Apprehensions, lest these Gentlemen, during the intervals of a long Peace, should find leisure to pick Holes in the weak sides of Religion and Government.[1] To prevent which, there has been much Thought employ'd of late upon certain Projects for taking off the Force, and Edge of those formidable Enquirers, from canvasing and reasoning upon such delicate Points. They have at length fixed upon one, which will require some Time as well as Cost, to perfect. Mean while the Danger hourly increasing, by new Levies of Wits all appointed (as there is Reason to fear) with Pen, Ink, and Paper

[1] Cf. Temple, *Of Poetry, ad fin.*: 'The Academy set up by Cardinal *Richlieu*, to amuse the Wits of that Age and Country, and divert them from raking into his Politicks and Ministery'; and Addison, *Spectator*, No. 262: 'Among those Advantages, which the Publick may reap from this Paper, it is not the least, that it draws Mens Minds off from the Bitterness of Party, and furnishes them with Subjects of Discourse that may be treated without Warmth or Passion. This is said to have been the first Design of those Gentlemen who set on Foot the Royal Society; and had then a very good Effect, as it turned many of the greatest Genius's of that Age to the Disquisitions of natural Knowledge, who, if they had engaged in Politicks with the same Parts and Application, might have set their Country in a Flame. The Air-Pump, the Barometer, the Quadrant, and the like Inventions, were thrown out to those busy Spirits, as Tubs and Barrels are to a Whale, that he may let the Ship sail on without Disturbance, while he diverts himself with those innocent Amusements.'

which may at an hours Warning be drawn out into
Pamphlets, and other Offensive Weapons, ready for
immediate Execution: It was judged of absolute necessity, that some present Expedient be thought on, till
the main Design can be brought to Maturity. To this
End, at a Grand Committee,[1] some Days ago, this
important Discovery was made by a certain curious
and refined Observer; That Sea-men have a Custom
when they meet a *Whale*, to fling him out an empty *Tub*,
by way of Amusement, to divert him from laying violent
Hands upon the Ship. This Parable was immediately
mythologiz'd: The *Whale* was interpreted to be *Hobs*'s[2]
Leviathan,[3] which tosses and plays with all other
Schemes of Religion and Government, whereof a great
many are hollow, and dry, and empty, and noisy, and
wooden, and given to Rotation.[4] This is the *Leviathan*
from whence the terrible Wits of our Age are said to
borrow their Weapons. The *Ship* in danger, is easily
understood to be its old Antitype the *Commonwealth*.[5]
But, how to analyze the *Tub*, was a Matter of difficulty;
when after long Enquiry and Debate, the literal Meaning was preserved: And it was decreed, that in order to
prevent these *Leviathans* from tossing and sporting
with the *Commonwealth*, (which of it self is too apt to

---

[1] Either a committee of the
whole house, or one of the four committees (for religion, grievances,
courts of justice, and trade) an-
nually appointed by the House of
Commons, until 1832.

[2] '*Hobs*'s' edd. 1–4; '*Hob*'s' ed.
5; '*Hobbes*'s' 1720. Cf. p. 277, l. 9.

[3] A book sufficiently known;
very much esteemed by some, and
held by others very dangerous for
the maximes of Religion and Government it contains [1720].

[4] Swift refers to the schemes of
government discussed by the Rota
Club, and especially to Harring-
ton's *Oceana* (1656) and *Rota*
(1660). Cf. Swift's *Contests and
Dissensions at Athens and Rome*:
'to leave us and themselves in a
very uncertain state, and in a sort
of rotation, that the author of the
Oceana never dreamed on'.

[5] So Horace, lib. 1. Od. xiv.
'O Navis! referent in mare te
novi Fluctus?' [*MS. Pate*].

fluctuate) they should be diverted from that Game by a
Tale of a Tub. And my Genius being conceived to lye
not unhappily that way, I had the Honor done me to be
engaged in the Performance.

THIS is the sole Design in publishing the following
Treatise, which I hope will serve for an *Interim* of some
Months to employ those unquiet Spirits, till the per-
fecting of that great Work: into the Secret of which, it
is reasonable the courteous Reader should have some
little Light.

IT is intended that a large Academy be erected,
capable of containing nine thousand seven hundred
forty and three Persons; which by modest Computation
is reckoned to be pretty near the current Number of
Wits in this Island.[1] These are to be disposed into the
several Schools of this Academy, and there pursue those
Studies to which their Genius most inclines them. The
Undertaker himself will publish his Proposals with all
convenient speed, to which I shall refer the curious
Reader for a more particular Account, mentioning at
present only a few of the Principal Schools.[2] There is
first, a large *Pederastick* School, with *French* and *Italian*
Masters. There is also, the *Spelling* School,[3] *a very*

[1] The number of livings in
England [*MS. Pate*].

There does not seem to be any
precise statement of the number
of livings in England at this time.
The number in the reign of Elizabeth was said to be 8,803 (see
Collier's *Ecclesiastical History*, ed.
Lathbury (1852), vol. ix, p. 362
and Index). The second edition
of Spelman's *Villare Anglicum*
(1678) gives 8,870 parishes in
England and 965 in Wales. The
number of livings in John Ec-
ton's *Liber Valorum et Decimarum*

(1711) is about 9,500 for England
and Wales together. See also *Valor
Beneficiorum* (1695). In the *Argument against abolishing Christianity* Swift says 'above ten thousand
parsons'.

[2] Accademy and Schools proper for different sorts of Rakes and
Beaus [1720; 1734 adds 'that pretend to be Wits'].

[3] Although spelling was not uni-
form in Swift's time he was very
particular about it. There are many
references to Stella's spelling in
the *Journal*; and in the *Proposal*

spacious *Building*: The School of *Looking Glasses*: The School of *Swearing*: The School of *Criticks*: The School of *Salivation*: The School of *Hobby-Horses*: The School of *Poetry*: *The School of *Tops*: The School of *Spleen*: The School of *Gaming*: with many others too tedious to recount. No Person to be admitted Member into any of these Schools, without an Attestation under two sufficient Persons Hands, certifying him to be a *Wit*.

BUT, to return. I am sufficiently instructed in the Principal Duty of a Preface, if my Genius were capable of arriving at it. Thrice have I forced my Imagination to make the *Tour* of my Invention,[1] and thrice it has returned empty; the latter having been wholly drained by the following Treatise. Not so, my more successful Brethren the *Moderns*, who will by no means let slip a Preface or Dedication, without some notable distinguishing Stroke, to surprize the Reader at the Entry, and kindle a Wonderful Expectation of what is to

* *This I think the Author should have omitted, it being of the very same Nature with the* School of Hobby-Horses, *if one may venture to censure one who is so severe a Censurer of others, perhaps with too little Distinction.*

for Correcting, Improving, and Ascertaining the English Tongue (1712), Swift says that 'it is sometimes a difficult matter to read modern books and pamphlets; where the words are so curtailed, and varied from their original spelling, that whoever has been used to plain English, will hardly know them by sight'. Cf. his letter to *The Tatler*, No. 230, and the Introduction to *Polite Conversation*.

The 'School of Tops' may perhaps refer to 'rotation' in government: see p. 40, note 4.

[1] Cf. Dryden, *Letter to Sir Robert Howard*, prefixed to *Annus Mirabilis*: 'wit in the Poet . . . is no other than the faculty of imagination in the Writer; which like a nimble Spaniel, beats over and ranges through the field of Memory, till it springs the Quarry it hunted after . . . So then, the first happiness of the Poet's Imagination is properly Invention, or the finding of the thought . . . The quickness of the Imagination is seen in the Invention.'

ensue. Such was that of a most ingenious Poet,[1] who solliciting his Brain for something new, compared himself to the *Hangman,* and his Patron to the *Patient*: This was **Insigne, recens, indictum ore alio.*[2] * *Hor.* When I went thro' That necessary and noble †Course of Study,[3] I had the happiness to † *Reading* observe many such egregious Touches, which *Prefaces, &c.* I shall not injure the Authors by transplanting: Because I have remarked, that nothing is so very tender as a *Modern* Piece of Wit, and which is apt to suffer so much in the Carriage. Some things are extreamly witty *to day,* or *fasting,* or *in this place,* or *at eight a clock,* or *over a Bottle,* or *spoke by Mr.* What d'y'call'm,[4] or *in a Summer's Morning*: Any of which, by the smallest Transposal or Misapplication, is utterly annihilate. Thus, *Wit* has its Walks and Purlieus, out of which it may not stray the breadth of a Hair,[5] upon peril of being lost. The *Moderns* have artfully fixed this *Mercury,*[6] and reduced it to the Circumstances of Time, Place and Person. Such a Jest there is, that will not pass out of *Covent-Garden*;[7] and such a one, that is no where intelligible but at *Hide-Park* Corner. Now, tho' it sometimes tenderly affects me to consider, that all the towardly Passages I shall deliver in the following Treatise, will grow quite out of date and relish with the first shifting

* *Something extraordinary, new and never hit upon before.*

[1] Not identified.

[2] Horace, *Odes,* iii. xxv. 7–8.

[3] It is one of the charges brought against Bentley in the *Examination* (e.g. pp. 193, 227) that he is learned in prefaces and introductions. Cf. pp. 97, 131.

[4] 'Whatdicall'um' edd. 1–3.

[5] 'an hair' ed. 5; cf. p. 81, l. 16.

[6] This is in origin an alchemical phrase, denoting the conversion of mercury into a solid by combination with some other substance. It was generally used at this time with reference to wit or volatility of character. Cf. *Essay on Man,* ii. 177.

[7] 'Convent-Garden' edd. 1, 2. 4; 'Convent Garden' ed. 3. See p. 52, note 2.

of the present Scene: yet I must need subscribe to the Justice of this Proceeding: because, I cannot imagine why we should be at Expence to furnish Wit for succeeding Ages, when the former have made no sort of Provision for ours; wherein I speak the Sentiment of the very newest, and consequently the most Orthodox Refiners,[1] as well as my own. However, being extreamly sollicitous, that every accomplished Person who has got into the Taste of Wit, calculated for this present Month of *August*, 1697,[2] should descend to the very *bottom* of all the *Sublime* throughout this Treatise; I hold fit to lay down this general Maxim. Whatever Reader desires to have a thorow Comprehension of an Author's Thoughts, cannot take a better Method, than by putting himself into the Circumstances and Postures[3] of Life, that the Writer was in, upon every important Passage as it flow'd from his Pen; For this will introduce a Parity and strict Correspondence of Idea's between the Reader and the Author. Now, to assist the diligent Reader in so delicate an Affair, as far as brevity will permit, I have recollected, that the shrewdest Pieces of this Treatise, were conceived in Bed, in a Garret: At other times (for a Reason best known to my self) I thought fit to sharpen my Invention with Hunger; and in general, the whole Work was begun, continued, and ended, under a long Course of Physick, and a great want of Money. Now, I do affirm, it will be absolutely impossible for the candid Peruser to go along with me in a great many bright Passages, unless upon the several Difficulties emergent, he will please to capacitate and prepare himself by these

---

[1] i.e. those who depreciate the ancients in favour of the moderns. Cf. Temple, *Of Poetry ad init.*: 'Few things in the world or none, will bear too much refining, a Thred too fine spun will easily break, and the point of a Needle too finely filed.'

[2] At this date Swift was probably with Temple at Moor Park.

[3] 'Posture' edd. 1–4. Cf. *Essay on Criticism*, ll. 233 ff.

Directions. And this I lay down as my principal *Postulatum*.

BECAUSE I have profess'd to be a most devoted Servant of all *Modern* Forms: I apprehend some curious *Wit* may object against me, for proceeding thus far in a Preface, without declaiming, according to the Custom, against the Multitude of Writers whereof the whole Multitude of Writers most reasonably complains. I am just come from perusing some hundreds of Prefaces, wherein the Authors do at the very beginning address the gentle Reader concerning this enormous Grievance. Of these I have preserved a few Examples, and shall set them down as near as my Memory has been able to retain them.[1]

One begins thus;

For a Man to set up for a Writer, when the Press swarms with, &c.

Another;

The Tax upon Paper[2] *does not lessen the Number of Scriblers, who daily pester*, &c.

Another;

When every little Would-be-wit takes Pen in hand, 'tis in vain to enter the Lists, &c.

Another;

To observe what Trash the Press swarms with, &c.

Another;

SIR, *It is meerly in Obedience to your Commands that I venture into the Publick; for who upon a less Consideration would be of a Party with such a Rabble of Scriblers,* &c.

NOW, I have two Words in my own Defence, against this Objection. First: I am far from granting the

[1] For examples of these complaints see Dryden's *Discourse on Satire* (ed. Ker, ii. 21), Addison's dedication to Halifax of vol. ii of *Musarum Anglicanarum Analecta* (1699), and Ayloffe's preface to Sedley's *Works* (1702). Cf. Marvell's *Rehearsal Transpros'd* (1672), p. 9.

[2] Imposed in 1696 (8° & 9° Gul. III. c. 7.)

Number of Writers, a Nuisance to our Nation, having strenuously maintained the contrary in several Parts of the following Discourse. Secondly: I do not well understand the Justice of this Proceeding, because I observe many of these polite Prefaces, to be not only from the same Hand, but from those who are most voluminous in their several Productions. Upon which I shall tell the Reader a short Tale.

A Mountebank in Leicester-Fields,[1] *had drawn a huge Assembly about him. Among the rest, a fat unweildy Fellow, half stifled in the Press, would be every fit*[2] *crying out, Lord! what a filthy Crowd is here; Pray, good People, give way a little, Bless me! what a Devil has rak'd this Rabble together: Z-----ds, what squeezing is this! Honest Friend, remove your Elbow. At last, a* Weaver *that stood next him could hold no longer: A Plague confound you* (said he) *for an over-grown Sloven; and who* (in the Devil's Name) *I wonder, helps to make up the Crowd half so much as your self? Don't you consider* (with a Pox) *that you take up more room with that Carkass than any five here? Is not the Place as free for us as for you? Bring your own Guts to a reasonable Compass* (and be d———n'd) *and then I'll engage we shall have room enough for us all.*

THERE are certain common Privileges of a Writer, the Benefit whereof, I hope, there will be no Reason to doubt; Particularly, that where I am not understood, it shall be concluded, that something very useful and profound is coucht underneath: And again, that whatever

---

[1] Now Leicester Square. There were fine houses on the north side, but the inhabitants of Cranbourne Alley and its neighbourhood frequented the square. Little attention was given to the field in the centre. Swift lodged here in 1711 (*Journal to Stella*, Nov. 28). Cf. Tom Brown, *Amusements Serious and Comical* (*Works*, vol. iii (1719), p. 73): 'In Leicester-fields I saw a Mountebank on the Stage, with a Congregation of Fools about him.'

There is a similar story in Prior's *Alma*, Canto III (ed. Waller (1905), i. 249).

[2] i.e. 'every now and then'.

word or Sentence is Printed in a different Character,[1] shall be judged to contain something extraordinary either of *Wit* or *Sublime*.

AS for the Liberty I have thought fit to take of praising my self, upon some Occasions or none; I am sure it will need no Excuse, if a Multitude of great Examples be allowed sufficient Authority: For it is here to be noted, that *Praise* was originally a Pension paid by the World: but the *Moderns* finding the Trouble and Charge too great in collecting it, have lately bought out the *Fee-Simple*; since which time, the Right of Presentation is wholly in our selves. For this Reason it is, that when an Author makes his own Elogy,[2] he uses a certain form to declare and insist upon his Title, which is commonly in these or the like words, *I speak without Vanity*;[3] which I think plainly shews it to be a Matter of Right and Justice. Now, I do here once for all declare, that in every Encounter of this Nature, thro' the following Treatise, the Form aforesaid is imply'd; which I mention, to save the Trouble of repeating it on so many Occasions.

'TIS a great Ease to my Conscience that I have writ

---

[1] Cf. Marvell, *The Rehearsal Transpros'd* (1672), p. 192: 'wheresoever there is a pretty Conceit, it shall be marked out in another Character'; also Swift, *On Poetry* (1733):

To Statesmen wou'd you give
    a Wipe,
You print it in *Italick Type*.
When Letters are in vulgar
    Shapes,
'Tis ten to one the Wit escapes;
But when in *Capitals* exprest,
The dullest Reader smoaks the
    Jest:
Or else perhaps he may invent

A better than the Poet meant.
[2] Cf. p. 38, note 1.
[3] There is an example of this affectation in Boyle's *Examination* (1698), p. 202: 'I abhor Vanity . . . yet this I will be bold to say; that even in those Translations of the Greek Authors, which are esteem'd the Best, would a man of some knowledge in Criticism exercise all the spite and skill he has that way to find out Mistakes, he might be able to muster up such a Plentiful Number of 'em, as would keep my Poor Version and Notes in Countenance.'

so elaborate and useful a Discourse without one grain
of Satyr intermixt; which is the sole point wherein
I have taken leave to dissent from the famous Originals
of our Age and Country.[1] I have observ'd some Satyrists
to use the Publick much at the Rate that Pedants do
a naughty Boy ready Hors'd for Discipline: First expostulate the Case, then plead the Necessity of the Rod,
from great Provocations, and conclude every Period
with a Lash. Now, if I know any thing of Mankind,
these Gentlemen might very well spare their Reproof
and Correction: For there is not, through all Nature,
another so callous and insensible a Member as the
World's Posteriors, whether you apply to it the *Toe* or
the *Birch*. Besides, most of our late Satyrists seem to
lye under a sort of Mistake, that because Nettles have
the Prerogative to Sting, therefore all *other Weeds* must
do so too. I make not this Comparison out of the least
Design to detract from these worthy Writers: For it is
well known among *Mythologists*, that *Weeds* have the
Preeminence over all other Vegetables; and therefore
the first *Monarch* of this Island,[2] whose Taste and Judgment were so acute and refined, did very wisely root out
the *Roses* from the Collar of the *Order*,[3] and plant the
Thistles in their stead as the nobler Flower of the two.
For which Reason it is conjectured by profounder Anti-
quaries, that the Satyrical Itch,[4] so prevalent in this part

[1] On the prevalence of satire at
this time cf. Temple's *Ancient and
Modern Learning, ad fin.*, and *Of
Poetry*, ed. 1696, pp. 351–2; and
cf. p. 234, l. 22.

[2] James I [*MS. Pate*; 1720].

[3] The Order of the Thistle was
revived, or instituted, by James II
in 1687, and again revived by
Anne in 1703. Its collar consists
of thistles alternately with sprigs
of rue. There was no 'rooting out'
of the roses of England. The roses
in the collar of the Order of the
Garter, the only older Order, remained as they were. See N. H.
Nicolas, *History of the Orders of
Knighthood*, iii, pp. 9 ff.

[4] In *Ancient and Modern
Learning, ad fin.*, Temple calls
satire 'the Itch of our Age and
Clymate'.

of our Island, was first brought among us from beyond the *Tweed*.[1] Here may it long flourish and abound; May it survive and neglect the Scorn of the World, with as much Ease and Contempt as the World is insensible to the Lashes of it. May their own Dullness, or that of their Party, be no Discouragement for the Authors to proceed; but let them remember, it is with *Wits* as with *Razors*, which are never so apt to *cut* those they are employ'd on, as when they have *lost their Edge*. Besides, those whose Teeth are too rotten to bite, are best of all others, qualified to revenge that Defect with their Breath.

I am not like other Men, to envy or undervalue the Talents I cannot reach; for which Reason I must needs bear a true Honour to this large eminent Sect of our *British* Writers. And I hope, this little Panegyrick will not be offensive to their Ears, since it has the Advantage of being only designed for themselves. Indeed, Nature her self has taken order, that Fame and Honour should be purchased at a better Pennyworth by Satyr, than by any other Productions of the Brain; the World being soonest provoked to *Praise* by *Lashes*, as Men are to *Love*. There is a Problem in an ancient Author, why Dedications, and other Bundles of Flattery run all upon stale musty Topicks, without the smallest Tincture of any thing New; not only to the torment and nauseating of the *Christian* Reader, but (if not suddenly prevented) to the universal spreading of that pestilent Disease, the Lethargy, in this Island: whereas, there is very little Satyr which has not something in it untouch'd before. The Defects of the former are usually imputed to the want of Invention among those who are Dealers in that kind: But, I think, with a great deal of Injustice; the Solution being easy and natural. For, the Materials of Panegyrick being very few in Number, have been long

---

[1] Scotland [*MS. Pate*].

since exhausted: For, as Health is but one Thing, and
has been always the same, whereas Diseases are by thousands, besides new and daily Additions; So, all the Virtues that have been ever in Mankind, are to be counted
upon a few Fingers, but his Follies and Vices are innu-
merable, and Time adds hourly to the Heap. Now, the
utmost a poor Poet can do, is to get by heart a List of
the Cardinal Virtues, and deal them with his utmost
Liberality to his Hero or his Patron: He may ring the
Changes as far as it will go, and vary his Phrase till he
has talk'd round; but the Reader quickly
Plutarch. finds, it is all *Pork*,[1] with a little variety of
Sawce: For there is no inventing Terms of Art beyond
our Idea's; and when Idea's are exhausted, Terms of
Art must be so too.

[1] Cf. Marvell, *The Rehearsal
Transpros'd* (1672), pp. 320–1:
'All the variety of his Treat is *Pork*
(he knows the story) but so little
disguised by good Cookery, that
it discovers the miserableness, or
rather the penury of the Host.'
See p. lx.

The story exists in many forms.
See A. C. Lee, *The Decameron:
its Sources and Analogues* (1909),
pp. 17–22: 'In the eleventh of the
"Proverbs" of Antonio Cornazano
(1431–1500) the story is told . . .
to illustrate the proverb . . . "E
tutta Fava". A wife desirous of
weaning her husband from the
attractions of other women made
him a sumptuous repast in which
each dish was composed of beans,
but with various extraordinary and
delicate flavours. The husband
asking "What is this?" she answers "Beans", and so on as re-

gards each dish, and at last she
said, "My husband, choose where
you list, it is all beans," whence he,
understanding the acute repre-
hension of his wife, changed his
mode of life.'

Among the different analogues
the dishes are made from eels,
partridges, woodcocks, chickens,
and rabbits. Cf. *Correspondence of
Gray, Walpole, West, and Ashton*,
ed. Toynbee (1915), ii, p. 43 and
note, and Burton, *Arabian Nights*
(1894), v, p. 43, and ix, p. 120.

The source of the story is Plutarch, as is stated in the margin.
It occurs in *The Life of Titus
Quintius Flaminius*, xvii, 7: ὡς
ὕεια πάντ' ἐστί, κ.τ.λ. Cf. Pliny,
Nat. Hist. viii. 51 (77), § 209:
'Neque alio ex animali numero-
sior materia ganeae. Quinquaginta
prope sapores, cum ceteris sin-
guli.'

BUT, tho' the Matter for Panegyrick were as fruitful as the Topicks of Satyr, yet would it not be hard to
find out a sufficient Reason, why the latter will be always[1] better received than the first. For, this being
bestowed only upon one or a few Persons at a time, is
sure to raise Envy, and consequently ill words from the
rest, who have no share in the Blessing: But Satyr being
levelled at all, is never resented for an offence by any,[2]
since every individual Person makes bold to understand
it of others, and very wisely removes his particular Part
of the Burthen upon the shoulders of the World, which
are broad enough, and able to bear it. To this purpose,
I have sometimes reflected upon the Difference between
Athens and *England*, with respect to the Point before us.
In the *Attick** Commonwealth,[3] it was the
Privilege and Birth-right of every Citizen   **Vid. Xenoph.*
and Poet, to rail aloud and in publick, or to expose
upon the Stage by Name, any Person they pleased, tho'
of the greatest Figure, whether a *Creon*,[4] an *Hyperbolus*,
an *Alcibiades*, or a *Demosthenes*: But on the other side,
the least reflecting word let fall against the *People* in
general, was immediately caught up, and revenged upon
the Authors, however considerable for their Quality or
their Merits. Whereas, in *England* it is just the Reverse
of all this. Here, you may securely display your utmost
Rhetorick against Mankind, in the Face of the World;
tell them,[5] *"That all are gone astray; That there is none*
"that doth good, no not one; That we live in the very Dregs

---

[1] 'alway' edd. 1–3.
[2] Cf. the 'Preface of the Author'
prefixed to the *Battle of the Books*,
p. 215.
[3] Swift refers to the political
pamphlet 'On the Polity of the
Athenians', ii. 18, formerly attributed to Xenophon. It was written
by an 'Oligarch' in 424 B.C., when
Xenophon was a child.
[4] Creon is a mistake for Cleon.
Hyperbolus and Cleon are mentioned together by Aristophanes,
Clouds, 549–51.
[5] Psalm xiv. 3 [1720].

"*of Time; That Knavery and Atheism are Epidemick as*
"*the Pox; That Honesty is fled with Astræa*; with any other
Common places *equally* new and eloquent, which are
furnished by the *Splendida bilis.[1] And when

Hor.

you have done, the whole Audience, far from
being offended, shall return you thanks as a Deliverer
of precious and useful Truths. Nay farther; It is but to
venture your Lungs, and you may preach in *Convent-*
Garden[2] against Foppery and Fornication, and *something*
else: Against Pride, and Dissimulation, and Bribery, at
White Hall: You may expose Rapine[3] and Injustice in
the *Inns* of *Court* Chappel: And in a *City* Pulpit be as
fierce as you please, against Avarice, Hypocrisie and
Extortion.[4] 'Tis but a *Ball* bandied to and fro, and every
Man carries a *Racket* about Him to strike it from himself among the rest of the Company. But on the other
side, whoever should mistake the Nature of things so
far, as to drop but a single Hint in publick, How *such*

* *Spleen.*

[1] Horace, *Sat.* II. iii. 141.
[2] '*Covent-Garden*' edd. 1–3; cf.
p. 43, l. 21. The form 'Convent',
though found as often as the other
in the early editions of the *Tale*,
was at this time passing out of use.
For another example see Blackmore's preface to *King Arthur*
(1697): 'I was so great a stranger
to the *Muses*, and by no means free
of the *Poets Company*, having never
Kiss'd their Governour's hands,
nor made the least Court to the
Committee that sits in *Convent*
Garden.'
[3] 'Rapine' edd. 1–3; misprinted 'Rapins' edd. 4, 5.
[4] As Swift read Collier's *Essays*

in 1697, the following passage
from the essay 'Of Popularity' has
a special interest:

If an Ecclesiastick 'intends to
keep Fair with the World . . . If
he is in the City, he must avoid
haranguing against Circumvention
in Commerce, and unreasonable
Imposing upon the Ignorance or
Necessity of the Buyer. . . . If his
Cure lyes among the Lawyers, let
there be nothing said against En-
tangling Property, Spinning out
of Causes, Squeezing of *Clients*,
and making the *Laws* a greater
Grievance than those who break
them . . .' (ed. 1697, Part ii, pp.
69, 70).

a one, starved half the Fleet, and half-poison'd the rest:[1] How *such a one*, from a true Principle of *Love* and *Honour*, pays no Debts but for *Wenches* and *Play*: How *such a one* has got a Clap and runs out of his Estate: *How *Paris* bribed by *Juno* and *Venus*, loath to offend either Party, slept out the whole Cause on the Bench: Or, how *such an Orator* makes long Speeches in the Senate with much Thought, little Sense, and to no Purpose; whoever, I say, should venture to be thus particular, must expect to be imprisoned for *Scandalum Magnatum*: to have *Challenges* sent him; to be sued for *Defamation*; and to be *brought before the Bar of the House*.

BUT I forget that I am expatiating on a Subject, wherein I have no concern, having neither a Talent nor an Inclination for Satyr; On the other side, I am so entirely satisfied with the whole present Procedure of human Things, that I have been for some Years preparing Materials towards *A Panegyrick upon the World*;[2]

* *Juno *and* Venus *are Money and a Mistress, very powerful Bribes to a Judge, if Scandal says true. I remember such Reflexions were cast about that time, but I cannot fix the Person intended here.*

[1] Complaints about the victualling of the navy were very common both before and after the publication of *A Tale of a Tub*. See Clowes, *The Royal Navy* (1898), vol. ii, chap. xxii.

Among the many pamphlets that dealt with this abuse at the time when the *Tale* was in preparation the following may be mentioned: *Great Britain's Groans, or an Account of the Oppression, Ruin, and Destruction of the Loyal Seamen of England* (1695); *Remarks upon the Navy, The Second Part* (1700); and *An Historical and Political Treatise of the Navy* (1703). An investigation was ordered in 1703, and the proceedings were published under the title, *A True and Exact Account of many great Abuses Committed in the Victualling Her Majesties Navy, From February 3, 170⅔, to July 1703. As Appears by the Informations and Depositions of several Witnesses, with the Proceedings thereupon, both at the Admiralty-Office, Hicks's-Hall, and Elsewhere. For the Information of the Parliament and Publick. Price 6d.*

[2] See the Catalogue before the Title [1720].

to which I intended to add a Second Part, entituled, *A Modest Defence of the Proceedings of the Rabble in all Ages*. Both these I had Thoughts to publish by way of Appendix[1] to the following Treatise; but finding my Common-Place-Book fill much slower than I had reason to expect, I have chosen to defer them to another Occasion. Besides, I have been unhappily prevented in that Design, by a certain Domestick Misfortune, in the Particulars whereof, tho' it would be very seasonable, and much in the *Modern* way, to inform the *gentle Reader*, and would also be of great Assistance towards extending this Preface into the Size now in Vogue, which by Rule ought to be *large* in proportion as the subsequent Volume is *small*; Yet I shall now dismiss our impatient Reader from any farther Attendance at the *Porch*; and having duly prepared his Mind by a preliminary Discourse, shall gladly introduce him to the sublime Mysteries that ensue.

[1] Swift refers to Bentley's *Dissertation* of 1697, printed as an appendix to the second edition of Wotton's *Reflections*.

A
TALE
OF A
TUB, &c.

SECT. I.

The INTRODUCTION.

WHOEVER hath an Ambition to be heard in a Crowd, must press, and squeeze, and thrust, and climb with indefatigable Pains, till he has exalted himself to a certain Degree of Altitude above them.[1] Now, in all Assemblies, tho' you wedge them ever so close, we may observe this peculiar Property; that, over their Heads there is Room enough; but how to reach it, is the difficult Point; It being as hard to get quit of *Number* as of *Hell*;

——Evadere ad auras,
Hoc opus, hic labor est.[2]

* *But to return, and view the cheerful Skies;*
In this the Task and mighty Labour lies.

[1] Cf. *Hudibras*, Part III, ii. 971:
For charlatans can do no good
Until they're mounted in a crowd.

[2] Virgil, *Aen.* vi. 128–9. The translation in the footnote is from Dryden's *Virgil*, 1697, p. 418.

TO this End, the Philosopher's Way in all Ages has been by erecting certain *Edifices in the Air*;[1] But, whatever Practice and Reputation these kind of Structures have formerly possessed, or may still continue in, not excepting even that of *Socrates*, when he was suspended in a Basket to help Contemplation;[2] I think, with due Submission, they seem to labour under two Inconveniences.[3] *First*, That the Foundations being laid too high, they have been often out of *Sight*, and ever out of *Hearing*. *Secondly*, That the Materials, being very transitory, have suffer'd much from Inclemencies of Air, especially in these North-West Regions.

THEREFORE, towards the just Performance of this great Work, there remain but three Methods that I can think on; Whereof the Wisdom of our Ancestors being highly sensible, has, to encourage all aspiring Adventurers, thought fit to erect three wooden Machines, for the Use of those Orators who desire to talk much without Interruption. These are, the *Pulpit*, the *Ladder*, and the *Stage-Itinerant*. For, as to the *Bar*, tho' it be compounded of the same Matter, and designed for the same Use, it cannot however be well allowed the Honor of a fourth, by reason of its level or inferior Situation, exposing it to perpetual Interruption from Collaterals. Neither can the *Bench* it self, tho raised to a proper Eminency, put in a better Claim, whatever its Advocates insist on. For if they please to look into the original Design of its Erection, and the Circumstances or Adjuncts subservient to that Design, they will soon acknowledge the present Practice exactly correspondent to the Primitive Institution, and both to answer the

[1] Systems of philosophy, which are ill founded and generally unintelligible, and quickly fall to pieces, especially those of English philosophers. For the reference to England in 'North-West Regions' cf. p. 113, ll. 2–3.
[2] Aristophanes, *Clouds*, 218 ff.
[3] 'Inconveniencies' edd. 1–4.

Original Design

Etymology of the Name, which in the *Phœnician* Tongue is a Word of great Signification, importing, if literally interpreted, *The Place of Sleep*; but in common Acceptation, *A Seat well bolster'd and cushion'd, for the Repose of old and gouty Limbs: Senes ut in otia tuta recedant.*[1] Fortune being indebted to them this Part of Retaliation, that, as formerly, they have long *Talkt*, whilst others *Slept*, so now they may *Sleep* as long whilst others *Talk*.

BUT if no other Argument could occur to exclude the *Bench* and the *Bar* from the List of Oratorial Machines, it were sufficient, that the Admission of them would overthrow a Number which I was resolved to establish, whatever Argument it might cost me; in imitation of that prudent Method observed by many other Philosophers and great Clerks, whose chief Art in Division has been, to grow fond of some proper mystical Number,[2] which their Imaginations have rendred Sacred, to a Degree, that they force common Reason to find room for it in every part of Nature; reducing, including, and adjusting every *Genus* and *Species* within that Compass, by coupling some against their Wills, and banishing others at any Rate. Now among all the rest, the profound Number *THREE* is that which hath most employ'd my sublimest Speculations, nor ever without wonderful Delight. There is now in the Press, (and will be publish'd next Term)[3] a Panegyrical Essay of mine upon this Number, wherein I have by most convincing Proofs, not only reduced the *Senses* and the *Elements* under its Banner, but brought

---

[1] Horace, *Sat.* i. i. 31.

[2] As Sir Thomas Browne grows fond of the number five in *The Garden of Cyrus*, seeing 'quincunxes in heaven above, quincunxes in earth below, and quincunxes in the water beneath the earth; quincunxes in deity, quincunxes in the mind of man, quincunxes in bones, in the optic nerves, in roots of trees, in leaves, in petals, in every thing' (Coleridge, letter to Sarah Hutchinson, 10 March 1804).

[3] See the list before the Title [1720].

over several Deserters from its two great Rivals *SEVEN* and *NINE*.[1]

NOW, the first of these Oratorial Machines in Place as well as Dignity, is the *Pulpit*. Of *Pulpits* there are in this Island several sorts; but I esteem only That made of Timber from the *Sylva Caledonia*,[2] which agrees very well with our Climate. If it be upon its Decay, 'tis the better, both for Conveyance of Sound, and for other Reasons to be mentioned by and by.[3] The Degree of Perfection in Shape and Size, I take to consist, in being extreamly narrow, with little Ornament, and best of all without a Cover; (for by antient Rule, it ought to be the only uncover'd *Vessel*[4] in every Assembly where it is rightfully used) by which means, from its near Resemblance to a Pillory, it will ever have a mighty Influence on human Ears.

OF *Ladders* I need say nothing: 'Tis observed by Foreigners themselves, to the Honor of our Country,[5] that we excel all Nations in our Practice and Under-

---

[1] Seven times seven, and seven times nine, the two climactericks [*MS. Pate*].

The numbers *seven* and *nine* were supposed to have a certain inherent and fatal power annexed to them, especially in computing the years of human life. Hence the great importance formerly attached to the sixty-third year of human life, which number, being produced by the multiplication of *seven* by *nine*, was termed the Grand Climacteric. The arrival of this aera was dreaded, and it was accounted a favour of fate, and a pledge of longevity, when it was safely passed over. See More's Vulgar Errors, book iv, chap. 12 [Scott]. 'More' of course should be 'Browne'.

[2] The Opinions of the greatest part of our Dissenters falling in with those of the Scotch Kirk by law established, makes the Author recommend this wood for pulpits; and their affected plainness and simplicity is exposed by the figure and size here prescribed [1720]. Scotland [*MS. Pate*].

[3] See p. 62.

[4] In Plate 2 the preacher and congregation all have their heads covered. Cf. p. 268, note 4. For 'vessel', here used with a play on the word, cf. Acts ix. 15.

[5] It is not usual in other Countrys as in Britain, for every one to make a Speech before they be executed [1720].

standing of this Machine. The ascending Orators do not only oblige their Audience in the agreeable Delivery, but the whole World in their *early* Publication of these Speeches;[1] which I look upon as the choicest Treasury of our *British* Eloquence, and whereof I am informed, that worthy Citizen and Bookseller, Mr. *John Dunton*, hath made a faithful and painful Collection, which he shortly designs to publish in Twelve Volumes in Folio, illustrated with Copper-Plates. A Work highly useful and curious, and altogether worthy of such a Hand.

THE last Engine of Orators, is the *Stage-Itinerant,* erected with much Sagacity, †*sub Jove pluvio, in triviis & quadriviis.* It is the great Seminary of the two former, and its Orators are sometimes[2] preferred to the One,

---

* *Is the* Mountebank's Stage, *whose Orators the Author determines either to the* Gallows *or a* Conventicle.

† *In the open Air, and in Streets where the greatest Resort is.*

---

[1] Paul Lorraine's papers, then ordinary of Newgate [*MS. Pate*].

Paul Lorrain was appointed ordinary [i.e. chaplain] of Newgate in 1698. From that date until his death in 1719 he compiled the official accounts of the dying speeches of criminals condemned to capital punishment. See Swift's *Remarks upon a Pamphlet* (1711); *An Essay on English Bubbles* (1720); *The Last Speech and Dying Words of Ebenezer Elliston*; *The Tatler*, No. 63; Bolingbroke's letter to Swift (14 Dec. 1725; *Correspondence*, vol. iii, 296). The following is the title of one of the official accounts: *The Ordinary of Newgate his account of the behaviour, confessions, and dying-words, of J. P. Dramatti, Elizabeth Tetherington, alias Smith, and Jane Bowman, who were executed at Tyburn ... 21th* [sic] *of July, 1703.*

Each such account fills a single folio sheet, and it would not have been difficult to make a collection of 'volumes in folio'. But there is no reason to believe that Dunton had formed this project, and that it was one of the 'many' which he 'left unmentioned' in his *Life and Errors* (1705, p. 277).

Dunton's greatest project was *The Athenian Mercury*, to which Swift had sent from Moor-Park, on 14 Feb. 1691, his 'Ode to the Athenian Society'. The *Life and Errors* accordingly contains (p. 260) a short note on 'Mr. Swift, a Country Gentleman'.

[2] 'sometimes' edd. 1–4; 'sometime' ed. 5.

and sometimes to the Other, in proportion to their Deservings, there being a strict and perpetual Intercourse between all three.

FROM this accurate Deduction it is manifest, that for obtaining Attention in Publick, there is of necessity required a *superiour Position of Place.* But, altho' this Point be generally granted, yet the Cause is little agreed in; and it seems to me, that very few Philosophers have fallen into a true, natural Solution of this *Phænomenon.* The deepest Account, and the most fairly digested of any I have yet met with, is this, That Air being a heavy Body, and therefore (according to the System *Lucret.* of *Epicurus*) continually descending, must Lib. 2. needs be more so, when loaden and press'd down by Words; which are also Bodies of much Weight and Gravity, as it is manifest from those deep *Impressions* they make and leave upon us; and therefore must be delivered from a due Altitude, or else they will neither carry a good Aim, nor fall down with a sufficient Force.

Corpoream quoque enim vocem constare fatendum est,
Et sonitum, quoniam possunt impellere Sensus.
                              Lucr. *Lib.* 4.[1]

AND I am the readier to favour this Conjecture, from a common Observation; that in the several Assemblies of these Orators, Nature it self hath instructed the Hearers, to stand with their Mouths open, and erected parallel to the Horizon, so as they may be intersected by a perpendicular Line from the Zenith to the Center of the Earth.[2] In which Position, if the Audience be

* *'Tis certain then, that* Voice *that thus can wound*
    Is all Material; Body *every* Sound.

[1] Lucretius, iv. 526–7. The translation in the footnote is from Creech's *Lucretius* (ed. 1683, p. 118).

[2] Swift seems to have in mind the following passage of Browne's *Vulgar Errors*, book iv, chap. i: '. . . the arms lie parallel to the

well compact, every one carries home a Share, and little or nothing is lost.

I confess, there is something yet more refined in the Contrivance and Structure of our Modern Theatres. For, First; the Pit is sunk below the Stage with due regard to the Institution above-deduced; that whatever *weighty* Matter shall be delivered thence (whether it be *Lead* or *Gold*) may fall plum into the Jaws of certain *Criticks* (as I think they are called) which stand ready open to devour them. Then, the Boxes are built round, and raised to a Level with the Scene, in deference to the Ladies, because, That large Portion of Wit laid out in raising Pruriences and Protuberances,[1] is observ'd to run much upon a Line, and ever in a Circle. The whining Passions, and little starved Conceits, are gently wafted up by their own extreme Levity, to the middle Region, and there fix and are frozen by the frigid Understandings of the Inhabitants. Bombast[2] and Buffoonry, by Nature lofty and light, soar highest of all, and would be lost in the Roof, if the prudent Architect had not with much Foresight contrived for them a fourth Place, called *the Twelve-Peny Gallery*, and there planted a suitable Colony, who greedily intercept them in their Passage.

NOW this Physico-logical Scheme of Oratorial Receptacles or Machines, contains a great Mystery, being a Type, a Sign, an Emblem, a Shadow, a Symbol, bearing Analogy to the spacious Commonwealth of Writers, and to those Methods by which they must exalt themselves to a certain Eminency above the inferiour World. By the *Pulpit* are adumbrated the Writings of our *Modern Saints* in *Great Britain*, as they have spiritualized and

---

horizon, so that a line through their navel will pass through the zenith and centre of the earth.'

[1] 'Protuberencies' edd. 1, 2, 3.
[2] 'Bombast' edd. 1–4. Ed. 5 has 'Bombastry', evidently a printer's coinage due to assimilation with 'Buffoonry'. No other instance of this form appears to be known.

refined them from the Dross and Grossness of *Sense* and *Human Reason*. The Matter, as we have said, is of rotten Wood, and that upon two Considerations; Because it is the Quality of rotten Wood to give[1] *Light* in the Dark: And secondly, Because its Cavities are full of Worms: which is a * Type with a Pair of Handles, having a Respect to the two principal Qualifications of the Orator, and the two different Fates attending upon his Works.

THE *Ladder* is an adequate Symbol of *Faction* and of *Poetry*, to both of which so noble a Number of Authors are indebted for their Fame. *Of *Faction*, because *

	*	*	*	*	*	*	*	*
Hiatus in	*	*	*	*	*	*	*	*
MS.								
	*	*	*	*	*	*	*	*

* * * *   Of *Poetry*, because its Orators do *perorare* with a Song;[2] and because climbing up by slow

* *The Two Principal Qualifications of a Phanatick Preacher are, his Inward Light, and his Head full of Maggots, and the Two different Fates of his Writings are, to be burnt or Worm eaten.*

* *Here is pretended a Defect in the Manuscript, and this is very frequent with our Author, either when he thinks he cannot say any thing worth Reading, or when he has no mind to enter on the Subject, or when it is a Matter of little Moment, or perhaps to amuse his Reader (whereof he is frequently very fond) or lastly, with some Satyrical Intention.*

[1] 'give' is omitted in edd. 2, 3, 4.

[2] Cf. *Hudibras*, iii. i. 55–56.
'. . . if they cannot read one verse
I'th' Psalms, must sing it, and that's worse'.
On this Zachary Grey writes: 'In Hudibras's days they used to sing a psalm at the gallows; and therefore he that, by not being able to read a verse in the *Psalms*, was condemned to be hanged, must sing, or at least hear a verse sung under the gallows before he was turned off. Mr. Cotton alludes to this in the following lines:
Ready, when Dido gave the word,
To be advanc'd into the halter,
Without the benefit on's Psalter.—
Then 'cause she would, to part the sweeter,
A portion have of Hopkins' metre,

Degrees, Fate is sure to turn them off[1] before they can reach within many Steps of the Top: And because it is a Preferment attained by transferring of Propriety, and a confounding of *Meum* and *Tuum*.

UNDER the *Stage-Itinerant* are couched those Productions designed for the Pleasure and Delight of Mortal Man; such as *Six-peny-worth of Wit*, Westminster *Drolleries*, *Delightful Tales*, *Compleat Jesters*, and the like;[2] by which the Writers of and for *GRUB-STREET*, have in these latter[3] Ages so nobly triumph'd over *Time*; have[4] clipt his Wings, pared his Nails, filed his Teeth, turn'd back his Hour-Glass, blunted his Scythe, and drawn the Hob-Nails out of his Shoes. It is under this Classis, I have presumed to list my present Treatise, being just come from having the Honor conferred upon me, to be adopted a Member of that Illustrious Fraternity.

As people use at execution,
For the decorum of conclusion,
Being too sad to sing, she says—
    Virgil Travestie, Book IV.
'Tis reported of one of the chaplains to the famous Montrose, that being condemned in Scotland to die, for attending his master in some of his glorious exploits; and being upon the ladder, and ordered to set out a psalm, expecting a reprieve, he named the 119th psalm (with which the officers attending the execution complied, the Scots Presbyterians being great psalm-singers), and 'twas well for him he did so; for they had sung it half through before the reprieve came; any other psalm would have hanged him.'

[1] Cf. John Chappelow, *The Right Way to be Rich* (1717), p. 64: 'The Executioner has him upon the Ladder, with a Rope about his Neck, and turns him off in an Instant.'

[2] Cf. Bentley's *Dissertation* (1697), p. 148: 'Who can read, with any patience, that silly Discourse between *Xanthus* and his man *Æsop*; not a bit better than our *Penny-Merriments*, printed at *London-Bridge*?'

The *Westminster Drolleries* (1671 and 1672) have been edited by the Rev. J. F. Ebsworth (1875).

The Universal Jester: or a Complete Book of Jests was repeatedly advertised in *The London Post* in 1704.

[3] 'later' edd. 1–4.

[4] 'have clipt' edd. 1, 2, 3, 5; 'clipt' ed. 4.

NOW, I am not unaware, how the Productions of the *Grub-street* Brotherhood, have of late Years fallen under many Prejudices, nor how it has been the perpetual Employment of two *Junior* start-up Societies, to ridicule them and their Authors, as unworthy their established Post in the Commonwealth of Wit and Learning. Their own Consciences will easily inform them, whom I mean; Nor has the World been so negligent a Looker on, as not to observe the continual Efforts made by the Societies of *Gresham*[1] and of *Will's to edify a Name and Reputation upon the Ruin of OURS. And this is yet a more feeling Grief to Us upon the Regards of Tenderness as well as of Justice, when we reflect on their Proceedings, not only as unjust, but as ungrateful, undutiful, and unnatural. For, how can it be forgot by the World or themselves, (to say nothing of our own Records, which are full and clear in the Point) that they both are Seminaries, not only of our *Planting*, but our *Watering* too? I am informed, Our two *Rivals* have lately made an Offer to enter into the Lists with united Forces, and Challenge us to a Comparison of Books, both as to *Weight* and *Number*. In Return to which, (with Licence from our *President*) I humbly offer two Answers: First, We say, the proposal is

* Viz. *About* like that which *Archimedes* made upon a *moving the Earth.* *smaller Affair, including an impossibility in the Practice; For, where can they find Scales of *Capacity* enough for the first, or an Arithmetician of *Capacity* enough for the Second. Secondly, We are ready to accept the Challenge, but with this

---

* Will'*s* Coffee-House *was formerly the Place where the Poets usually met, which tho it be yet fresh in memory, yet in some Years may be forgot, and want this Explanation.*

[1] The Royal Society met in Gresham College until 1710. See C. R. Weld, *History of the Royal* *Society* (1848), vol. i, chap. iv, and p. 395.

Condition, that a third indifferent Person be assigned, to whose impartial Judgment it shall be left to decide, which Society each Book, Treatise or Pamphlet do most properly belong to. This Point, God knows, is very far from being fixed at present; For, We are ready to produce a Catalogue of some Thousands, which in all common Justice ought to be entitled to Our Fraternity, but by the revolted and new-fangled Writers, most perfidiously ascribed to the others. Upon all which, we think it very unbecoming our Prudence, that the Determination should be remitted to the Authors themselves; when our Adversaries by Briguing[1] and Caballing, have caused so universal a Defection from us, that the greatest Part of our Society hath already deserted to them, and our nearest Friends begin to stand aloof, as if they were half-ashamed to own Us.

THIS is the utmost I am authorized to say upon so ungrateful and melancholy a Subject; because We are extreme unwilling to inflame a Controversy, whose Continuance may be so fatal to the Interests of Us All, desiring much rather that Things be amicably composed; and We shall so far advance on our Side, as to be ready to receive the two *Prodigals* with open Arms, whenever they shall think fit to return from their *Husks* and their *Harlots*;[2] which I think from the *present Course of their Studies they most properly may be said to be engaged in; and like an indulgent Parent, continue to them our Affection and our Blessing.

* *Virtuoso Experiments, and Modern Comedies.*

[1] Intriguing (Fr. *briguer*, intrigue for). The word occurs frequently in Bernier's *Histoire du Grand Mogol* (1670), which Swift read in 1697, and is used by Rabelais; but it was fully naturalized in English by Swift's time.

[2] A reminiscence of the parable of the Prodigal Son: 'husks', because Swift thought experimental research useless, and 'harlots' because of the immorality of the stage. Jeremy Collier's *Short View of the Immorality and Profaneness of the Stage* appeared in 1698.

BUT the greatest Maim given to that general Reception, which the Writings of our Society have formerly received, (next to the transitory State of all sublunary Things,) hath been a superficial Vein among many Readers of the present Age, who will by no means be persuaded to inspect beyond the Surface and the Rind of Things; whereas, *Wisdom* is a *Fox*, who after long hunting, will at last cost you the Pains to dig out: 'Tis a *Cheese*, which by how much the richer, has the thicker, the homelier, and the courser Coat; and whereof to a judicious Palate,[1] the *Maggots* are the best. 'Tis a *Sack-Posset*, wherein the deeper you go, you will find it the sweeter. *Wisdom* is a *Hen*, whose *Cackling* we must value and consider, because it is attended with an *Egg*; But then, lastly, 'tis a *Nut*, which unless you chuse with Judgment, may cost you a Tooth, and pay you with nothing but a *Worm*. In consequence of these momentous Truths, the *Grubæan*[2] Sages have always chosen to convey their Precepts and their Arts, shut up within the Vehicles of Types and Fables, which having been perhaps more careful and curious in adorning, than was altogether necessary, it has fared with these Vehicles after the usual Fate of Coaches over-finely painted and gilt; that the transitory Gazers have so dazzled their Eyes, and fill'd their Imaginations with the outward Lustre, as neither to regard or consider, the Person or the Parts of the Owner within. A Misfortune we undergo with somewhat less Reluctancy, because it has been common to us with *Pythagoras*, *Æsop*, *Socrates*,[3] and other of our Predecessors.

HOWEVER, that neither the World nor our selves may any longer suffer by such misunderstandings, I

---

[1] 'Palate' edd. 1–4; 'Pate' ed. 5.
[2] i.e. 'of Grub-street'; apparently first used by Swift.
[3] Pythagoras, Æsop, and Socrates were all men of mean or ugly appearance. On Æsop's 'ugliness' see Boyle's *Examination*, pp. 268 ff.

have been prevailed on, after much importunity from my Friends, to travel in a compleat and laborious Dissertation upon the prime Productions of our Society, which besides their beautiful Externals for the Gratification of superficial Readers, have darkly and deeply couched under them, the most finished and refined Systems of all Sciences and Arts; as I do not doubt to lay open by Untwisting or Unwinding, and either to draw up by Exantlation,[1] or display by Incision.

THIS great Work was entred upon some Years ago, by one of our most eminent Members: He began with the History of *Reynard the Fox,*[2] but neither lived to publish his Essay, nor to proceed farther in so useful an Attempt which is very much to be lamented, because the Discovery he made, and communicated with his Friends, is now universally received; nor, do I think, any of the Learned will dispute, that famous Treatise

* *The Author seems here to be mistaken, for I have seen a Latin Edition of* Reynard *the Fox, above an hundred Years old, which I take to be the Original; for the rest it has been thought by many People to contain some Satyrical Design in it.*

[1] The action of drawing out, as water from a well (Lat. *exantlare*). Cf. Sir Th. Browne, *Vulgar Errors*, book i, chap. v: 'Truth which wise men say doth lye in a well, is not recoverable but by exantlation'.

[2] As the footnote remarks, the *History of Reynard the Fox* was not one of the productions of Grubstreet. The 'Latin edition' is probably Hartmann Schopper's *Opus Poeticum de admirabili fallacia et astutia Vulpeculae Reinikes* (Frankfort, 1567). The stories were often used for political satire, so that there is distinct point in Swift's

calling the History 'a complete body of civil knowledge'. A free rendering of Schopper's Latin into English verse, entitled 'The Crafty Courtier', was issued in 1706 by Swift's publisher, John Nutt.

Another metrical version, by John Shurley, was issued in 1681 under the title *The Most Delightful History of Reynard the Fox: in Heroic Verse . . . containing Wisdom and Policies of State.* It was based on the current prose version, which was derived from Caxton's translation. In the Epistle to the Reader what Swift here says of

to be a compleat Body of Civil Knowledge, and the *Revelation*, or rather the *Apocalyps* of all State-*Arcana*. But the Progress I have made is much greater, having already finished my Annotations upon several Dozens; From some of which, I shall impart a few Hints to the candid Reader, as far as will be necessary to the Conclusion at which I aim.

THE first Piece I have handled is that of *Tom Thumb*,[1] whose Author was a *Pythagorean* Philosopher. This dark Treatise contains the whole Scheme of the *Metempsychosis*,[2] deducing the Progress of the Soul thro' all her Stages.

THE next is Dr. *Faustus*, penn'd by *Artephius*, an Author *bonæ notæ*, and an *Adeptus*; He published it in the *nine hundred eighty fourth Year of his Age; this Writer proceeds wholly by *Reincrudation*, or in the *via humida*: And the Marriage between *Faustus* and *Helen*, does most conspicuously dilucidate the fermenting of the *Male* and *Female Dragon*.[3]

* *He lived a thousand.*

WHITTINGTON *and his Cat*, is the Work of that Mysterious *Rabbi*, *Jehuda Hannasi*, containing a Defence of the *Gemara* of the *Jerusalem Misna*, and its just

the Treatise by way of satire is seriously claimed for it. 'In this piece as in a Crystal Mirror', says Shurley, 'may the Politick Statesman see his shadow . . . if it be seriously weighed and thorowly understood, it is the only Book to study men by, and to observe the Conditions both of high and low.'

[1] *Tom Thumb, Dr. Faustus, Whittington and his Cat, the Wise Men of Gotham.* Swift probably refers to the versions of these stories which were issued in chapbooks at the end of the seventeenth

or beginning of the eighteenth century. They will be found in Ashton's *Chap-books of the Eighteenth Century.*

Cf. the 'Treatise' entitled *A Comment upon the History of Tom Thumb,* published in 1711, and afterwards included in *Miscellaneous Works of Dr. William Wagstaffe.*

[2] 'Metempsychosis' edd. 3, 4; 'Metampsycosis' edd. 1, 5; 'Metampsychosis' ed. 2.

[3] On all this paragraph see Appendix F, pp. 354–5.

preference to that of *Babylon,* contrary to the vulgar Opinion.

THE *Hind and Panther.* This is the Master-piece of a famous Writer † now living, intended for a compleat Abstract of sixteen thousand †Viz *in the Year* 1698.[1] Schoolmen from *Scotus* to *Bellarmin.*

TOMMY POTTS.[2] Another Piece supposed by the same Hand, by way of Supplement to the former.

THE *Wise Men of* Gotham,[3] *cum Appendice.* This is a Treatise of immense Erudition, being the great Original and Fountain of those Arguments, bandied about both in *France* and *England,* for a just Defence of the *Modern*[4] Learning and Wit, against the Presumption, the Pride, and the Ignorance of the *Antients.* This unknown Author hath so exhausted the Subject, that a penetrating Reader will easily discover, whatever hath been written since upon that Dispute, to be little more than Repetition. *An Abstract of this Treatise hath been lately published by a *worthy Member* of our Society.

THESE Notices may serve to give the Learned Reader an Idea as well as a Taste of what the whole Work is likely to produce: wherein I have now altogether circumscribed my Thoughts and my Studies; and if I can bring it to a Perfection before I die, shall

---

* *This I suppose*[5] *to be understood of Mr.* W-tt-ns *Discourse of Antient and Modern Learning.*

[1] '1697' edd. 1, 2, 3. Dryden died 1 May 1700.

[2] Swift refers to the ballad entitled 'The Lovers Quarrel: or Cupid's Triumph. Being The Pleasant History of fair Rosamond of Scotland. Being Daughter to the Lord *Arundel,* whose Love was obtained by the Valour of *Tommy Pots:* who conquered the Lord *Phenix,* and wounded him, and after obtained her to be his Wife. Being very delightful to Read. *London,* Printed by *A. P.* for *F. Coles, T. Vere,* and *J. Wright'* [? 1675].

[3] 'Gotham' edd. 1–3; 'Goatham', edd. 4, 5. See p. xlv.

[4] '*Modern*' edd. 1, 2 (cf. note*); '*Moderns*' edd. 3–5.

[5] 'is, I suppose', *Notes* 1711.

reckon I have well employ'd the *poor Remains of an unfortunate Life.[1] This indeed is more than I can justly expect from a Quill worn to the Pith in the Service of the State, in *Pro's* and *Con's* upon *Popish Plots*, and † *Meal-Tubs*,[2] and *Exclusion Bills*, and *Passive Obedience*, and *Addresses of Lives and Fortunes*; and *Prerogative*, and *Property*,[3] and *Liberty of Conscience*, and *Letters to a Friend:* From an Understanding and a Conscience, thread-bare and ragged with perpetual turning; From a Head broken in a hundred places, by the Malignants of the opposite Factions, and from a Body spent with Poxes ill cured, by trusting to Bawds and Surgeons, who, (as it afterwards appeared) were profess'd Enemies to Me and the Government, and revenged their Party's Quarrel upon my Nose and Shins. Fourscore and eleven Pamphlets have I written[4] under three Reigns, and for the Service of six and thirty Factions.[5]

* *Here the Author seems to personate L'Estrange, Dryden, and some others, who after having past their Lives in Vices,[6] Faction and Falshood, have the Impudence to talk of Merit and Innocence and Sufferings.*

† *In King* Charles *the* II. *Time, there was an Account of a* Presbyterian *Plot, found in a Tub*,[7] *which then made much Noise.*

[1] On the footnote see p. 7.

[2] The Meal-tub Plot was the conspiracy invented and revealed by Thomas Dangerfield in 1679. The papers relating to the plot were said to have been hidden in a *Meal-tub* in the house of Mrs. Cellier, a Roman Catholic lady.

[3] 'Popery' ed. 3.

[4] 'writ' edd. 1, 2, 3.

[5] Cf. 'On each side of the Gate was a small Window ... into that on the Left side, the King's Smiths conveyed fourscore and eleven Chains ... which were locked to my left Leg with six and thirty Padlocks' (*Gulliver's Travels* (1762),

part i, chap. i).

'From the curious coincidence of the numbers in these two passages, Professor Porson inferred that both were written by the same person, that is, that Swift was the author of the *Tale of a Tub*' (*Tracts and Miscellaneous Criticisms of Richard Porson*, ed. T. Kidd (1815), p. 317).

The passage is intended as a parody of L'Estrange in particular, but cf. Dryden's 'Postscript to the Reader' in his *Virgil*.

[6] 'Vice' *Notes* 1711.

[7] 'Meal-Tub' *Notes* 1711.

But finding the State has no farther Occasion for Me and my Ink, I retire willingly to draw it out into Speculations more becoming a Philosopher, having, to my unspeakable Comfort, passed a long Life, with a Conscience void of Offence.[1]

BUT to return. I am assured from the Reader's Candor, that the brief Specimen I have given, will easily clear all the rest of our Society's Productions from an Aspersion grown, as it is manifest, out of Envy and Ignorance: That they are of little farther Use or Value to Mankind, beyond the common Entertainments of their Wit and their Style: For these I am sure have never yet been disputed by our keenest Adversaries: In both which, as well as the more profound and mystical Part, I have throughout this Treatise closely followed the most applauded Originals. And to render all compleat, I have with much Thought and Application of Mind, so ordered, that the chief Title prefixed to it, (I mean, That under which I design it shall pass in the common Conversations of Court and Town) is modelled exactly after the Manner peculiar to *Our* Society.

I confess to have been somewhat liberal in the Business of *Titles, having observed the Humor of multiplying them, to bear great Vogue among certain Writers, whom I exceedingly Reverence. And indeed, it seems not unreasonable, that Books, the Children of the Brain, should have the Honor to be Christned with variety of Names, as well as other Infants of Quality. Our famous *Dryden* has ventured to

* *The Title Page in the Original was so torn, that it was not possible to recover several Titles which the Author here speaks of.*

---

[1] Acts xxiv. 16 [1720].
Edd. 1–4 read 'with a *Conscience void of Offence towards God and* *towards Man*' ('*Men*' edd. 2–4).
Cf. p. 7, note 3.

* *See* Virgil *translated,* &c.

proceed a Point farther, endeavouring to introduce also a Multiplicity of *God-fathers;*[1] which is an Improvement of much more Advantage, upon a very obvious Account. 'Tis a Pity this admirable Invention has not been better culti-vated, so as to grow by this time into general Imitation, when such an Authority serves it for a Precedent. Nor have[2] my Endeavours been wanting to second so useful an Example: But it seems, there is an unhappy Ex-pence usually annexed to the Calling of a God-Father, which was clearly out of my Head, as it is very reason-able to believe. Where the Pinch lay, I cannot certainly affirm; but having employ'd a World of Thoughts and Pains, to split my Treatise into forty Sections, and hav-ing entreated forty Lords of my Acquaintance, that they would do me the Honor to stand, they all made it a[3] Matter of Conscience, and sent me their Excuses.

[1] Dryden dedicated his transla-tion of Virgil to three patrons: the *Eclogues* to Lord Clifford, the *Georgics* to the Earl of Chester-field, and the *Aeneid* to the Mar-quis of Normanby. He was not the first so to divide a book. Fuller's *Church History* (1655) has twelve title-pages, besides the general one, and as many particular dedications, as well as fifty or sixty inscrip-tions to benefactors. Sir Balthasar Gerbier has forty-one dedicatory epistles in his *Counsel and Advise to all Builders* (1663).

Hawkesworth took Swift to re-fer to the three patrons of the different parts; cf. Malone, *Prose Works of Dryden* (1800), vol. i, p. 237. But would Swift have used the word 'multiplicity' had he thought only of them, or also of the other patrons named in Dryden's 'Postscript to the Read-er'? Does he not refer to the plates in Dryden's translation? There were two sets of subscriptions, five guineas and two guineas; and those who paid the larger sum had one of the full-page engravings in-scribed to them. The list of these 'Subscribers to the Cuts of Virgil' (printed at the beginning of the volume) contains no fewer than 101 names.

Dryden, or rather his publisher, was not the first to employ this method. Its beginnings are found in Thomas Heywood's *Hierarchie of the blessed Angels* (1635), where each plate bears the name of the patron at whose expenses it had been provided. It was employed by Ogilby in his *Homer* (1669).

[2] 'have' edd. 1–4; 'has' ed. 5.

[3] 'a' omitted edd. 2, 3, 4.

Original Design

SECTION II

ONCE upon a Time, there was a Man who had Three* Sons by one Wife, and all at a Birth, neither could the Mid-Wife tell certainly which was the Eldest. Their Father died while they were young, and upon his Death-Bed, calling the Lads to him, spoke thus,

SONS; *because I have purchased no Estate, nor was born to any,*[1] *I have long considered some good Legacies to bequeath You; And at last, with much Care as well as Expence, have provided each of you* (here they are) *a new* †*Coat.*[2] *Now, you are to understand, that these Coats have two Virtues contained in them: One is, that with good wearing, they will last you fresh and sound as long as you live: The other is, that they will grow in the same proportion with your Bodies, lengthning and widening of themselves, so as to be always fit. Here, let me see them on you before I die. So, very well, Pray Children, wear them clean, and brush them often. You will find in my* ‡*Will* (here it is) *full Instructions in every particular concerning the Wearing and Management of your Coats; wherein you must be very exact,*

* *By these three Sons,* Peter, Martyn *and* Jack; Popery, *the* Church of England, *and our Protestant* Dissenters *are designed.* W. Wotton.

† *By his Coats which he gave his Sons, the Garments of the* Israelites. W. Wotton.

An Error (with Submission) of the learned Commentator; for by the Coats are meant the Doctrine and Faith of Christianity, *by the Wisdom of the Divine Founder fitted to all Times, Places and Circumstances.* Lambin.

‡ *The New Testament.*

[1] See Math. viii. 20. [1734.]

[2] The Scripture [*MS. Pate*] —strictly the Gospels. See note †, which was evidently written by Swift. The name of Lambin —the French scholar (1516–72) who wrote commentaries on Horace, Lucretius, Cicero, Demosthenes, Plautus, and other classical authors—is added to the note merely for the purpose of humorous mystification.

to avoid the Penalties I have appointed for every Transgression or Neglect, upon which your future Fortunes will entirely depend. I have also commanded in my Will, that you should live together in one House like Brethren and Friends, for then you will be sure to thrive, and not otherwise.

HERE the Story says, this good Father died, and the three Sons went all together[1] to seek their Fortunes.

I shall not trouble you with recounting what Adventures they met for the first seven Years,[2] any farther than by taking notice, that they carefully observed their Father's Will, and kept their Coats in very good Order; That they travelled thro' several Countries, encountred a reasonable Quantity of Gyants, and slew certain Dragons.[3]

BEING now arrived at the proper Age for producing themselves, they came up to Town, and fell in love with the Ladies, but especially three, who about that time were in chief Reputation: The *Dutchess *d' Argent*, *Madame de Grands Titres*, and the Countess *d' Orgueil*. On their first Appearance, our three Adventurers met with a very bad Reception; and soon with great Sagacity guessing out the Reason, they quickly began to improve in the good Qualities of the Town: They[4] Writ, and Raillyed,[5] and Rhymed, and Sung, and Said, and said Nothing; They Drank, and Fought, and Whor'd, and Slept, and Swore, and took Snuff: They went to new Plays on the first Night, haunted the *Chocolate*-Houses,

* *Their Mistresses are the* Dutchess d'Argent, Madamoiselle de Grands Titres, *and the* Countess d'Orgueil, *i.e.* Covetousness, Ambition *and* Pride, *which were the three great Vices that the ancient Fathers inveighed against as the first Corruptions[6] of Christianity.* W. Wotton.

---

[1] 'altogether' ed. 1.
[2] The first seven centuries: Cf. Curll's *Key* (p. 333).
[3] The enemys of Christianity, & Hereticks. [1734.]

[4] A List of some of the good qualitys of the Town Rakes [1720].
[5] 'Rallyed' edd. 2, 3, 4.
[6] 'Corrupters' Wotton.

beat the Watch, lay on Bulks,[1] and got Claps: They bilkt
Hackney-Coachmen, ran in Debt with Shop-keepers,
and lay with their Wives: They kill'd Bayliffs, kick'd
Fidlers down Stairs, eat at *Locket*'s,[2] loytered at *Will*'s:
They talk'd of the Drawing-Room and never came
there, Dined with Lords they never saw; Whisper'd
a Dutchess, and spoke never a Word; exposed the
Scrawls of their Laundress for Billets-doux[3] of Quality:
came ever just from Court and were never seen in it;
attended the Levee *sub dio*; Got a list of Peers by heart
in one Company, and with great Familiarity retailed
them in another. Above all, they constantly attended
those Committees of Senators who are silent in the *House*,
and loud in the *Coffee-House*, where they nightly ad-
journ to chew the Cud of Politicks, and are encompass'd
with a Ring of Disciples, who lye in wait to catch up
their Droppings. The three Brothers had acquired forty
other Qualifications of the like Stamp, too tedious to recount, and by consequence, were justly reckoned the
most accomplish'd Persons in Town:[4] But all would
not suffice, and the Ladies aforesaid continued still in-
flexible: To clear up which Difficulty, I must with the
Reader's good Leave and Patience, have recourse to
some Points of Weight, which the Authors of that Age
have not sufficiently illustrated.

---

[1] A bulk is a stall outside a shop,
or, in Johnson's words, 'a part of
a building jutting out'. Cf. *Dunciad*, ii. 420, 'stretch'd on bulks, as
usual, Poets lay,' and Johnson's
Life of Savage (1744), p. 127:
'walked about the Streets till he
was weary and lay down in the
Summer upon a Bulk.' Cf. also
Othello, v. i. 1, and *Humphrey
Clinker*, letter of 10 June.

[2] A fashionable ordinary at
Charing Cross, so called from
Adam Locket, its first landlord.
Its reputation, which was made as
early as 1675, continued throughout the reign of Anne, but ceased
shortly thereafter. See Cunningham and Wheatley, *London*, vol.
ii, pp. 413–14.

[3] 'Billets-doux' ed. 1; 'Billet-
doux' edd. 2–5.

[4] 'in the Town' edd. 4, 5.

FOR, *about this Time it happened a Sect arose, whose Tenents[1] obtained and spread very far, especially in the *Grand Monde*, and among every Body of good Fasion. They worshipped a sort of *Idol*,[2] who, as their Doctrine delivered, did daily create Men, by a kind of Manufactory Operation. This †*Idol* they placed in the highest Parts of the House, on an Altar erected about three Foot: He was shewn in the Posture of a *Persian* Emperor, sitting on a *Superficies*, with his Legs interwoven under him. This God had a *Goose*[3] for his Ensign; whence it is, that some Learned Men pretend to deduce his Original from *Jupiter Capitolinus*. At his left Hand, beneath the Altar, *Hell*[4] seemed to open, and catch at the Animals the *Idol* was creating; to prevent which, certain of his Priests hourly flung in Pieces of the uninformed Mass, or Substance, and sometimes whole Limbs already enlivened, which that horrid Gulph insatiably swallowed, terrible to behold. The *Goose* was also held a subaltern Divinity, or *Deus minorum Gentium*, before whose Shrine was sacrificed that Creature,[5] whose hourly Food is Human[6] Gore, and who is in

* *This is an Occasional Satyr upon Dress and Fashion, in order to introduce what follows.*

† *By this* Idol *is meant a Taylor.*

[1] This form, which means strictly the opinions held by more than one person, went out of use in the first half of the eighteenth century. It is recorded as a variant of 'tenet' in Johnson's *Dictionary*. 'Tenets' occurs in 'The Apology', p. 8, l. 3.

[2] Tailors [*MS. Pate*].

[3] A tailor's smoothing-iron (with a handle like a goose's neck). The latter part of the sentence refers to the sacred geese which

saved the Capitol.

[4] The place into which the tailor throws pieces or shreds of cloth: cf. p. 102, l. 2, and *Hudibras*, i. i. 476.

[5] 'To prick a louse' was at this time and earlier a proverbial phrase for 'to be a tailor'.

[6] 'Human' edd. 1–4; 'humane' ed. 5. The modern distinction between 'human' and 'humane' was not fully established till about the middle of the eighteenth century.

so great Renown abroad, for being the Delight and Favourite of the *Ægyptian Cercopithecus.[1] Millions of these Animals were cruelly slaughtered every Day, to appease the Hunger of that consuming Deity. The chief *Idol* was also worshipped as the Inventor of the *Yard* and the *Needle*, whether as the God of Seamen, or on Account of certain other mystical Attributes, hath not been sufficiently cleared.

THE Worshippers of this Deity had also a System of their Belief, which seemed to turn upon the following Fundamental. They held the Universe to be a large *Suit of Cloaths*, which *invests* every Thing: That the Earth is *invested* by the Air; The Air is *invested* by the

* *The Ægyptians worship'd a Monkey, which Animal is very fond of eating Lice, styled here Creatures that feed on Human Gore.*

[1] 'This long-tailed monkey is, by the classical authors generally, associated with the worship of the ancient Egyptians. Everyone remembers Juvenal's lines (xv. 4):

Effigies sacri nitet aurea cerco-
    pitheci,
Dimidio magicae resonant ubi
    Memnone chordae
Atque vetus Thebe centum
    iacet obruta portis.

Martial is also familiar with the animal (xiv. 202):

Si mihi cauda foret, cercopithe-
    cus eram;

and Pliny describes, among the monsters of Aethiopia (viii. 72, ed. Sillig): "cercopithecos, nigris capitibus, pilo asini, et dissimiles ceteris voce." Cuvier's note on this passage (in Didot's edition, 1827) is very remarkable: "non desunt in India simiae quibus longior cauda, pilus leucophaeus, facies nigra; quales *entellus* et *malbrouk* (simia faunus)." The name of "Malbrouk", or Marlborough, must have been given to this variety of ape during the great war of the Spanish succession, and Swift may have heard of it, as he did hear most things. Beyond the fact that Swift was a Whig and Marlborough a Tory at the time of the writing of the *Tale of a Tub*, there is indeed no reason for supposing that Swift entertained at that early date the strong antipathy he afterwards felt for the great general: but it is at least a curious and hitherto unnoticed coincidence that the lice-eating long-tailed monkey of the *Tub* should have been known by the name of Malbrouk' (*Prose Writings of Swift*, selected by Stanley Lane-Poole, 1884, p. 266).

Stars; and the Stars are *invested* by the *Primum Mobile*. Look on this Globe of Earth, you will find it to be a very compleat and fashionable *Dress*. What is that which some call *Land*, but a fine Coat faced with Green? or the Sea, but a Wastcoat of Water-Tabby?[1] Proceed to the particular Works of the Creation, you will find how curious *Journey-man* Nature hath been, to trim up the *vegetable* Beaux: Observe how sparkish a Perewig adorns the Head of a *Beech*, and what a fine Doublet of white Satin is worn by the *Birch*. To conclude from all, what is Man himself but a *Micro-Coat, or rather a compleat Suit of Cloaths with all its Trimmings? As to his Body, there can be no dispute; but examine even the Acquirements of his Mind, you will find them all contribute in their Order, towards furnishing out an exact Dress: To instance no more; Is not Religion a *Cloak*, Honesty a *Pair of Shoes*,[2] worn out in the Dirt, Self-love a *Surtout*, Vanity a *Shirt*, and Conscience a *Pair of Breeches*, which, tho' a Cover for Lewdness as well as Nastiness, is easily slipt down for the Service of both.

THESE *Postulata* being admitted, it will follow in due Course of Reasoning, that those Beings which the World calls improperly *Suits of Cloaths*, are in Reality the most refined Species of Animals, or to proceed higher, that they are Rational Creatures, or Men. For, is it not manifest, that They live, and move, and talk, and perform all other Offices of Human Life? Are not

---

* *Alluding to the Word* Microcosm, *or a little World, as Man hath been called by Philosophers.*

[1] 'Tabby' was a waved or watered silk; derived, through the Fr. *tabis* and the Ital., Span., or Portug. *tabi*, from the Persian *'ottāby*, so called from a district of Bagdad where the stuff was made.

[2] Such comparisons are frequent with some Divines, who think them authorized by several places of Scripture. See Ephes. vi. 14–17. [1720.]

Beauty, and Wit, and Mien, and Breeding, their inseparable Proprieties? In short, we see nothing but them, hear nothing but them. Is it not they who walk the Streets, fill up *Parliament—*, *Coffee—*, *Play—*, *Bawdy-Houses*? 'Tis true indeed, that these Animals, which are vulgarly called *Suits of Cloaths*, or *Dresses*, do according to certain Compositions receive different Appellations. If one of them be trimm'd up with a Gold Chain, and a red Gown, and a white Rod, and a great Horse,[1] it is called a *Lord-Mayor*; If certain Ermins and Furs be placed in a certain Position, we stile them a *Judge*, and so, an apt Conjunction of Lawn and black Sattin, we intitle a *Bishop*.[2]

OTHERS of these Professors, though agreeing in the main System, were yet more refined upon certain Branches of it; and held that Man was an Animal compounded of two *Dresses*, the *Natural* and the *Celestial Suit*, which were the Body and the Soul: That the Soul was the outward, and the Body the inward Cloathing;[3] that the latter was *ex traduce*;[4] but the former of daily Creation and Circumfusion. This last they proved by *Scripture*, because, *in Them we Live, and Move, and have*

---

[1] See p. 205, note 1.

[2] *Omnia vanitas*: All is meer outside [1720].

[3] Cf. *All's Well*, ii. v. 49: 'the soul of this man is his clothes'.

[4] Swift alludes to the theological controversy about the origin of the soul. The doctrine of 'traduction' (or 'traducianism' as it is now generally called) maintained that the soul of man is transmitted from his parents, just as his body is derived from them; its opponents held that only the body is so derived, and that a new soul is created immediately at birth. Cf.

Sir Thomas Browne, *Religio Medici*, i, 36, and Sir Kenelm Digby, *Observations upon Religio Medici* (1643): 'it is not *Ex traduce*, and yet hath a strange kind of neere dependence on the body; which is, as it were, Gods instrument to create it by'; also Dryden, *Ode to Mrs. Anne Killigrew*, l. 23.

The phrase is used in Collier's *Essays* (see above, p. 52, note 4), ed. 1697, Part i, p. 52. At p. 97 of the same book Collier writes, 'the Taylors, &c., are the *Fountains of Honour*'.

our Being:[1] As likewise by Philosophy, because they are *All in All*,[2] and *All in every Part*.[3] Besides, said they, separate these two, and you will find the Body to be only a sensless unsavory Carcass. By all which it is manifest, that the outward Dress must needs be the Soul.

TO this System of Religion were tagged several subaltern Doctrines, which were entertained with great Vogue: as particularly, the Faculties of the Mind were deduced by the Learned among them in this manner: *Embroidery*, was *Sheer wit*;[4] *Gold Fringe* was *agreeable Conversation*, *Gold Lace* was *Repartee*, a huge long *Periwig* was *Humor*, and a *Coat full of Powder* was very good *Raillery*: All which required abundance of *Finesse* and *Delicatesse* to manage with Advantage, as well as a strict Observance after Times and Fashions.[5]

I have with much Pains and Reading, collected out of antient Authors, this short Summary of a Body of Philosophy and Divinity, which seems to have been composed by a Vein and Race[6] of Thinking, very different from any other Systems, either *Antient* or *Modern*. And it was not meerly to entertain or satisfy the Reader's Curiosity, but rather to give him Light into several

---

[1] Acts xvii. 28.

[2] 1 Cor. xv. 28: 'That God may be all in all.'

[3] i.e. the Philosophy of Anaxagoras. Sir Henry Craik suggests (*Selections from Swift* (1892), p. 387) that Swift knew the doctrine as expressed by Lucretius, bk. i. 876, 'Ut omnibus omnes Res putet immixtas rebus latitare.'

[4] Cf. Buckingham's *Essay on Poetry*, l. 269:

That silly thing Men call *Sheer-Wit* avoid,
With which our Age so nauseously is cloy'd.

Also *The Rehearsal*, iii. i.

[5] Those of a refined taste presently judge of every one's genius, by their dress [1720].

[6] Swift follows Temple in his use of this word. Strictly applied to the characteristic flavour of wines, it is said by Johnson (*Dictionary*, and *Life of Thomson, ad fin.*) to have been first employed in a literary sense by Temple. See *Ancient and Modern Learning* (ed. 1696), p. 59: 'I think the Epistles of *Phalaris* to have more Race ... than any others.' Cf. Wotton's MS. note, p. 314.

Circumstances of the following Story: that knowing the State of Dispositions and Opinions in an Age so remote, he may better comprehend those great Events which were the issue of them. I advise therefore the courteous Reader, to peruse with a world of Application, again and again, whatever I have written upon this Matter. And so[1] leaving these broken Ends, I carefully gather up the chief Thread of my Story, and proceed.

THESE Opinions therefore were so universal, as well as the Practices of them, among the refined Part of Court and Town, that our three Brother-Adventurers, as their Circumstances then stood, were strangely at a loss. For, on the one side, the three Ladies they address'd themselves to, (whom we have named already) were ever at the very Top of the Fashion, and abhorred all that were below it, but the breadth of a Hair. On the other side, their Father's Will was very precise, and it was the main Precept in it, with the greatest Penalties annexed, not to add to, or diminish from their Coats,[2] one Thread, without a positive Command in the Will. Now, the Coats their Father had left them were, 'tis true, of very good Cloth, and besides, so neatly sown,

The first part of the Tale *is the History of* Peter; *thereby* Popery *is exposed, every Body knows the* Papists *have made great Additions to* Christianity, *that indeed is the great Exception which the* Church of England *makes against them, accordingly* Peter *begins his Pranks, with adding a* Shoulder-knot *to his Coat.* W. Wotton.

His Description of the Cloth of which the Coat was made, has a farther meaning than the Words may seem to import, 'The Coats their Father had left them, were of very good Cloth, and besides so neatly Sown, you would swear it had been all of a Piece, but at the same time very plain with little or no Ornament.' *This is the distinguishing Character of the Christian Religion.* Christiana Religio absoluta & simplex, *was* Ammianus Marcellinus's *Description of it, who was himself a Heathen.* W. Wotton.

---

[1] 'And so' edd. 1–4; 'And' ed. 5.

[2] See Apocal. xxii. 18, 19 [1734].

you would swear they were all of a Piece, but at the same time, very plain, and with little or no Ornament; And it happened, that before they were a Month in Town, great *Shoulder-knots*[1] came up; Strait, all the World was *Shoulder-knots*; no approaching the Ladies *Ruelles*[2] without the *Quota* of *Shoulder-knots: That Fellow*, cries one, *has no Soul; where is his Shoulder-knot?* Our three Brethren soon discovered their Want by sad Experience, meeting in their Walks with forty Mortifications and Indignities. If they went to the *Play-house*, the Door-keeper shewed them into the Twelve-peny Gallery.[3] If they called a Boat, says a Water-man, *I am first Sculler*:[4] If they stept to the *Rose*[5] to take a Bottle,

* *By this is understood the first introducing of Pageantry, and unnecessary Ornaments in the Church, such as were neither for Convenience nor Edification, as a* Shoulder-knot, *in which there is neither Symmetry nor Use.*

[1] Knots of ribbon or lace, sometimes enriched with jewels, worn on the shoulders. They were introduced from France about 1670. See Plates 4 and 5 for illustrations, pp. 122, 136.

[2] It was customary under Louis XIV for ladies to receive morning visitors in their bedrooms; hence 'ruelle', the passage by the side of a bed, came to signify a boudoir of ladies of fashion. The word is found in English in 1676, in Etherege's *Man of Mode*, iv. ii. Cf. Addison, *Spectator*, Nos. 45 and 530.

[3] Cf. p. 61, l. 22.

[4] 'Finding my Companion thus agreeable to my Humour, I steer'd him down *Black Friers* towards the *Thames*-side, 'till coming near the Stairs, where from their lousy

Benches up started such a noisy Multitude of old grizly *Tritons* . . . hallowing and hooting out, *Next Oars* and *Skullers* . . .' (Tom Brown, 'A Walk round London and Westminster,' *Works*, ed. 1719, vol. iii, pp. 322–3).

'The little Boats upon the *Thames*, which are only for carrying of Persons, are light and pretty; some are row'd but by one Man, others by two; the former are call'd *Scullers*, and the latter *Oars*. . . . It is easy to conceive that the *Oars* go faster than the *Sculls*, and accordingly their Pay is double' (Misson's *Memoirs and Observations in his Travels over England, &c.* (1719), p. 21).

[5] The Rose was a tavern in Russell Street frequented by men of fashion. Cf. *The Hind and the*

Original Design

the Drawer would cry, *Friend, we sell no Ale.* If they went to visit a Lady, a Footman met them at the Door with, *Pray send up your Message.* In this unhappy Case, they went immediately to consult their Father's Will, read it over and over, but not a Word of the *Shoulder-knot.* What should they do? What Temper[1] should they find? Obedience was absolutely necessary, and yet *Shoulder-knots* appeared extreamly requisite. After much Thought, one of the Brothers who happened to be more *Book-learned* then the other two, said he had found an Expedient. *'Tis true,* said he, *there is nothing here in this Will,* *totidem verbis, *making mention of* Shoulder-knots, *but I dare conjecture, we may find them* inclusivè, *or* totidem syllabis.[2] This Distinction was immediately approved by all; and so they fell again to examine the Will. But their evil Star had so directed the Matter, that the first Syllable was not to be found in the whole Writing. Upon which Disappointment, he, who found the former Evasion, took heart and said, *Brothers, there is yet Hopes; for tho' we cannot find them* totidem verbis, *nor* totidem syllabis, *I dare engage we shall make them out* tertio modo, *or* totidem literis. This Discovery was also

---

* *When the Papists cannot find any thing which they want in Scripture, they go to* Oral Tradition: *Thus* Peter *is introduced satisfy'd with the Tedious way of looking for all the Letters of any Word, which he has occasion for in the* Will, *when neither the constituent Syllables, nor much less the whole Word, were there* in Terminis. W. Wotton.

Panther Transvers'd, ad init., *The Spectator,* No. 2, and Swift's verses *On the Death of Dr. Swift*:
> Suppose me dead, and then suppose
> A club assembled at the Rose.

It was next to Drury Lane Theatre, and was demolished when the theatre was enlarged by Garrick in 1776. It is supposed to be the scene of Plate 3 in Hogarth's *Rake's Progress.*

[1] Middle course, compromise. Cf. Burnet, *Pastoral Care* (1692), ch. viii, p. 192: 'so strongly does the World love Extreams, and avoid a Temper'.

[2] Distinctions useful to find out in the Scriptures what was never in them [1720].

highly commended, upon which they fell once more to
the Scrutiny, and soon[1] picked out *S, H, O, U, L, D,*
E, R; when the same Planet, Enemy to their Repose,
had wonderfully contrived, that a *K* was not to be found.
Here was a weighty Difficulty! But the distinguishing
Brother (for whom we shall hereafter find a Name) now
his Hand was in, proved by a very good Argument,
that *K* was a modern illegitimate Letter, unknown to
the Learned Ages, nor any where to be found in antient
Manuscripts. 'Tis true, said he, the Word[2] *Calendæ*

    * *Quibusdam*   hath in **Q.V.C.* been sometimes writ
Veteribus Codi-   with a *K*, but erroneously, for in the
cibus.   best Copies it is ever spelt with a *C*. And
by consequence it was a gross Mistake in our Language
to spell *Knot* with a *K*, but that from henceforward, he
would take care it should be writ with a *C*. Upon this,
all farther Difficulty vanished; *Shoulder-Knots* were made
clearly out, to be *Jure Paterno*,[3] and our three Gentlemen
swaggered with as large and as flanting ones as the best.

    BUT, as human Happiness is of a very short Dura-
tion, so in those Days were human Fashions, upon
which it entirely depends. *Shoulder-Knots* had their
Time, and we must now imagine them in their Decline;
for a certain Lord came just from *Paris*, with fifty Yards
of *Gold Lace*[4] upon his Coat, exactly trimm'd after the
Court-Fashion of that *Month*. In two Days, all Mankind
appear'd closed up in Bars of †*Gold Lace*: whoever

---

    * *Some antient Manuscripts.*
    † *I cannot tell whether the Author means any new Innovation by this*
Word, or whether it be only to introduce the new Methods of forcing and
perverting Scripture.

---

    [1] 'soon' omitted ed. 5.
    [2] ''Tis true ... Word', forming
a line in edd. 1–4, omitted in ed. 5,
evidently through an oversight of
the printer.

    [3] What ever serves the present
turn or occasion must be made out
to be *Jure divino* [1720].
    [4] See Planché, *Cyclopædia of*
Costume, vol. i, pp. 333–4.

durst peep abroad without his Complement of *Gold Lace*, was as scandalous as a ——, and as ill received among the Women. What should our three Knights do in this momentous Affair? They had sufficiently strained a Point already, in the Affair of *Shoulder-Knots*: Upon Recourse to the Will, nothing appeared there but *altum silentium*.[1] That of the *Shoulder-Knots* was a loose, flying, circumstantial[2] Point; but this of *Gold Lace*, seemed too considerable an Alteration without better Warrant; it did *aliquo modo essentiæ adhærere*, and therefore required a positive Precept. But about this time it fell out, that the Learned Brother aforesaid, had read *Aristotelis Dialectica*, and especially that wonderful Piece *de Interpretatione*,[3] which has the Faculty of teaching its Readers to find out a Meaning in every Thing but it self; like Commentators on the *Revelations*, who proceed Prophets without understanding a Syllable of the Text. *Brothers*, said he, **You are to be informed, that, of Wills*, duo sunt genera, †*Nuncupatory*[4] *and scriptory: that in*[5] *the Scriptory Will here before us, there is no*

---

* *The next Subject of our Author's Wit, is the Glosses and Interpretations of Scripture, very many absurd ones of which are allow'd in the most Authentick Books of the* Church of Rome. W. Wotton.

† *By this is meant* Tradition, *allowed to have equal Authority with the Scripture, or rather greater.*

[1] Virgil, *Aen.* x. 63.
[2] Adventitious, unimportant. Cf. John Sharp, 'Sermon', *c.* 1714, *Works*, ed. 1754, vol. vii, p. 168: 'We must therefore distinguish between . . . what enters the nature of the action, and what is merely circumstantial.'
[3] *Aristotelis Dialectica*, any Latin translation or compendium of Aristotle's logical treatises; *de Interpretatione*, περὶ ἑρμηνείας, a treatise on the expression of thought by language. It is not one of the more difficult of Aristotle's writings, and its doctrines are taught today in elementary grammars and logics, but Swift chooses to represent it as an organum of interpreting everything but itself.
[4] By word of mouth, nuncupative.
[5] 'to' ed. 5, following a misprint in ed. 4.

Precept or Mention about Gold Lace, conceditur: *But,* si idem affirmetur de nuncupatorio, negatur, *For Brothers, if you remember, we heard a Fellow say when we were Boys, that he heard my Father's Man say, that he heard my Father say, that he would advise his Sons to get* Gold Lace *on their Coats,*[1] *as soon as ever they could procure Money to buy it. By* G—— *that is very true,* cries the other; *I remember it perfectly well,* said the third. And so without more ado they got the largest *Gold Lace* in the Parish, and walk'd about as fine as Lord.

A while after, there came up *all in Fashion,* a pretty sort of *flame Coloured Sattin* for Linings, and the *Mercer* brought a Pattern of it immediately to our three Gentlemen, *An please your Worships* (said he) †*My Lord* C—, *and Sir* J. W.[2] *had Linings out of this very Piece last*

* *This is Purgatory, whereof he speaks more particularly hereafter, but here only to shew how Scripture was perverted to prove it, which was done by giving equal Authority with the* Canon *to* Apocrypha, *called here a* Codicil *annex'd.*

It is likely the Author, in every one of these Changes in the Brother's Dresses, refers to some particular Error in the Church of Rome; *tho' it is not easy I think to apply them all, but by this of* Flame Colour'd Satin *is manifestly intended* Purgatory; *by* Gold Lace *may perhaps be understood, the lofty Ornaments and Plate in the Churches. The* Shoulder-Knots *and* Silver Fringe, *are not so obvious, at least to me; but the* Indian Figures *of Men, Women and Children plainly relate to the Pictures in the* Romish Churches, *of God like an old Man, of the Virgin* Mary *and our Saviour as a Child.*

† *This shews the Time the Author writ, it being about fourteen Years since those two Persons were reckoned the fine Gentlemen of the Town.*[2]

[1] Traditions about rich vestments for the clergy [*MS. Pate*].

[2] Note † is headed 'Lord *Cl-ff-rd* and Sir *J-n W-t-rs*' in *Notes* 1711. In ed. 1720 the names are printed '*my Lord* Cuts *and* Sir John Walters'. Nichols gives the former as 'my lord Conway'; cf. Wotton's MS. note, p. 314.

Clifford is probably Charles Boyle, second Earl of Burlington 1698, died 1704, rather than Hugh Lord Clifford, Dryden's patron. Sir John Walter, or Walters, of Sarsden, was M.P. for Appleby in 1697; cf. *Journal to Stella,* 1 Oct. 1711.

Night; it takes wonderfully, and I shall not have a Remnant left, enough to make my Wife a Pin-cushion by to morrow Morning at ten a Clock. Upon this, they fell again to romage the Will, because the present Case also required a positive Precept, the Lining[1] being held by Orthodox Writers to be of the Essence of the Coat. After long search, they could fix upon nothing to the Matter in hand, except a short Advice of their Fathers in the Will, *to take care of *Fire*, and put out their *Candles* before they went to Sleep. This tho' a good deal for the Purpose, and helping very far towards Self-Conviction, yet not seeming wholly of Force to establish a Command; and being resolved to avoid farther Scruple, as well as future Occasion for Scandal, says He that was the Scholar; *I remember to have read in Wills, of a Codicil annexed, which is indeed a Part of the Will, and what it contains hath equal authority with the rest. Now, I have been considering of this same Will here before us, and I cannot reckon it to be compleat for want of such a Codicil.[2] I will therefore fasten one in its proper Place very dexterously; I have had it by me some Time, it was written by a* †*Dog-keeper of my Grand-father's,[3] and talks a great deal (as good Luck would have it) of this very flame-colour'd Sattin.* The Project was immediately approved by the other two; an old Parchment Scrowl was tagged on according to Art, in the Form of a *Codicil annext,* and the *Sattin* bought and worn.

NEXT Winter, a *Player,* hired for the Purpose by the Corporation of *Fringe-makers,* acted his Part in a

---

* *That is, to take care of Hell, and, in order to do that, to subdue and extinguish their Lusts.*

† *I believe this refers to that part of the* Apocrypha *where mention is made of* Tobit *and his* Dog.

[1] Curll's *Key* takes 'lining' as 'praying for the dead'. See p. 334.

[2] Apocrypha [*MS. Pate*].

[3] This seems to hint at *Tobias* and his Dog. See *Tobit* v. 16, xi. 4 [1734].

new Comedy, all covered with *Silver Fringe,*[1] and according to the laudable Custom gave Rise to that Fashion. Upon which, the Brothers consulting their Father's Will, to their great Astonishment found these Words; Item, *I charge and command my said three Sons, to wear no sort of* Silver Fringe *upon or about their said Coats,* &c. with a Penalty in case of Disobedience, too long here to insert. However, after some Pause the Brother so often mentioned for his Erudition, who was well Skill'd in Criticisms, had found in a certain Author, which he said should be nameless, that the same Word which in the Will is called *Fringe,* does also signifie a *Broom-stick*; and doubtless ought to have the same Interpretation in this Paragraph. This, another of the Brothers disliked, because of that Epithet, *Silver,* which could not, he humbly conceived, in Propriety of Speech be reasonably applied to a *Broom-stick*: but it was replied upon him, that this Epithet was understood in a *Mythological,* and *Allegorical* Sense. However, he objected again, why their Father should forbid them to wear *Broom-stick* on their Coats, a Caution that seemed unnatural and impertinent; upon which he was taken up short, as one that spoke irreverently of a *Mystery,*[2] which doubtless was very useful and significant, but ought not to be over-curiously pryed into, or nicely reasoned upon. And in short, their Father's Authority being now considerably sunk, this Expedient was allowed to serve as a lawful Dispensation, for wearing their full Proportion of *Silver Fringe.*

* *This is certainly the farther introducing the Pomps of Habit and Ornament.*[3]

[1] Habits of the clergy [*MS. Pate*].

[2] When Church men find their account in any Doctrine or Custom introduced, tho directly against the plain literal meaning of Scripture, whoever speaks against it shall be cried down as a Libertin or despiser of Mysterys and Religion [1720].

[3] 'Habits and Ornaments' *Notes* 1711.

A while after, was revived an old Fashion, long anti-
quated, of *Embroidery*[1] with **Indian Figures* of Men,
Women and Children. Here they had no Occasion to
examine the Will. They[2] remembred but too well,
how their Father had always abhorred this Fashion;
that he made several Paragraphs on purpose, importing
his utter Detestation of it, and bestowing his everlasting Curse to his Sons whenever they should wear it. For
all this, in a few Days, they appeared higher in the
Fashion than any Body else in the Town. But they
solved he Matter by saying, that these Figures were
not at all the *same* with those that were formerly worn,
and were meant in the Will. Besides, they did not wear
them in that Sense, as forbidden by their Father, but
as they were a commendable Custom, and of great Use
to the Publick. That these rigorous Clauses in the Will
did therefore require some *Allowance*, and a favourable
Interpretation, and ought to be understood *cum grano
Salis*.

BUT, Fashions perpetually altering in that Age, the
Scholastick Brother grew weary of searching farther
Evasions, and solving everlasting Contradictions. Re-
solved therefore at all Hazards, to comply with the
Modes of the World, they concerted Matters together,
and agreed unanimously, to †lock up their Father's

---

* *The Images of Saints, the Blessed Virgin, and our Saviour as an*[3]
Infant.
   Ibid. *Images in the* Church of Rome *give him but too fair a Handle.*
The Brothers remembred, *&c. The Allegory here is direct.* W. Wotton.
   † *The Papists formerly forbad the People the Use of Scripture in a
Vulgar Tongue,* Peter *therefore* locks up his Father's Will in a Strong
Box, brought out of *Greece* or *Italy. Those Countries are named because
the* New Testament *is written in* Greek; *and the* Vulgar Latin, *which
is the Authentick Edition of the* Bible *in the Church of* Rome, *is in the
Language of old* Italy. W. Wotton.

---

[1] Image worship [*MS. Pate*].   omitted by an oversight in ed. 5.
[2] 'had no . . . They' edd. 1–4;   [3] 'as an' *Notes* 1711; *an* ed. 5.

Will in a *Strong-Box*, brought out of *Greece* or *Italy*, (I have forgot which) and trouble themselves no farther to examine it, but only refer to its Authority whenever they thought fit. In consequence whereof, a while after, it grew a general Mode to wear an infinite Number of *Points*,[1] most of them *tagg'd with Silver*: Upon which the Scholar pronounced *ex Cathedra, that Points* were absolutely *Jure Paterno*, as they might very well remember. 'Tis true indeed, the Fashion prescribed somewhat more than were directly named in the Will; However, that they, as Heirs general of their Father, had power to make and add certain Clauses for publick Emolument,[2] though not deducible, *totidem verbis*, from the Letter of the Will, or else, *Multa absurda sequerentur*. This was understood for *Canonical*, and therefore on the following *Sunday* they came to Church all covered with *Points*.

THE Learned Brother so often mentioned, was reckon'd the best Scholar in all that or the next Street to it; insomuch, as having run something behind-hand with the World, he obtained the Favour from a †*certain*

---

* *The* Popes *in their Decretals and Bulls, have given their Sanction to very many gainful Doctrines which are now received in the* Church of Rome *that are not mention'd in Scriptures, and are unknown to the Primitive Church.* Peter *accordingly pronounces* ex Cathedra, *That* Points tagged with Silver were absolutely *Jure Paterno, and so they wore them in great Numbers.* W. Wotton.

† *This was* Constantine the Great, *from whom the* Popes *pretend a Donation of St.* Peter's *Patrimony, which they have been never*[3] *able to produce.*

---

[1] Tagged laces or cords for attaching the hose to the doublet, or fastening the dress where buttons are now used. Cf. Peacham, *The Worth of a Peny* (1647), p. 17: '*Charles* the first was so naturally sparing, that if a point from his hose had broken, he would have tied the same upon a knot, and made it to serve againe.' See p. 136, note 1.

[2] The Church claims a power to ordain every thing she finds necessary for good order, so it be not directly contrary to Scripture [1720].

[3] 'never been' *Notes* 1711.

Lord, to receive him into his House, and to teach his Children. A while after, the *Lord* died, and he by long Practice upon[1] his Father's Will, found the way of contriving a *Deed of Conveyance* of that House to Himself and his Heirs:[2] Upon which he took Possession, turned the young Squires out, and received his Brothers in their stead.

Ibid. *The Bishops of* Rome *enjoyed their Priviledges in* Rome *at first by the favour of Emperors, whom at last they shut out of their own Capital City, and then forged a Donation from* Constantine the Great, *the better to justifie what they did. In Imitation of this,* Peter having run something behind hand in the World, obtained Leave of a certain Lord, *&c.* W. Wotton.

[1] 'Practice upon' edd. 1–3; 'Practice of' edd. 4, 5.

[2] Thus the Pope, upon the decease of the duke of Ferrara without lawful issue, seized the dutchy, as falling to the holy see, *jure divino* [*MS. Pate*].

Ferrara was claimed as a papal fief, and then on the failure of the direct line of Este the Popes refused to grant a reinvestiture of the fief on the plea that papal regulations had forbidden this. See Ranke, *History of the Popes*, vol. ii, bk. vi, §§ vii and viii, and vol. i, bk. i, c. iii.

SECT. III.

A Digression concerning Criticks.

THO' I have been hitherto as cautious as I could, upon all Occasions, most nicely to follow the Rules and Methods of Writing, laid down by the Example of our illustrious *Moderns*; yet has the unhappy shortness of my Memory led me into an Error, from which I must immediately extricate my self, before I can decently pursue my Principal Subject. I confess with Shame, it was an unpardonable Omission to proceed so far as I have already done, before I had performed the due Discourses, Expostulatory, Supplicatory, or Deprecatory with my *good Lords* the *Criticks*. Towards some Atonement for this grievous Neglect, I do here make humbly bold to present them with a short Account of themselves and their *Art*, by looking into the Original and Pedigree of the Word, as it is generally understood among us, and very briefly considering the antient and present State thereof.

BY the Word, *Critick*, at this Day so frequent in all Conversations, there have sometimes been distinguished three very different Species of Mortal Men, according as I have read in *Antient Books and Pamphlets*. For first, by this Term was[1] understood such Persons as invented or drew up Rules for themselves and the World, by observing which, a careful Reader might be able to pronounce upon the productions of the *Learned*, form his Taste to a true Relish of the *Sublime* and the *Admirable*, and divide every Beauty of Matter or of Style from the Corruption that Apes it: In their common perusal of Books, singling out the Errors and Defects, the Nauseous, the Fulsome, the Dull, and the Imperti-

---

[1] 'were' edd. 1–4.

nent, with the Caution of a Man that walks thro' *Eden-borough* Streets in a Morning,[1] who is indeed as careful as he can, to watch diligently, and spy out the Filth in his Way, not that he is curious to observe the Colour and Complexion of the Ordure, or take its Dimensions, much less to be padling in,[2] or tasting it: but only with a Design to come out as cleanly as he may. These men seem, tho' very erroneously, to have understood the Appellation of *Critick* in a literal Sence; That one principal part of his Office was to Praise and Acquit; and, that a *Critick*, who sets up to Read, only for an Occasion of Censure and Reproof, is a Creature as barbarous as a *Judge*, who should take up a Resolution to hang all Men that came before him upon a Tryal.

AGAIN; by the Word *Critick*, have been meant, the Restorers[3] of Antient Learning from the Worms, and Graves, and Dust of Manuscripts.[4]

NOW, the Races of these two have been for some Ages utterly extinct: and besides, to discourse any farther of them would not be at all to my purpose.

THE Third, and Noblest Sort, is that of the *TRUE CRITICK*, whose Original is the most Antient of all.

---

[1] See *Old and New Edinburgh*, by James Grant, vol. i, pp. 192–3 and 203; and cf. Melford's letter to Sir Watkin Phillips (18 July) in *Humphrey Clinker*, and Boswell, *Tour to the Hebrides*, 14 Aug. 1773.

[2] 'in it' ed. 4.

[3] 'Restorer' edd. 1–3.

[4] Cf. Temple's *Thoughts upon reviewing the Essay of Antient and Modern Learning* (*Miscellanea*, 1701, pp. 257–8): "'Tis to them [the critics] we owe the Editions of all the antient Authors, the best Translations of many out of *Greek*, the restoring of the old Copies, maimed with Time or Negligence, the correcting of others mistaken in the transcribing, the explaining Places obscure, in an Age so ignorant of the Stile or Customs or the Antients: And in short, endeavouring to recover those old Jewels out of the Dust and Rubbish, wherein they had been so long lost or soiled; to restore them to their native Lustre, and make them appear in their true Light.' Temple's *Miscellanea* of 1701 ('The Third Part') was published by Swift.

Every *True Critick* is a Hero born, descending in a direct Line from a Celestial Stem, by *Momus* and *Hybris*, who begat *Zoilus*, who begat *Tigellius*, who begat *Etcætera* the Elder, who begat *B–tly*, and *Rym–r*, and *W–tton*, and *Perrault*, and *Dennis*, who begat *Etcætera* the Younger.[1]

AND these are the *Criticks* from whom the Commonwealth of Learning has in all Ages received such immense benefits, that the Gratitude of their Admirers placed their Origine in Heaven, among those of *Hercules*, *Theseus*, *Perseus*, and other great Deservers of Mankind. But Heroick Virtue[2] it self hath not been exempt from the Obloquy of Evil Tongues.[3] For it hath been objected, that those Antient Heroes, famous for their Combating so many Giants, and Dragons, and Robbers, were in their own Persons a greater Nuisance to Mankind, than any of those Monsters they subdued;[4] and therefore, to render their Obligations more Compleat, when all *other* Vermin were destroy'd, should in Conscience have concluded with the same Justice upon themselves: as[5] *Hercules* most generously did,[6] and hath upon that Score, procured to himself more Temples and Votaries than the best of his Fellows. For these

---

[1] *Zoilus* attacked Homer; *Tigellius* attacked Horace.

For the descent of the *True Critick* cf. the *Battle of the Books*, p. 240.

[2] Cf. Temple's essay *Of Heroick Virtue* (*Miscellanea*, Second Part, ed. 1696, p. 148): 'Though it be easier to describe Heroick Virtue, by the Effects and Examples, than by Causes or Definitions; yet it may be said to arise from some great and native Excellency of Temper or Genius transcending the common race of Mankind, in Wisdom, Goodness and Fortitude.'

[3] Cf. Milton, *Par. Lost*, vii. 26, and Virgil, *Ecl.* vii. 28.

[4] Cf. Collier, *Essays* (1697), part ii, p. 5: 'You say it [Fame] produces Heroes; so much the worse. 'Twas well if there were fewer of them: For I scarcely ever heard of any, excepting *Hercules*, but did more Mischief than Good.'

[5] 'as' edd. 1–4; omitted ed. 5.

[6] Cf. Horace, *Epistles*, ii. i. 10–14.

Reasons, I suppose, it is why some have conceived, it would be very expedient for the Publick Good of Learning, that every *True Critick*, as soon as he had finished his Task assigned, should immediately deliver himself up to Ratsbane, or Hemp, or from some convenient *Altitude*, and that no Man's Pretensions to so illustrious a Character, should by any means be received, before That Operation were performed.

NOW, from this Heavenly Descent of *Criticism*, and the close Analogy it bears to *Heroick Virtue*, 'tis easie to Assign the proper Employment of a *True Antient Genuine Critick*; which is, to travel thro' this vast World of Writings: to pursue and hunt those Monstrous Faults bred within them: to drag out the lurking Errors like *Cacus* from his Den; to multiply them like *Hydra*'s Heads; and rake them together like *Augeas*'s[1] Dung. Or else to drive[2] away a sort of *Dangerous Fowl*, who have a perverse Inclination to plunder the best Branches of the *Tree of Knowledge*, like those *Stymphalian*[3] Birds that eat up the Fruit.

THESE Reasonings will furnish us with an adequate Definition of a *True*[4] *Critick*; that, He is *a Discoverer and Collector of Writers Faults*. Which may be farther put beyond Dispute by the following Demonstration: That whoever will examine the Writings in all kinds, wherewith this antient Sect has honour'd the World, shall immediately find, from the whole Thread and Tenour of them, that the Idea's of the Authors have been altogether conversant, and taken up with the Faults and Blemishes, and Oversights, and Mistakes of other Writers; and let the Subject treated on be whatever it will, their Imaginations are so entirely possess'd and replete with the Defects of other Pens, that the very Quintessence of what is bad, does of necessity distill into their own: by which

[1] '*Augea*'s' edd. 4, 5.
[2] 'else drive' edd. 3–5.
[3] '*Stimphalian*' ed. 5.
[4] 'a true' edd. 3–5.

means the Whole appears to be nothing else but an *Abstract* of the *Criticisms* themselves have made.

HAVING thus briefly consider'd the Original and Office of a *Critick*, as the Word is understood in its most noble and universal Acceptation, I proceed to refute the Objections of those who argue from the Silence and Pretermission of Authors; by which they pretend to prove, that the very Art of *Criticism*, as now exercised, and by me explained, is wholly *Modern*; and consequently, that the *Criticks* of *Great Britain* and *France*, have no Title to an Original so Antient and Illustrious as I have deduced. Now, If I can clearly make out on the contrary, that the most Antient Writers have particularly described, both the Person and the Office of a *True Critick*, agreeable to the Definition laid down by me; their Grand Objection, from the Silence of Authors, will fall to the Ground.

I confess to have for a long time born a part in this general Error; from which I should never have acquitted my self, but thro' the Assistance of our Noble *Moderns*; whose most edifying Volumes I turn indefatigably over Night and Day,[1] for the Improvement of my Mind, and the good of my Country: These have with unwearied Pains[2] made many useful Searches into the weak sides of the *Antients*, and given us a comprehensive List of them. *Besides, they have proved beyond contradiction, that the very finest Things delivered of old, have been long since invented, and brought to Light by much later Pens, and that the noblest Discoveries those *Antients* ever made, of Art or of Nature, have all been produced by the transcending Genius of the present Age. Which clearly shews, how little Merit those *Antients*

* *See* Wotton *of Antient and Modern Learning.*

[1] Horace, *Ars Poetica*, 269.
[2] Cf. Pope on Bentley, *Dunciad*, iv. 211:

Thy mighty Scholiast, whose
    unweary'd pains
Made Horace dull. . .

can justly pretend to; and takes off that blind Admiration paid them by Men in a Corner, who have the Unhappiness of conversing too little with *present Things.* Reflecting maturely upon all this, and taking in the whole Compass of Human Nature, I easily concluded, that these *Antients,* highly sensible of their many Imperfections, must needs have endeavoured from some Passages in their Works, to obviate, soften, or divert the Censorious Reader, by *Satyr,* or *Panegyrick* upon the *True Criticks,* in Imitation of their *Masters* the *Moderns.* Now, in the *Common-Places* of *both these, I was plentifully instructed, by a long Course of useful Study in *Prefaces* and *Prologues*;[1] and therefore immediately resolved to try what I could discover of either, by a diligent Perusal of the most Antient Writers, and especially those who treated of the earliest Times. Here I found to my great Surprize, that although they all entred, upon Occasion, into particular Descriptions of the *True Critick,* according as they were governed by their Fears or their Hopes: yet whatever they touch'd of that kind, was with abundance of Caution, adventuring no farther than *Mythology* and *Hieroglyphick.*[2] This, I suppose, gave ground to superficial Readers, for urging the Silence of Authors, against the Antiquity of the *True Critick*; tho' the *Types* are so apposite, and the Applications so necessary and natural, that it is not easy to conceive, how any Reader of a *Modern Eye* and *Taste* could over-look them. I shall venture from a great Number to produce a few, which

Satyr, and Panegyrick upon Criticks.

[1] Cf. p. 43, note 3; p. 131, note 3.

[2] Cf. Bacon, *Advancement of Learning,* book ii. iv. 3: 'Allusive or parabolical [poetry] was much more in use in the ancient times, as by the fables of Æsop, and the brief sentences of the seven, and the use of hieroglyphics may appear. . . . And as hieroglyphics were before letters, so parables were before arguments.' See also Sir Thomas Browne, *Vulgar Errors,* book v, chap. 20.

I am very confident, will put this Question beyond
Dispute.

IT well deserves considering, that these *Antient
Writers* in treating Enigmatically upon the Subject, have
generally fixed upon the very *same Hieroglyph*, varying
only the Story according to their Affections or their
Wit. For first: *Pausanias* is of Opinion, that the Perfection
of Writing correct was entirely owing to the Institution
of *Criticks*; and, that he can possibly mean no other than
the *True Critick*, is, I think, manifest enough from the
following Description. He says, *They were a Race of
Men, who delighted to nibble at the Superfluities, and Excrescencies of Books; which the Learned at length observing,
took Warning of their own Accord, to lop the Luxuriant, the
Rotten, the Dead, the Sapless, and the Overgrown Branches
from their Works.* But now, all this he cunningly shades

* *Lib*—— under the following Allegory; *that the* *Nau-
plians *in* Argia,[1] *learned the Art of pruning
their Vines, by observing, that when an* ASS *had browsed*

† *Lib.* 4. *upon one of them, it thrived the better, and bore
fairer Fruit.*[2] But †*Herodotus* holding the very
same *Hieroglyph*, speaks much plainer, and almost *in
terminis*. He hath been so bold as to tax the *True Criticks*,
of Ignorance and Malice; telling us openly, for I
think nothing can be plainer, that *in the Western Part
of* Libya, *there were* ASSES *with*

‡ Vide *excerpta* HORNS:[3] Upon which Relation
ex eo apud Pho- ‡*Ctesias* yet refines, mentioning the
tium. very same Animal about *India*, adding,
That whereas all other ASSES *wanted a* Gall, *these
horned ones were so redundant in that Part, that their Flesh
was not to be eaten because of its extream* Bitterness.[4]

NOW, the Reason why those Antient Writers treated

[1] 'Argos' Hawkesworth 1755.
[2] Pausanias, ii. 38.
[3] Herodotus, iv. 191.
[4] Photius, *Bibliotheca*, ed. Bekker (1824), pp. 48–49.

this Subject only by Types and Figures, was, because they durst not make open Attacks against a Party so Potent and so Terrible, as the *Criticks* of those Ages were: whose very Voice was so Dreadful, that a Legion of Authors would tremble, and drop their Pens at the Sound; For so *Herodotus tells us expressly in another Place, how *a vast Army of* Scythians *was put to flight in a Panick Terror, by the Braying of an* ASS.[1] From hence it is conjectured by certain profound *Philologers*, that the great Awe and Reverence paid to a *True Critick*, by the Writers of *Britain*, have been derived to Us, from those our *Scythian* Ancestors.[2] In short, this Dread was so universal, that in process of Time, those Authors who had a mind to publish their Sentiments more freely, in describing the *True Criticks* of their several Ages, were forced to leave off the use of the former *Hieroglyph*, as too nearly approaching the *Prototype*, and invented other Terms instead thereof that were more cautious and mystical; so †*Diodorus* speaking to the same purpose, ventures no farther than to say, That *in the Mountains of* Helicon *there grows a certain* Weed, *which bears a Flower of so damned a Scent, as to poison those who offer to smell it.*[3]

* *Lib.* 4.

† *Lib.*

[1] Herodotus, iv. 129.

[2] Cf. Temple, *Introduction to the History of England*: "'Tis more difficult to find out the Original of the *Scots*, or the Time of their Entrance upon those North-west Regions; but as far as can be gathered out of the Dust or Rubbish of such barbarous Times and Writings, and what remains still of known Appellations and Events, it seems probable, that vast numbers of a savage People, called *Scyths*, at some certain time, began and atchieved the Conquest of the Northern Parts both of *Britain* and *Ireland,* and by an easie Change of the word, were called *Scots*' (ed. 1695, p. 22). Swift read Temple's *Introduction* in 1697.

[3] Swift seems to be mistaken in the reference to Diodorus (the side-note omits to name the book). Pausanias (ix. xxviii. 1) says that none of the plants that grow on Helicon are at all poisonous to man. Diodorus may be a slip for

Lucretius gives exactly the Same Relation,
   ‖ *Est etiam in magnis Heliconis montibus arbos,*
      Floris odore hominem tetro consueta necare.[1] Lib. 6.

BUT *Ctesias*, whom we lately quoted, hath been a great deal bolder; He had been used with much severity by the *True Criticks* of his own Age,[2] and therefore could not forbear to leave behind him, at least one deep Mark of his Vengeance against the whole Tribe. His Meaning is so near the Surface, that I wonder how it possibly came to be overlook'd by those who deny the Antiquity of the[3] *True Criticks*. For pretending to make a Description of many strange Animals about *India*, he hath set down these remarkable Words. *Amongst the rest*, says he, *there is a* Serpent *that wants* Teeth, *and consequently cannot bite, but if its* Vomit (*to which it is much addicted*) *happens to fall upon any Thing, a certain Rottenness or Corruption ensues: These* Serpents *are generally found among the Mountains where* Jewels *grow, and they frequently emit a* poisonous Juice *whereof, whoever drinks, that Person's* Brains *flie out of his Nostrils*.[4]

THERE was also among the *Antients* a sort of *Critick*, not distinguisht in *Specie* from the Former, but

   ‖ *Near* Helicon, *and round the Learned Hill, Grow Trees, whose Blossoms with their Odour kill.*

Dicaearchus. In his note on Lucretius vi. 787 Munro, after quoting a passage from Plutarch, *Sympos.* III. i. 647 F, about the shade of the yew killing people who sleep under it at its time of flowering, adds: 'Dicaearchus, frag. 60, in Mueller, *frag. hist. Graec.* ii, p. 261, tells the same of a plant on Pelion, τοὺς δ' ἁψαμένους αὐτῆς ἀναιρεῖ τῇ ὀσμῇ.' Perhaps Swift found the passage in some note on Lucretius.
   [1] Lucretius, vi. 786–7. In edd.

1–5 'tetro' is misprinted 'retro'. The verse translation in the footnote is from Creech (1683), p. 209.
   [2] Ctesias is not known to have been 'used with severity' by the Critics of his own age, though later Greek historians discredited him. Swift is probably inventing a reason for the attack on the critics which he professes to find in the description of the serpents.
   [3] 'the' omitted ed. 5.
   [4] Photius, *Bibliotheca*, ed. Bekker, p. 47.

in Growth or Degree, who seem to have been only the
Tyros's or *junior* Scholars; yet, because of their differing
Employments, they are frequently mentioned as a Sect
by themselves. The usual exercise of these younger
Students, was to attend constantly at Theatres, and
learn to Spy out the *worst Parts* of the Play, whereof
they were obliged carefully to take Note, and render
a rational Account, to their Tutors. Flesht at these
smaller Sports, like young Wolves, they grew up in
Time, to be nimble and strong enough for hunting
down large Game. For it hath been observed both
among Antients and Moderns, that a *True Critick* hath
one Quality in common with a *Whore* and an *Alderman*,
never to change his Title or his Nature; that a *Grey
Critick* has been certainly a *Green* one, the Perfections
and Acquirements of his Age being only the improved
Talents of his Youth; like *Hemp*, which some Naturalists
inform us, is bad for *Suffocations*, tho' taken but in the
Seed. I esteem the Invention, or at least the Refinement
of *Prologues*, to have been owing to these younger Pro-
ficients, of whom *Terence* makes frequent and honourable mention, under the Name of *Malevoli*.[1]

NOW, 'tis certain, the Institution of the *True Criticks*,
was of absolute Necessity to the Commonwealth of
Learning. For all Human Actions seem to be divided
like *Themistocles* and his Company; One Man can *Fiddle*,
and another can make *a small Town a great City*, and he
that cannot do either one or the other, deserves to be
kick'd out of the Creation.[2] The avoiding of which
Penalty, has doubtless given the first Birth to the Nation
of *Criticks*, and withal, an Occasion for their secret
Detractors to report; that a *True Critick* is a sort of
Mechanick, set up with a Stock and Tools for his
Trade, at as little Expence as a *Taylor*; and that there

[1] See the Prologues to *Andria*,   [2] See Plutarch, *Themistocles*, ii
Heautontimoroumenos, and *Adelphi*.   (*Opera*, Didot, vol. i, p. 134).

is much Analogy between the Utensils and Abilities of both: That the *Taylor's Hell* is the Type of a Critick's *Common-Place-Book*, and his Wit and Learning held forth by the *Goose*:[1] That it requires at least as many of these, to the making up of one Scholar, as of the others to the Composition of a Man:[2] That the Valour of both is equal, and their *Weapons* near of a Size.[3] Much may be said in answer to those[4] invidious Reflections; and I can positively affirm the first to be a Falshood: For, on the contrary, nothing is more certain, than that it requires greater Layings out, to be free of the *Critick's* Company, than of any other you can name. For, as to be a *true Beggar*, it will cost the richest Candidate every Groat he is worth; so, before one can commence a *True Critick*, it will cost a man all the good Qualities of his Mind; which, perhaps, for a less Purchase, would be thought but an indifferent Bargain.

HAVING thus amply proved the Antiquity of *Criticism*, and described the Primitive State of it; I shall now examine the present Condition of this Empire, and shew how well it agrees with its antient self. *A certain Author, whose Works have many Ages since been entirely lost, does in his fifth Book and eighth Chapter, say of *Criticks*, that *their Writings are the Mirrors of Learning*. This I understand in a literal Sense, and suppose our Author must mean, that whoever designs to be a perfect Writer, must inspect into the Books of *Criticks*, and correct his Invention

* *A Quotation after the manner of a great Author. Vide* Bently's *Dissertation, &c.*[5]

[1] Cf. pp. 76–77.
[2] 'Nine tailors make a man.'
[3] Cf. *Henry IV, Part II*, iii. ii. 163 and foll.
[4] 'these' edd. 1–4.
[5] Cf. Bentley's *Dissertation* (1697), pp. 19, 36, and 54–55: 'The Summ *Talent*, in the *Sicilian* Accompt, contained no more in Specie than Three *Attic* Drachms, or *Roman* Denares; as plainly appears from *Aristotle*, in his now lost Treatise of the *Sicilian* Government'; and Boyle's *Examination* (1698), pp. 98 and 232.

there as in a Mirror. Now, whoever considers, that the *Mirrors* of the Antients were made of *Brass*, and *sine Mercurio*,[1] may presently apply the two Principal Qualifications of a *True Modern Critick*, and consequently, must needs conclude, that these have always been, and must be for ever the same. For, *Brass* is an Emblem of Duration, and when it is skilfully burnished, will cast *Reflections* from its own *Superficies*, without any Assistance of *Mercury* from behind. All the other Talents of a *Critick* will not require a particular Mention, being included, or easily deducible to these. However, I shall conclude with three Maxims,[2] which may serve both as Characteristicks to distinguish a *True Modern Critick* from a Pretender, and will be also of admirable Use to those worthy Spirits, who engage in so useful and honourable an Art.

THE first is, That *Criticism*, contrary to all other Faculties of the Intellect, is ever held the truest and best, when it is the very *first* Result of the *Critick*'s Mind: As Fowlers reckon the first aim for the surest, and seldom fail of missing the Mark, if they stay[3] for a Second.

SECONDLY; The *True Criticks* are known by their Talent of swarming about the noblest Writers, to which they are carried meerly by Instinct, as a Rat to the best Cheese, or a Wasp to the fairest Fruit. So, when the *King* is a Horse-back, he is sure to be the *dirtiest* Person of the Company, and they that make their Court best, are such as *bespatter* him most.

LASTLY; A *True Critick*, in the Perusal of a Book, is like a *Dog* at a Feast, whose Thoughts and Stomach are wholly set upon what the Guests *fling away*, and

---

[1] Cf. p. 43, l. 18.

[2] The whole of this Digression, and particularly the concluding Maxims, may be compared with the character of a Good Critic in Boyle's *Examination*, pp. 224-7, where five consecutive paragraphs begin with 'A Good Critic' or 'A Critic Really such'.

[3] 'stay not' edd. 2–5.

consequently, is apt to *Snarl* most, when there are the fewest *Bones*.[1]

THUS much, I think, is sufficient to serve by way of Address to my Patrons, the *True Modern Criticks*, and may very well atone for my past Silence, as well as That which I am like to observe for the future. I hope I have deserved so well of their whole *Body*, as to meet with generous and tender Usage at their *Hands*. Supported by which Expectation, I go on boldly to pursue those Adventures already so happily begun.

[1] And how they're disappointed when they're pleas'd. CONGREVE [*MS. Pate*].

The line quoted is in the Epilogue to Congreve's tragedy *The Mourning Bride*, produced in 1697.

SECT. IV.

A TALE of a TUB.

I HAVE now with much Pains and Study, conducted the Reader to a Period, where he must expect to hear of great Revolutions. For no sooner had Our *Learned Brother*, so often mentioned, got a warm House of his own over his Head, than he began to look big, and to take mightily upon him: insomuch, that unless the Gentle Reader out of his great Candour, will please a little to exalt his Idea, I am afraid he will henceforth hardly know the *Hero* of the Play, when he happens to meet Him; his part, his Dress, and his Mien being so much altered.

HE told his Brothers, he would have them to know, that he was their Elder, and consequently his Father's sole Heir; Nay, a while after, he would not allow them to call Him, *Brother*,[1] but Mr. *PETER*; And then he must be styl'd, *Father PETER*; and sometimes, *My Lord PETER*. To support this Grandeur, which he soon began to consider, could not be maintained without a Better *Fonde*[2] than what he was born to; After much Thought, he cast about at last, to turn *Projector*[3] and *Virtuoso*, wherein he so well succeeded, that many famous Discoveries, Projects and Machines, which bear great Vogue and Practice at present in the World, are owing entirely to *Lord Peter's* Invention. I will deduce the best Account I have been able to collect of the Chief amongst them, without considering much the Order they came out in; because, I think, Authors are not well agreed as to that Point.

[1] 'Brother' edd. 4, 5.
[2] Foundation; cf. p. 147, l. 25.
[3] Cf. in particular Swift's *Voy-age to Laputa*, iv, v, and vi; also Defoe's *Essay upon Projects*.

I hope, when this Treatise of mine shall be translated into Foreign[1] Languages,[2] (as I may without Vanity affirm, That the Labour of collecting, the Faithfulness in recounting, and the great Usefulness of the Matter to the Publick, will amply deserve that Justice) that the worthy Members of the several *Academies* abroad, especially those of *France* and *Italy*,[3] will favourably accept these humble Offers, for the Advancement of Universal Knowledge. I do also advertise the most Reverend Fathers the *Eastern* Missionaries,[4] that I have purely for their Sakes, made use of such Words and Phrases, as will best admit an easie Turn into any of the *Oriental* Languages, especially the *Chinese*. And so I proceed with great Content of Mind, upon reflecting, how much Emolument this whole Globe of Earth is like to reap by my Labours.

THE first Undertaking of Lord *Peter*, was to purchase a *Large Continent, lately said to have been discovered in *Terra Australis incognita*.[5] This Tract of Land he bought at a very great Penny-worth[6] from the Discoverers themselves, (tho' some pretended to doubt whether they had ever been there) and then retailed

* *That is Purgatory.*

[1] 'Forein' edd. 1–4; cf. p. 110, l. 18.

[2] A French translation and a French adaptation (*Les Trois Justaucorps*) appeared in 1721, a German translation in 1729, and a Dutch in 1735. See pp. lxxiv–lxxvi.

[3] Cf. Wotton's *Reflections*, p. 410. Like Dryden and others, Swift was in favour of an English Academy, but not for 'the Advancement of Universal Knowledge'. See his *Proposal for Correcting the English Tongue* (1712).

[4] Among the books which Swift read in 1697 were several by Jesuit missionaries to the East.

[5] The West Indies, sold by the Pope to the King of Spain [*MS. Pate*]. This Continent is taken by some to mean Purgatory, and by others Heaven [1720]. See the account of 'Terra Australis Incognita' in Heylyn's *Cosmography*, Appendix, ed. 1677, p. 158, and cf. p. 125, note 3, and p. 195, note 2.

[6] A bargain; cf. p. 49, l. 19.

it into several Cantons to certain Dealers, who carried over Colonies, but were all Shipwreckt in the Voyage. Upon which, *Lord Peter* sold the said Continent to other Customers *again*, and *again*, and *again*, and *again*, with the same Success.

THE second Project I shall mention, was his *Sovereign Remedy for the *Worms*,[1] especially those in the *Spleen*.† The Patient was to eat nothing after Supper for three Nights: as soon as he went to Bed, he was carefully to lye on one Side, and when he grew weary, to turn upon the other: He must also duly confine his two Eyes to the same Object; and by no means break Wind at both Ends together, without manifest Occasion. These Prescriptions diligently observed, the *Worms* would void insensibly by Perspiration, ascending thro' the *Brain*.

A third Invention, was the Erecting of a ‡*Whispering-Office*,[2] for the Publick Good and Ease of all such as

* Penance *and* Absolution *are plaid upon under the Notion of a* Sovereign Remedy for the Worms, *especially in the Spleen, which by* observing Peters Prescription *would void sensibly by Perspiration ascending thro' the Brain, &c.* W. Wotton.

† *Here the Author ridicules the Penances of the Church of* Rome, *which may be made as easy to the Sinner as he pleases, provided he will pay for them accordingly.*

‡ *By his* Whispering-Office, *for the Relief of Eves-droppers, Physitians, Bawds, and Privy-counsellours, he ridicules Auricular Confession, and the Priest who takes it, is described by the Asses Head.* W. Wotton.

[1] The Worms here signifie scruples and qualms of Conscience on account of sins; alluding to Mark ix. 44, 46, 48 . . . [1720].
Fasting days in Lent [*MS. Pate*].
Swift parodies the advertisements of quack medicines. 'Moore's Worm Powder' is notorious because of *The Spectator*, No. 547, and Pope's verses (ed. Elwin and Courthope, iv, pp. 484–5); cf. also *Curll Papers* (1879), pp. 23–24. But similar advertisements are found in *The Post-Man* and *The London Post* in 1703. For the operation of the remedy cf. Swift's *Voyage to Laputa*, chap. v, last paragraph.

[2] Confession [*MS. Pate*].

are Hypochondriacal, or troubled with the Cholick; as likewise of all Eves-droppers, Physicians,[1] Midwives, small Politicians, Friends fallen out, Repeating Poets,[2] Lovers Happy or in Despair, Bawds, Privy-Counsellours, Pages, Parasites and Buffoons; In short, of all such as are in Danger of bursting with too much *Wind*. An *Asse*'s Head was placed so conveniently, that the Party affected might easily with his Mouth accost either of the Animal's Ears; which he was to apply close for a certain Space, and by a fugitive Faculty, peculiar to the Ears of that Animal, receive immediate Benefit, either by Eructation, or Expiration, or Evomition.

ANOTHER very beneficial Project of *Lord Peter*'s was an *Office of Ensurance*, for Tobacco-Pipes,[3] Martyrs of the Modern Zeal; Volumes of Poetry, Shadows, ⸺ ⸺ ⸺ ⸺ and Rivers: That these, nor any of these shall receive Damage by *Fire*.[4] From whence our *Friendly Societies*[5] may plainly find themselves, to be only Transcribers from this Original; tho' the one and the other have been of *great* Benefit to the Undertakers, as well as of *equal* to the Publick.

* *This I take to be the Office of* Indulgences, *the gross Abuses whereof first gave Occasions for the Reformation.*

[1] 'likewise . . . Physicians', forming a line in edd. 1–4, omitted in ed. 5. Cf. p. 84, n. 2.

[2] Poets who repeat or recite their own verses.

[3] Indulgences [*MS. Pate*].

[4] As the Insurance-Offices, for a certain summ, ensure houses from fire, &c., so in the Romish Church whoever pays for Indulgences and Pardons may be insured from scorching after he's dead. The things here mentioned seem either not to deserve, or not to stand in need of insurance; and that which is left out between *Shadows* and *Rivers*, seems to be somthing as little susceptible of fire as the first, and in as little danger of being hurt by it as the last; such as Spirits, or immaterial Beings [1720].

[5] The Friendly Society was the name of a company for insurance against fire. Others were 'The Phœnix' and 'The Amicable Contributors'. See Ashton's *Social Life in the Reign of Queen Anne*, pp. 50–51.

LORD *Peter* was also held the Original Author of
*Puppets and *Raree-Shows*;[1] the great Usefulness whereof
being so generally known, I shall not enlarge farther
upon this Particular.

BUT, another Discovery for which he was much
renowned, was his famous Universal †*Pickle*.[2] For
having remark'd how your ‡Common *Pickle* in use
among Huswives, was of no farther Benefit than to
preserve dead Flesh, and certain kinds of Vegetables;
Peter, with great Cost as well as Art, had contrived
a *Pickle* proper for Houses, Gardens, Towns, Men,
Women, Children, and Cattle; wherein he could preserve them as Sound as Insects in Amber. Now, this
Pickle to the Taste, the Smell, and the Sight, appeared
exactly the same, with what is in common Service for
Beef, and Butter, and Herrings, (and has been often
that way applied with great Success) but for its many
Sovereign Virtues was a quite[3] different Thing. For
Peter would put in a certain Quantity of his ‖*Powder*

---

* *I believe are the Monkeries and ridiculous Processions,* &c. *among
the Papists.*

† *Holy Water, he calls an* Universal Pickle *to preserve Houses,
Gardens, Towns, Men, Women, Children and Cattle, wherein he could
preserve them as sound as Insects in Amber.* W. Wotton.

‡ *This is easily understood to be Holy Water, composed of the same
Ingredients with many other Pickles.*

‖ *And because Holy Water differs only in Consecration from common
Water, therefore he tells us that his Pickle by the Powder of* Pimperlimpimp *receives new Virtues though it differs not in Sight nor Smell from
the common Pickle, which preserves Beef, and Butter, and Herrings.*
W. Wotton.

---

[1] Ceremonies [*MS. Pate*].

By Puppets and Raree-shows
are represented the Images, Paintings and other gaudy ornaments
of the Popish Worship [1720].

[2] Holy water [*MS. Pate*].

The universal Pickle is the
Holy-water, to which superstitious
people attribute so many virtues
[1720]. The consecration which
makes the only difference between
it and common-water, is called by
this Author the powder of Pimper-
lim-pimp, a term used by Juglers
[added in 1734].

[3] 'was quite a' edd. 1–4.

Pimperlim pimp,[1] after which it never failed of Success. The Operation was performed by *Spargefaction*[2] in a proper Time of the Moon. The Patient who was to be *pickled*, if it were a House, would infallibly be preserved from all Spiders, Rats, and Weazels; If the Party affected were a Dog, he should be exempt from Mange, and Madness, and Hunger. It also infallibly took away all Scabs and Lice, and scall'd Heads from Children, never hindring the Patient from any Duty, either at Bed or Board.[3]

BUT of all *Peter*'s Rarities,[4] he most valued a certain Set of *Bulls, whose Race was by great Fortune preserved in a lineal Descent from those that guarded the *Golden Fleece*. Tho' some who pretended to observe them curiously, doubted the Breed had not been kept entirely chast; because they had degenerated from their Ancestors in some Qualities, and had acquired others very extraordinary, but a Forein Mixture. The *Bulls* of

* *The Papal* Bulls *are ridicul'd by Name, So that here we are at no loss for the Authors Meaning.* W. Wotton.

Ibid. *Here the Author has kept the Name, and means the* Popes Bulls, *or rather his Fulminations and Excommunications, of Heretical Princes, all sign'd with Lead and the Seal of the Fisherman.*

[1] Barrett in his *Essay on the Earlier Part of the Life of Swift* (1808), p. 35, says that a pamphlet published about 1690, called *A Dialogue between Dr Sherlock, the King of France, the Great Turk, and Dr Oates,* contains the following passage: 'This famous Doctor (Sherlock) plays the Merry Andrew with the world, and like the Powder of Pimper le Pimp, turns up what trump the Knave of Clubs calls for.' No pamphlet with this title appears to be in the British Museum, or the Bodleian, or Trinity College, Dublin—of which Barrett was Vice-Provost. The phrase *poudre de perlimpinpin* is given in Richelet's *Dictionnaire françois,* 1679. Littré defines it as 'poudre imaginaire qui donne aux sorciers un grand pouvoir, et figurément, médicament sans vertu'.

[2] Spargefication, sprinkling.

[3] The usual promise of quacks: see the advertisement of Susanna Kirleus in *The Spectator,* No. 331.

[4] 'Rarieties' ed. 5, an old spelling that had passed out of general use.

Colchos[1] are recorded to have *brazen Feet*; But whether it happen'd by ill Pasture and Running,[2] by an Allay from intervention of other Parents, from stolen Intrigues; Whether a Weakness in their Progenitors had impaired the seminal Virtue: Or by a Decline necessary thro' a long Course of Time, the Originals of Nature being depraved in these latter sinful Ages of the World; Whatever was the Cause, 'tis certain that *Lord Peter*'s *Bulls* were extreamly vitiated by the Rust of Time in the Mettal of their Feet, which was now sunk into common *Lead*.[3] However the terrible *roaring* peculiar to their Lineage, was preserved; as likewise that Faculty of breathing out *Fire* from their Nostrils; which notwithstanding many of their Detractors took to be a Feat of Art, and to[4] be nothing so terrible as it appeared; proceeding only from their usual Course of Dyet, which was of *Squibs and Crackers. However, they had two peculiar Marks which extreamly distinguished them from the *Bulls of Jason*, and which I have not met together in the Description of any other Monster, beside that in *Horace*;

Varias inducere plumas,
and
Atrum desinit in piscem.[5]

For, these had *Fishes Tails*,[6] yet upon Occasion, could

* *These are the Fulminations of the Pope threatning Hell and Damnation to those Princes who offend him.*

---

[1] '*Colchos*' edd. 1–5; '*Colchis*' Hawkesworth. See p. 161, note.
[2] Cf. White Kennett, *Parochial Antiquities* (1695), Gloss. s. v. *Porcus*, 'Dare porcos in bosco, to grant ... free running of hogs in such a wood'.
[3] The leaden Seal [1720].

[4] 'and to' edd. 1–4; 'to' ed. 5.
[5] Horace, *Ars Poetica*, 2–4.
[6] Sub annulo piscatoris [*MS. Pate*; 1720].
In this passage Swift does not distinguish between a Papal Bull and a Papal Brief. A Bull has the leaden *bulla* attached to it; the less

out-fly any Bird in the Air. *Peter* put these *Bulls* upon several Employs. Sometimes he would set them a *roaring* to fright *Naughty Boys, and make them quiet. Sometimes he would send them out upon Errands of great Importance; where it is wonderful to recount, and perhaps the cautious Reader may think much to believe it. An *Appetitus sensibilis*,[1] deriving itself thro' the whole Family, from their Noble Ancestors, Guardians of the *Golden-Fleece*; they continued so extremely fond of *Gold*, that if *Peter* sent them abroad, though it were only upon a Compliment,[2] they would *Roar*, and *Spit*, and *Belch*, and *Piss*, and *Fart*, and *Snivel* out *Fire*, and keep a perpetual Coyl,[3] till you flung them a Bit of *Gold*; but then, *Pulveris exigui jactu*,[4] they would grow calm and quiet as Lambs. In short, whether by secret Connivance, or Encouragement from their Master, or out of their own Liquorish Affection to Gold, or both; it is certain they were no better than a sort of sturdy, swaggering Beggars; and where they could not prevail to get an Alms, would make Women miscarry, and Children fall into Fits: who, to this very Day, usually call Sprites and Hobgoblins by the Name of *Bull-Beggars*.[5] They grew

* *That is Kings who incurr his Displeasure.*

formal Brief, addressed to an individual or community, ends with the words *sub annulo* or *sigillo piscatoris*, being sealed in wax with the private seal of the Pope, representing St. Peter fishing. See the Benedictine *Nouveau Traité de Diplomatique*, vol. v (1762), pp. 310–11, and Harry Bresslau, *Handbuch der Urkundenlehre für Deutschland und Italien*, Bd. I, 2te Auflage (1912), pp. 81–82.

[1] In Aquinas *appetitus sensibilis*, or *sensitivus*, or *animalis*, is distinguished from *appetitus intellectivus* or *rationalis*.

[2] 'Complement' edd. 4, 5.

[3] Disturbance, fuss. Cf. *All's Well*, II. i. 27, *King John*, II. i. 165, and *Hamlet*, III. i. 67.

[4] Virgil, *Georgics*, iv. 87.

[5] Spectres, scarecrows, bugbears. Cf. Marvell, *Rehearsal Transpros'd*, part ii (1673), p. 250: 'Private Conscience is . . . a Bulbegger fit to fright children.'

at last so very troublesome to the Neighbourhood, that some Gentlemen of the *North-West*,[1] got a Parcel of right *English Bull-Dogs*, and baited them so terribly, that they felt it ever after.

I must needs mention one more of *Lord Peter*'s Projects, which was very extraordinary, and discovered him to be Master of a high Reach, and profound Invention. Whenever it happened that any Rogue of *Newgate* was condemned to be hang'd, *Peter* would offer him a Pardon for a certain Sum of Money, which when the poor Caitiff had made all Shifts to scrape up and send; *His Lordship* would return a *Piece of Paper in this Form.

TO all Mayors, Sheriffs, Jaylors, Constables, Bayliffs, Hangmen, &c. Whereas we are informed that A. B. remains in the Hands of you, or any of you, under the Sentence of Death. We will and command you upon Sight hereof, to let the said Prisoner depart to his own Habitation, whether he stands condemned for Murder, Sodomy, Rape, Sacrilege, Incest, Treason, Blasphemy, &c. for which this shall be your sufficient Warrant: And if you fail hereof, G— d—mn You and Yours to all Eternity. And so we bid you heartily Farewell.[2]

Your most Humble
Man's Man,[3]
EMPEROR PETER.

* *This is a Copy of a General Pardon sign'd* Servus Servorum. Ibid. *Absolution* in Articulo Mortis, *and the Tax* Cameræ Apostolicæ *are jested upon in Emperor* Peter's *Letter.* W. Wotton.[4]

The word was sometimes used with a punning allusion to the Papal Bull and to Beggar. Cf. Ayliffe, *Parergon* (1726), p. 132: 'these Fulminations from the *Vatican* . . . were called *Bull-Beggars*'. Cf. also Temple, *Of Poetry*, ed. 1696, p. 344, and *The Tatler*, No. 212.

[1] Cf. p. 56, l. 12.
[2] This letter is referred to in *The Tatler*, No. 25.
[3] *Servus Servorum* [1720]. *Servus Servorum Dei* was a title adopted by the Pope.
[4] The Popes have granted Pardons for all sorts of crimes; and one may see the Fees to be paid at

THE Wretches trusting to this, lost their Lives and Money too.

I desire of those whom the *Learned* among Posterity will appoint for Commentators upon this elaborate Treatise; that they will proceed with great Caution upon certain dark points, wherein all who are not *Verè adepti*,[1] may be in Danger to form rash and hasty Conclusions, especially in some mysterious Paragraphs, where certain *Arcana* are joyned for brevity sake, which in the Operation must be divided. And, I am certain, that future Sons of Art, will return large Thanks to my Memory, for so grateful, so useful an *Innuendo*.[2]

IT will be no difficult Part to persuade the Reader, that so many worthy Discoveries met with great Success in the World; tho' I may justly assure him that I have related much the smallest Number; My Design having been only to single out such, as will be of most Benefit for Publick Imitation, or which best served to give some Idea of the Reach and Wit of the Inventor. And therefore it need not be wondred, if by this Time, *Lord Peter* was become exceeding[3] Rich. But alas, he had kept his Brain so long, and so violently upon the Rack, that at last it *shook* it self, and began to *turn round* for a little Ease. In short, what with Pride, Projects, and Knavery, poor *Peter* was grown distracted, and con-

---

the Office for expedition of those Pardons, in the *Taxa Cancellariæ Romanæ* so often printed [1720].

A 'Tax' at Rome is the charge on engrossing deeds, &c. Wotton evidently thought the charge for engrossing an indulgence was a payment for the indulgence itself. The 'Camera Apostolica' is the Papal Treasury.

[1] See p. 68 and Appendix F.

[2] The med. Lat. formula used especially in legal documents to introduce a parenthetical explanation of the precise reference of a preceding noun or pronoun, = meaning, to wit, that is to say. Hence, as substantive, the parenthetical explanation or specification itself; or the appended explanation of, or construction put upon a word, expression, or passage (*Oxford English Dictionary*).

[3] 'exceding' ed. 5.

Original Design

ceived the strangest Imaginations in the World. In the
Height of his Fits (as it is usual with those who run
mad out of Pride) He would call Himself *God Almighty*, and sometimes *Monarch of the Universe*. I have
seen him, (says my Author) take three old †*high-crown'd
Hats*, and clap them all on his Head, three Story high,
with a huge Bunch of ‡*Keys* at his Girdle, and an
Angling Rod in his Hand. In which Guise, whoever went
to take him by the Hand in the way of Salutation, *Peter*
with much Grace, like a well educated Spaniel, would
present them with his §*Foot*, and if they refused his
Civility, then he would raise it as high as their Chops,
and give them a damn'd Kick on the Mouth, which
hath ever since been call'd a *Salute*.[1] Whoever walkt by,
without paying him their Compliments,[2] having a wonderful strong Breath, he would blow their Hats off into
the Dirt. Mean time, his Affairs at home went upside
down; and his two Brothers had a wretched Time;
Where his first ‖*Boutade*[3] was, to kick both their ****** *Wives*

* *The Pope is not only allow'd to be the Vicar of* Christ, *but by several
Divines is call'd* God upon Earth, *and other blasphemous Titles.*
† *The Triple Crown.*
‡ *The Keys of the Church.*
Ibid. *The Pope's Universal Monarchy, and his Triple Crown,* [*and
Keys,*[4]] *and Fisher's Ring.* W. Wotton.
§ *Neither does his arrogant way of requiring men to kiss his Slipper,
escape Reflexion.* Wotton.
‖ *This Word properly signifies a sudden Jerk, or Lash of an Horse,
when you do not expect it.*
** *The* Celibacy of the *Romish* Clergy *is struck at in* Peter's *beating
his own and Brothers Wives out of Doors.* W. Wotton.

[1] 'call'd *Salute*' ed. 5.
[2] 'Complements' edd. 4, 5.
[3] A sudden motion or outbreak.
The word is found in English before Swift, but he felt the need of
explaining it in a letter to Mrs.
Pendarves, 7 Oct. 1734: 'It is,
you know, a French word, and
signifies a sudden jerk from a
horse's hinder feet which you did
not expect, because you thought
him for some months a sober
animal.' Cf. p. 314.
[4] 'and Keys' *Notes* 1711.

one Morning out of Doors, and his own too, and in their stead, gave Orders to pick up the first three Strolers could be met with in the Streets.[1] A while after, he nail'd up the Cellar-Door: and would not allow his Brothers a *Drop of *Drink* to their Victuals. Dining one Day at an Alderman's in the City, *Peter* observed him expatiating after the Manner of his Brethren, in the Praises of his Surloyn of Beef. *Beef*, said the Sage Magistrate, *is the King of Meat; Beef comprehends in it the Quintessence of Partridge, and Quail, and Venison, and Pheasant,*[2] *and Plum-pudding, and Custard.* When *Peter* came home, he would needs take the Fancy of cooking up this Doctrine into Use, and apply the Precept in default of a Surloyn, to his brown Loaf: *Bread*, says he, *Dear Brothers, is the Staff of Life; in which Bread is contained*, inclusivè, *the Quintessence of Beef, Mutton, Veal, Venison, Partridge, Plum-pudding, and Custard: And to render all compleat, there is intermingled a due Quantity of Water, whose Crudities are also corrected by Yeast or Barm, thro' which means it becomes a wholesome fermented Liquor, diffused thro' the Mass of the Bread.*[3] Upon the Strength of these Conclusions, next Day at Dinner was the brown Loaf served up in all the Formality of a City Feast. *Come Brothers*, said *Peter, fall to,*

* *The Pope's refusing the Cup to the Laity, persuading them that the Blood is contain'd in the Bread, and that the Bread is the real and entire Body of* Christ.

[1] "Gravius peccat sacerdos si uxorem ducat, quam si domi concubinam foveat" [*MS. Pate*].

[2] '*Pheasant*' edd. 1–4; '*Phesants*' ed. 5.

[3] 'Swift, who formed himself on Rabelais, has here exactly copied the famous speech of Panurge' (from a note signed 'Dr. Warton' in Swift's *Works*, ed. Nichols (1808), ii, p. 281; cf. the note on *The Dunciad*, i. 22 in Pope's *Works*, ed. Warton (1797), v, p. 81). No reference is given, and Swift's debt to Rabelais is absurdly overstated. Warton may have had a confused recollection of *Pantagruel*, iii. 2–4. For Swift's copy of Rabelais see p. lviii, note.

'A strange passage, which

*and spare not; here is excellent good *Mutton; or hold, now
my Hand is in, I'll help you.* At which word, in much
Ceremony, with Fork and Knife, he carves out two good
Slices of the[1] Loaf, and presents each on a Plate to his
Brothers. The Elder of the two not suddenly entring
into *Lord Peter*'s Conceit, began with very civil Language to examine the Mystery. *My Lord, said he, I
doubt, with great Submission, there may be some Mistake.
What, says Peter, you are pleasant; Come then, let us hear
this Jest, your Head is so big with. None in the World, my
Lord; but unless I am very much deceived, your Lordship
was pleased a while ago, to let fall a Word about Mutton,
and I would be glad to see it with all my Heart. How,* said
Peter, appearing in great Surprise, *I do not comprehend
this at all*—Upon which, the younger interposing, to
set the Business right; *My Lord, said he, My Brother,
I suppose is hungry, and longs for the Mutton, your Lordship
hath promised us to Dinner. Pray,* said Peter, *take me
along with you,[2] either you are both mad, or disposed to be
merrier than I approve of; If You there, do not like your
Piece, I will carve you another, tho' I should take that to be*

---

* Transubstantiation. Peter *turns his Bread into Mutton, and according to the Popish Doctrine of Concomitants, his Wine too, which in his
way he calls,* Pauming his damn'd Crusts upon the Brothers for Mutton.
W. Wotton.

Quevedo has put into the mouth
of a drunken bully, may, in the
opinion of Mr. T. Swift, have
suggested the noted ridicule on
transubstantiation. It occurs in the
tenth chapter of the History of
Paul the Sharper' (Scott, Swift's
Works (1824), i, p. 84). 'Mr. T.
Swift' is Theophilus Swift (1746–
1815), son of Deane Swift.

Another supposed source,
Buckingham's 'Conference with
an Irish Priest', is dealt with in the
'Apology', pp. 13–15. To all these
suggestions the reply there given is
sufficient. Swift was able to 'invent' this allegory, 'without enquiring what other People had
writ'.

[1] 'the' ed. 1; 'a' edd. 2–5.
[2] Cf. *1 Henry IV*, ii. iv. 512;
also id. 475 with 'very lewdly
given' p. 119, last line. Instances
of Shakespearian phrases are not
uncommon in Swift. Cf. *Correspondence*, iv, pp. 112 and 329.

the choice Bit of the whole Shoulder. *What then, my Lord,* replied the first, *it seems this is a shoulder of Mutton all this while. Pray Sir,* says *Peter, eat your Vittles, and leave off your Impertinence, if you please, for I am not disposed to relish it at present*: But the other could not forbear, being over-provoked at the affected Seriousness of *Peter*'s Countenance. *By G——, My Lord,* said he, *I can only say, that to my Eyes, and Fingers, and Teeth, and Nose, it seems to be nothing but a Crust of Bread.* Upon which, the second put in his Word: *I never saw a Piece of Mutton in my Life, so nearly resembling a Slice from a Twelve-peny Loaf. Look ye, Gentlemen,* cries *Peter* in a Rage, *to convince you, what a couple of blind, positive, ignorant, wilful Puppies you are, I will use but this plain Argument; By G——, it is true, good, natural Mutton as any in* Leaden-Hall *Market;*[1] *and G—— confound you both eternally, if you offer to believe otherwise.* Such a thundring Proof as this, left no farther Room for Objection: The two Unbelievers began to gather and pocket up their Mistake as hastily as they could. *Why, truly,* said the first, *upon more mature Consideration—Ay,* says the other, interrupting him, *now I have thought better on the Thing, your Lordship seems to have a great deal of Reason. Very well,* said *Peter, Here Boy, fill me a Beer-Glass of Claret. Here's to you both with all my Heart.* The two Brethren much delighted to see him so readily appeas'd returned their

---

[1] Craik (*Selections*, i, p. 397) points out that the speciality of this market was not mutton, according to Gay, in *Trivia*, ii. 543–6:

> Shall the large mutton smoke upon your boards?
> Such Newgate's copious market best affords.
> Would'st thou with mighty beef augment thy meal?

Seek Leaden-hall; St James's sends thee veal.

Swift's and Gay's references to Leaden-Hall are not inconsistent. The detailed account of it in Strype's *Survey of London*, 1720, ii, p. 89, shows that it contained three courts, of which the first was 'the Beef Market', and the second was 'now a market for Veal, Mutton, and Lamb'.

Original Design

most humble Thanks, and said, they would be glad to pledge His Lordship. *That you shall*, said Peter, *I am not a Person to refuse you any Thing that is reasonable; Wine moderately taken, is a Cordial; Here is a Glass apiece for you; 'Tis true natural Juice from the Grape; none of your damn'd* Vintners[1] *Brewings.* Having spoke thus, he presented to each of them another large dry Crust, bidding them drink it off, and not be bashful, for it would do them no Hurt. The two Brothers, after having performed the usual Office in such delicate Conjunctures, of staring a sufficient Period at *Lord Peter*, and each other; and finding how Matters were like to go, resolved not to enter on a new Dispute, but let him carry the Point as he pleased; for he was now got into one of his mad Fits, and to Argue or Expostulate further, would only serve to render him a hundred times more untractable.

I have chosen to relate this worthy Matter in all its Circumstances, because it gave a principal Occasion to that great and famous **Rupture*, which happened about the same time among these Brethren, and was never afterwards made up. But, of That, I shall treat at large in another Section.[2]

HOWEVER, it is certain, that *Lord Peter*, even in his lucid Intervals,[3] was very lewdly given in his

* *By this* Rupture *is meant the* Reformation.

[1] 'Vintner's' edd. 1–4. 'Vintners' is the possessive plural; the apostrophe *after* the plural termination dates from the latter part of the eighteenth century.

[2] Section VI.

[3] The Latin phrase 'non est compos mentis, sed gaudet lucidis intervallis' is common in English legal documents from the thirteenth to the fifteenth century (*Oxford English Dict.*). In *The Story of Bethlehem Hospital*, by E. G. O'Donoghue (1914), p. 221, there is reproduced the following title-page of a book by James Carcasse (or Carkesse): 'Lucida Intervalla: Containing divers Miscellaneous Poems, Written at Finsbury and Bethlem By the Doctors Patient extraordinary ... 1679.'

common Conversation, extream wilful and positive, and would at any time rather argue to the Death, than allow himself to be once in an Error. Besides, he had an abominable Faculty of telling huge palpable *Lies* upon all Occasions;[1] and swearing, not only to the Truth, but cursing the whole Company to Hell, if they pretended to make the least Scruple of believing Him. One time, he swore, he had a *Cow at home, which gave as much Milk at a Meal, as would fill three thousand Churches; and what was yet more extraordinary, would never turn Sower. Another time, he was telling of an old †*Sign-Post* that belonged to his *Father*, with Nails and Timber enough on it, to build sixteen large Men of War. Talking one Day of *Chinese* Waggons,[2] which were made so light as to sail over Mountains: *Z—nds*, said *Peter*, *where's the Wonder of that? By G—, I saw a* ‡*Large*

* *The ridiculous Multiplying of the Virgin* Mary's Milk *among the Papists, under the Allegory of a* Cow, *which gave as much Milk at a Meal, as would fill three thousand Churches.* W. Wotton.

† *By this Sign-Post is meant the* Cross *of our Blessed Saviour.*

‡ *The Chappel of* Loretto. *He falls here only upon the ridiculous Inventions of Popery: The Church of* Rome *intended by these Things, to gull silly, superstitious People, and rook them of their Money; that the World had been too long in Slavery, our*[3] *Ancestors gloriously redeem'd us from that Yoke. The Church of* Rome *therefore ought to be expos'd, and he deserves well of Mankind that does expose it.* W. Wotton.

Ibid. *The Chappel of* Loretto, *which travell'd from the* Holy Land *to*[4] Italy.

[1] Infallibility [*MS. Pate*].

[2] Cf. *Paradise Lost*, iii. 437–9, and the note by Masson in his edition: 'In the succinct Latin account of China and the Chinese accompanying the map of China in the pretty little Atlas of P. Bertius, with maps by Hondius, published at Amsterdam in 1616, the following sentence occurs: "They have invented chariots which they drive over the plains with spread sails without the help of cattle"; and the same account is repeated in the Cosmography of Milton's contemporary, Heylin.'

Cf. also the note in *Annotations on Milton's Paradise Lost* by P. H[ume], 1695, p. 115.

[3] 'money, the World . . . Slavery, and our' *Notes* 1711.

[4] 'into' *Notes* 1711.

House of Lime and Stone travel over Sea and Land (grant-
ing that it stopt sometimes to bait) above two thousand German *Leagues.* And that which was the good of it, he
would swear desperately all the while, that he never told
a Lye in his Life; And at every Word; *By G——, Gentle-*
men, I tell you nothing but the Truth; and the D——l broil
them eternally that will not believe me.

IN short, *Peter* grew so scandalous, that all the
Neighbourhood began in plain Words to say, he was
no better than a Knave. And his two Brothers long
weary of his ill Usage, resolved at last to leave him;
but first, they humbly desired a Copy of their Father's
Will, which had now lain by neglected, time out of
Mind. Instead of granting this Request, he called them
damn'd Sons of Whores, Rogues, Traytors, and the rest
of the vile Names he could muster up. However, while
he was abroad one Day upon his Projects, the two
Youngsters watcht their Opportunity, made a Shift to
come at the *Will,* *and took a *Copia vera,*[1] by which
they presently saw how grosly they had been abused:
Their Father having left them equal Heirs, and strictly
commanded, that whatever they got, should lye in common among them all. Pursuant to which, their next
Enterprise was to break open the Cellar-Door, and get
a little good †*Drink* to spirit and comfort their Hearts.
In copying the *Will,* they had met another Precept
against Whoring, Divorce, and separate Maintenance;

* *Translated the Scriptures into the vulgar Tongues.*
† *Administred the Cup to the Laity at the Communion.*

[1] This *Copia Vera,* it seems, has been lost, for the Critics have been long disputing about the true readings: But to the great comfort of all critical Believers, the learned and pious Dr. *Bentley* has now undertaken, with his usual modesty, to publish from his own elaborate conjectures, a more accurate and exact copy than ever has been known before or since the Originals were lost [1720].

Upon which, their next *Work was to discard their Concubines, and send for their Wives. Whilst all this was in agitation, there enters a Sollicitor from *Newgate*, desiring *Lord Peter* would please to procure a *Pardon* for a *Thief* that was to be *hanged* to morrow. But the two Brothers told him, he was a Coxcomb to seek Pardons from a Fellow, who deserv'd to be hang'd much better than his Client; and discovered all the Method of that Imposture, in the same Form I delivered it a while ago, advising the Sollicitor to put his Friend upon obtaining †a *Pardon from the King*. In the midst of all this Clutter and Revolution, in comes *Peter* with a File of ‡Dragoons[1] at his Heels, and gathering from all Hands what was in the Wind, He and his Gang, after several Millions of Scurrilities and Curses, not very important here to repeat, by main Force, very fairly §kicks them both out of Doors, and would never let them come under his Roof from that Day to this.

* *Allowed the Marriages of Priests.*

† *Directed Penitents not to trust to Pardons and Absolutions procur'd for Money, but sent them to implore the Mercy of God, from whence alone Remission is to be obtain'd.*

‡ *By* Peter's *Dragoons, is meant the Civil Power which those Princes, who were bigotted to the Romish Superstition, employ'd against the Reformers.*

§ *The Pope shuts all who dissent from him out of the Church.*

[1] In using the word 'dragoons' Swift has in mind the *dragonnades* of Louis XIV.

Original Design

SECT. V.

A Digression in the Modern Kind.

WE whom the World is pleased to honor with the Title of *Modern Authors*, should never have been able to compass our great Design of an everlasting Remembrance, and never-dying Fame, if our Endeavours had not been so highly serviceable to the general Good of Mankind. This, *O Universe,* is the Adventurous Attempt of me thy Secretary;

——— *Quemvis perferre laborem*
Suadet, & inducit noctes vigilare serenas.[1]

TO this End, I have some Time since, with a World of Pains and Art, dissected the Carcass of *Humane Nature,* and read many useful Lectures upon the several Parts, both *Containing* and *Contained*;[2] till at last it *smelt* so strong, I could preserve it no longer. Upon which, I have been at a great Expence to fit up all the Bones with exact Contexture, and in due Symmetry; so that I am ready to shew a very compleat Anatomy[3] thereof to all curious *Gentlemen and others.* But not to Digress

---

[1] Lucretius, i. 141–2.

[2] Cf. Wotton's *Reflections* (1697), p. 211: 'By *Anatomy,* there is seldom any thing understood but the Art of laying open the several Parts of the Body with a Knife, that so the Relation which they severally bear each to other may be clearly discerned. This is generally understood of the *containing* Parts, Skin, Flesh, Bones, Membranes . . . wherein only the Ancients busied themselves: As for the Examination of the Nature and particular Texture of the *contained* Parts, Blood, Chyle . . . and the like; they made very few Experiments'.

[3] Skeleton. Cf. Fuller, *Worthies* (1662), 'Essex', p. 320: 'the Anatomy of a Man lying in the Tombe above-said, onely the Bones remaining'. Cf. *Comedy of Errors,* v. i. 239, and *King John,* iii. iv. 40.

farther in the midst of a Digression, as I have known some Authors inclose Digressions in one another, like a Nest of Boxes; I do affirm, that having carefully cut up *Humane Nature*, I have found a very strange, new, and important Discovery; That the Publick Good of Mankind is performed by two Ways, *Instruction*, and *Diversion*. And I have farther proved in my said several Readings, (which, perhaps, the World may one day see, if I can prevail on any Friend to steal a Copy, or on certain Gentlemen of my Admirers, to be very Importunate) that, as Mankind is now disposed, he receives much greater Advantage by being *Diverted* than *Instructed*; His Epidemical Diseases being *Fastidiosity*, *Amorphy*, and *Oscitation*;[1] whereas in the present universal Empire of Wit and Learning, there seems but little Matter left for *Instruction*. However, in Compliance with a Lesson of Great Age and Authority, I have attempted carrying the Point in all its Heights; and accordingly throughout this Divine Treatise,[2] have skilfully kneaded up both together with a *Layer* of *Utile* and a *Layer of Dulce*.[3]

WHEN I consider how exceedingly our Illustrious *Moderns* have eclipsed the weak glimmering Lights of the *Antients*, and turned them out of the Road of all fashionable Commerce, to a degree, that our choice *Town-Wits of most refined Accomplishments, are in

* *The Learned Person here meant by our Author, hath been endeavouring to annihilate so many Antient Writers, that until he is pleas'd to stop his hand it will be dangerous to affirm, whether there have been [ever[4]] any Antients in the World.*

[1] Fastidiosity, a humorously pedantic form, not found before Swift; nor does an earlier instance of *Amorphy* appear to be known. *Oscitation* is used by Bentley, *Dissertation* (1697), p. 119: "'Tis a mere oscitation of our Scholiast, and of *Suidas* that gaped after him.' Cf. Boyle's *Examination* (1698), p. 136. Swift uses *Oscitancy*, p. 203, l. 27.

[2] Cf. pp. 181–2.

[3] Horace, *Ars Poetica*, l. 343.

[4] 'ever' *Notes* 1711.

grave Dispute, whether there have been ever any *Antients* or no:[1] In which Point we are like to receive wonderful Satisfaction from the most useful Labours and Lucubrations of that Worthy *Modern*, Dr. *B—tly:* I say, when I consider all this, I cannot but bewail, that no famous *Modern* hath ever yet attempted an universal System in a small portable Volume, of all Things that are to be Known, or Believed, or Imagined, or Practised in Life. I am, however, forced to acknowledge, that such an enterprise was thought on some Time ago by a great Philosopher of *O. Brazile*.[2] The Method he proposed,

* *This is an imaginary Island, of Kin to that which is call'd the* Painters Wives Island,[3] *placed in some unknown part of the* Ocean, *meerly at the Fancy of the Map-maker.*

[1] *Wotton* and *Bentley* maintain, that we of the present Age are the true Ancients, and that those commonly called so do not at all deserve that name. [1720; similar note in 1734, which adds 'as having lived in the Infancy of the World, before Arts or Sciences were brought to perfection'.]

Cf. Bacon, *Advancement of Learning*, i. v. i: 'And to speak truly, *Antiquitas sæculi juventus mundi*'; also *Novum Organum*, i. 84. For similar statements by Hobbes, Collier, Fontenelle, and Perrault see note on the *Battle of the Books*, p. 227, note 2.

[2] 'O-Brazile' edd. 1, 2. This island was supposed to lie to the west of Ireland and to be seen at times from the Isles of Arran. Two accounts of it were published in 1674, *O Brazile, or the Inchanted Island* and *The Western Wonder: or, O Brazeel, An Inchanted Island*

discovered. See Southey, *History of Brazil* (1810), vol. i, p. 22; James Hardiman, *Irish Minstrelsy* (1831), vol. i, pp. 367–76; and *The Tour of . . . M. de la Boullaye le Gouz*, ed. T. C. Croker (1837), pp. 68–78.

See also *A Long Ramble, Or several Years Travels, In the much Talk'd of, But never before Discover'd, wandering Island of O-Brazil* (1712); and *A Voyage to O'Brazeel* in *The Ulster Miscellany* (1752). The island is given in the 'Typus Orbis Terrarum' and 'Europa' of Ortelius (Antwerp, 1570), and is found in many seventeenth-century maps.

[3] See the *Geographical Journal* for September 1916, p. 276. The source of the story is Raleigh's *History of the World*, bk. ii, chap. 23, § 4 (1614, p. 574): 'I remember a pretie jeast of *Don Pedro de Sarmiento*, a worthie

was by a certain curious *Receipt*, a *Nostrum*, which after his untimely Death, I found among his Papers; and do here out of my great Affection to the *Modern Learned*, present them with it, not doubting, it may one Day encourage some worthy Undertaker.

Y O U take fair correct Copies, well bound in Calfs Skin, and Lettered at the Back, of all Modern Bodies of Arts and Sciences whatsoever, and in what Language you please. These you distil in balneo Mariæ,[1] *infusing* Quintessence of Poppy Q. S. *together with three Pints of* Lethe, *to be had from the Apothecaries. You cleanse away carefully the* Sordes *and* Caput mortuum, *letting all that is volatile evaporate. You preserve only the first Running, which is again to be distilled seventeen times, till what remains will amount to about two Drams. This you keep in a Glass Viol* Hermetically *sealed, for one and twenty Days. Then you begin your Catholick Treatise, taking every Morning fasting, (first shaking the Viol) three Drops of this* Elixir, *snuffing it strongly up your Nose. It will dilate it self about the Brain (where there is any) in fourteen Minutes, and you imme-*

Spanish Gentleman, who had beene emploied by his King in planting a Colonie vpon the Streights of *Magellan*: for when I asked him, being then my Prisoner, some question about an Iland in those streights, which me thought, might haue done either benefit or displeasure to his enterprise, he told me merrily, that it was to bee called the *Painters wiues Iland*; saying, That whilest the fellow drew that Mappe, his wife sitting by, desired him to put in one Countrie for her; that shee, in imagination, might haue an Iland of her owne.' The story is repeated in the account of 'Terra Australis Incognita' in Heylyn's *Cosmographie*, Appendix, ed. 1677, p. 161, and in such a way as to suggest that this, rather than Raleigh's *History*, was the immediate source of the note. From what Raleigh says, there is no reason to believe that the name was actually given in any map.

[1] The *balneum Mariae* is the *bain-marie* of the kitchen, in which a stewpan is surrounded by water that is boiled. 'Q.S.' = 'quantum sufficit.' 'Catholick' is used in the medical and Rosicrucian sense of universally applicable or efficient: cf. Robert Fludd's *Medicina Catholica*, 1629.

diately perceive in your Head an infinite Number of Abstracts, Summaries, Compendiums, Extracts, Collections, Medulla's, Excerpta quædam's, Florilegia's[1] *and the like, all disposed into great Order, and reducible upon Paper.*

I must needs own, it was by the Assistance of this *Arcanum,* that I, tho' otherwise *impar,* have adventured upon so daring an Attempt; never atchieved or undertaken before, but by a certain Author called *Homer,* in whom, tho' otherwise a Person not without some Abilities, and *for an Ancient,* of a tolerable Genius; I have discovered many gross Errors, which are not to be forgiven his very Ashes, if by chance any of them are left. For whereas, we are assured, he design'd his Work for a *compleat Body of all Knowledge Human, Divine, Political, and Mechanick; it is manifest, he hath wholly ne-

> * *Homerus omnes res humanas Poematis complexus est.* Xenoph. in conviv.[2]

glected some, and been very imperfect in the rest. For, first of all, as eminent a *Cabbalist*[3] as his Disciples would represent Him, his Account of the *Opus magnum* is extreamly poor and deficient; he seems to have read but very superficially, either *Sendivogius,*[4] *Behmen,* or† *Anthroposophia Theomagica.*[5] He is also quite mistaken

† *A Treatise written about fifty Years ago, by a* Welsh *Gentleman of* Cambridge, *his Name, as I remember, was* Vaughan, *as appears by the Answer to it, writ by the Learned Dr.* Henry Moor, *it is a Piece of the most unintelligible Fustian, that, perhaps, was ever publish'd in any Language.*

[1] 'Florilega's' edd. 1–4.

[2] Xenophon, *Convivium,* iv. 6. Cf. Temple, *Of Poetry,* ed. 1696, p. 321: 'the Greatest Masters have found in his [Homer's] Works the best and truest Principles of all their Sciences or Arts'.

[3] 'Cabalist' edd. 1, 2. Cf. p. 152, l. 6.

[4] 'Sendivogus' edd. 1, 2, 3, 5.

[5] Cf. *Hudibras,* 1. i. 541–2:
He Anthroposophus, and Floud, And Jacob Behmen, understood; . . .
In Rosicrucian lore as learned As he that *Verè adeptus* earned.
On this passage and footnote see Appendix F, p. 356.

about the *Sphæra Pyroplastica*, a neglect not to be attoned for; and (if the Reader will admit so severe a
Censure) *Vix crederem Autorem hunc, unquam audivisse
ignis vocem*. His Failings are not less prominent in several
Parts of the *Mechanicks*. For, having read his Writings
with the utmost Application usual among *Modern Wits*,
I could never yet discover the least Direction about the
Structure of that useful Instrument a *Save-all*.[1] For
want of which, if the *Moderns* had not lent their Assistance, we might yet have wandred *in the Dark*. But I
have still behind, a Fault far more notorious to tax this
Author with; I mean, *his gross Ignorance[2] in the
Common Laws of this Realm*, and in the Doctrine as well
as Discipline of the Church of *England*. A Defect indeed, for which both he and all the Ancients stand most
justly censured by my worthy and ingenious Friend
Mr. *W—tt—on*, Batchelor of Divinity, in his incom-
parable Treatise of *Ancient and Modern Learning*; A
Book never to be sufficiently valued, whether we consider the happy Turns and Flowings of the Author's
Wit, the great Usefulness of his sublime Discoveries

* Mr. W-tt-n (*to whom our Author never gives any Quarter*) *in his
Comparison of Antient and Modern Learning, Numbers Divinity, Law,
&c. among those Parts of Knowledge wherein we excel the Antients.*

[1] A device for holding candle-
ends, so that they may be wholly
burned. Cf. *Hudibras*, i. ii. 541–2:

> The mouse-trap men laid save-
>   alls by,
> And 'ganst Ev'l Counsellors
>   did cry.

In the list of Swift's plate there
was included a 'Cup and save-all'
which cost him £15 (*Correspondence*, vol. vi, p. 228).

[2] Here, as elsewhere, Swift is
parodying the language of Wotton,
e.g. '. . . in many material and very
curious Parts of Learning, the
Ancients were, comparatively
speaking, grossly ignorant' (*Reflections* (1697), Preface, p. iv).

Cf. Temple, *Some Thoughts
upon Reviewing the Essay of
Antient and Modern Learning*
(1701), p. 260: 'For Divinity,
wherein they give the Moderns
such a Preference above the
Antients, they might as well have
made them excell in the Know-
ledg of our Common Law'.

upon the Subject of *Flies* and *Spittle*,[1] or the laborious
Eloquence of his Stile. And I cannot forbear doing that
Author the Justice of my publick Acknowledgments,
for the great *Helps* and *Liftings* I had out of his incom-
parable Piece, while I was penning this Treatise.

BUT, besides these Omissions in *Homer* already
mentioned, the curious Reader will also observe several
Defects in that Author's Writings, for which he is not
altogether so accountable. For whereas every Branch
of Knowledge has received such wonderful Acquirements since his Age, especially within these last three
Years,[2] or thereabouts; it is almost impossible, he could
be so very perfect in Modern Discoveries, as his Advocates pretend. We freely acknowledge Him to be the
Inventor of the *Compass*, of *Gun-Powder*, and the *Circulation of the Blood*: But, I challenge any of his Admirers
to shew me in all his Writings, a compleat Account of
the *Spleen*; Does he not also leave us wholly to seek in
the Art of *Political Wagering*? What can be more defective and unsatisfactory than his long Dissertation upon
Tea? and as to his Method of *Salivation without Mercury*, so much celebrated of late, it is to my own Knowledge and Experience, a Thing very little to be relied on.

IT was to supply such momentous Defects, that I
have been prevailed on after long Sollicitation, to take
Pen in Hand; and I dare venture to Promise, the Judicious Reader shall find nothing neglected here, that
can be of Use upon any Emergency of Life. I am confident to have included and exhausted all that Human
Imagination can *Rise* or *Fall* to. Particularly, I recommend to the Perusal of the Learned, certain Discoveries
that are wholly untouch by others; whereof I shall only

---

[1] See Wotton's *Reflections upon Ancient and Modern Learning* (1697), chap. xxiii and chap. xvii, pp. 223–4: and cf. Temple's *Thoughts upon Reviewing the Essay* (1701), pp. 282–3.
    [2] i.e. since the publication of Wotton's *Reflections* (1694).

mention among a great many more; *My New Help of Smatterers*, or the *Art of being Deep-learned, and Shallow-read.*[1] *A curious Invention about Mouse-Traps.*[2] *An Universal Rule of Reason, or Every Man his own Carver*; Together with a most useful Engine for *catching of Owls.* All which the judicious Reader will find largely treated on, in the several Parts of this Discourse.

I hold my self obliged to give as much Light as is possible, into the Beauties and Excellencies of what I am writing, because it is become the Fashion and Humor most applauded among the first Authors of this Polite and Learned Age, when they would correct the ill Nature of Critical, or inform the Ignorance of Courteous Readers. Besides, there have been several famous Pieces lately published both in Verse and Prose; wherein, if the Writers had not been pleas'd, out of their great Humanity and Affection to the Publick, to give us a nice Detail of the *Sublime*, and the *Admirable* they contain; it is a thousand to one, whether we should ever have discovered one Grain of either. For my own particular, I cannot deny, that whatever I have said upon this Occasion, had been more proper in a Preface, and more agreeable to the Mode, which usually directs it there. But I here think fit to lay hold on that great and honourable Privilege of being the *Last Writer*; I claim an absolute Authority in Right, as the *freshest Modern*, which gives me a Despotick Power over all Authors before me. In the Strength of which Title, I do utterly disapprove and declare against that pernicious Custom, of making the Preface a Bill of Fare to the

---

[1] Bentley's opponents said that he took his learning from dictionaries and indexes: see p. 43, note 3.

[2] Mouse-traps were sold by street-vendors in London. See Ben Jonson, *Bartholomew Fair*, ii.

iv. 7, ed. P. Simpson, x. 190, and *Pecuniæ obediunt Omnia* (1698), p. 96. Swift may have had in mind Vaughan's *Man-Mouse taken in a Trap*: see p. 357.

Book. For I have always lookt upon it as a high Point
of Indiscretion in *Monster-mongers* and other *Retailers of
strange Sights*; to hang out a fair large Picture over the
Door, drawn after the Life, with a most eloquent Description underneath: This hath saved me many a Threepence, for my Curiosity was fully satisfied, and I never
offered to go in, tho' often invited by the urging and
attending Orator, with his last *moving* and *standing*
Piece of Rhetorick; *Sir, Upon my Word, we are just
going to begin.* Such is exactly the Fate, at this Time, of
*Prefaces, Epistles, Advertisements, Introductions, Prolego-
mena's, Apparatus's, To-the-Reader's*.[1] This Expedient
was admirable at first; Our Great *Dryden* has long
carried it as far as it would go, and with incredible
Success. He has often said to me in Confidence, that
the World would have never suspected him to be so
great a Poet, if he had not assured them so frequently
in his Prefaces, that it was impossible they could either
doubt or forget it. Perhaps it may be so; However,
I much fear, his Instructions have edify'd out of their
Place, and taught Men to grow Wiser in certain Points,
where he never intended they should; For it is lamentable to behold, with what a lazy Scorn, many of the
yawning Readers in our Age, do now a-days twirl over
forty or fifty Pages of *Preface* and *Dedication*, (which is
the usual *Modern* Stint[2]) as if it were so much *Latin*.
Tho' it must be also allowed on the other Hand that
a very considerable Number is known to proceed *Criticks*
and *Wits*, by reading nothing else.[3] Into which two

---

[1] '*To-the-Readers's*' edd. 1–4.
Cf. Boyle's *Examination*, p. 193:
'as *Prefaces, Prolegomena, Apparatus's, Introductions*, &c.'

[2] The Dedication of Dryden's
Juvenal runs to fifty-three folio
pages, and the Dedication of the
Æneis to forty-seven.

[3] Cf. pp. 43 and 97. Also
Swift's *On Poetry* (1733):
 Judicious *Rymer* oft review:
 Wise *Dennis*, and profound
  Bossu.
 Read all the *Prefaces* of *Dryden*

Factions, I think, all present Readers may justly be divided. Now, for my self, I profess to be of the former Sort; and therefore having the *Modern* Inclination to expatiate upon the Beauty of my own Productions, and display the bright Parts of my Discourse; I thought best to do it in the Body of the Work, where, as it now lies, it makes a very considerable Addition to the Bulk of the Volume, *a Circumstance by no means to be neglected by a skilful Writer*.

HAVING thus paid my due Deference and Acknowledgment to an establish'd Custom of our newest Authors, by *a long Digression unsought for*, and *an universal Censure unprovoked*; By forcing into the Light, with much Pains and Dexterity, my own Excellencies and other Mens Defaults, with great Justice to my self and Candor to them; I now happily resume my Subject, to the Infinite Satisfaction both of the Reader and the Author.

For these our Criticks much confide in,
(Though meerly writ at first for filling
To raise the Volume's Price, a Shilling.)
And cf. this last line with the last line of the paragraph.

SECT. VI.

A TALE of a TUB.

WE left *Lord Peter* in open Rupture with his two Brethren; both for ever discarded from his House, and resigned to the wide World, with little or nothing to trust to. Which are Circumstances that render them proper Subjects for the Charity of a Writer's Pen to work on; Scenes of Misery, ever affording the fairest Harvest for great Adventures. And in this, the World may perceive the Difference between the Integrity of a generous Author, and that of a common Friend. The latter is observed to adhere close in Prosperity, but on the Decline of Fortune, to drop suddenly off. Whereas, the generous Author, just on the contrary, finds his Hero on the Dunghil, from thence by gradual Steps, raises Him to a Throne, and then immediately withdraws, expecting not so much as Thanks for his Pains: in imitation of which Example, I have placed *Lord Peter* in a Noble House, given Him a Title to wear, and Money to spend. There I shall leave Him for some Time; returning where common Charity directs me, to the Assistance of his two Brothers, at their lowest Ebb. However, I shall by no means forget my Character of an Historian, to follow the Truth, step by step, whatever happens, or where-ever it may lead me.

THE two Exiles so nearly united in Fortune and Interest, took a Lodging together; Where, at their first Leisure, they began to reflect on the numberless Misfortunes and Vexations of their Life past, and could not tell, on the sudden, to what Failure in their Conduct they ought to impute them; When, after some Recollection, they called to Mind the Copy of their Father's *Will*, which they had so happily recovered. This was immediately produced, and a firm Resolution taken between them, to alter whatever was already amiss, and reduce all their future Measures to the strictest Obedience prescribed therein. The main Body of the *Will* (as the Reader cannot easily have forgot) consisted in certain admirable Rules about the wearing of their Coats; in the Perusal whereof, the two Brothers at every Period duly comparing the Doctrine with the Practice, there was never seen a wider Difference between two Things; horrible down-right Transgressions of every Point. Upon which, they both resolved without further Delay, to fall immediately upon reducing the Whole, exactly after their Father's Model.

B U T, here it is good to stop the hasty Reader, ever impatient to see the End of an Adventure, before We Writers can duly prepare him for it. I am to record, that these two Brothers began to be distinguished at this Time, by certain Names. One of them desired to be called **MARTIN*, and the other took the Appellation of *†JACK*. These two had lived in much Friendship and Agreement under the Tyranny of their Brother *Peter*, as it is the Talent of Fellow-Sufferers to do; Men in Misfortune, being like Men in the Dark, to whom all Colours are the same:[1] But when they came forward into the World, and began to display themselves to each other, and to the Light, their Complexions[2] appear'd extreamly different; which the present Posture of their Affairs gave them sudden Opportunity to discover.

B U T, here the severe Reader may justly tax me as a Writer of short Memory, a Deficiency to which a true

* *Martin Luther.*   † *John Calvin.*

[1] Cf. Bacon's essay 'Of Unity in Religion': 'For all Colours will agree in the Darke.'

[2] Dispositions, temperaments. Cf. *The English Theophrastus* (1702), p. 120: 'Men that are *Cowards* by Complexion, are hardly to be made Valiant by Discourse.'

Modern cannot but of Necessity be a little subject: Because, *Memory* being an Employment of the Mind upon things past, is a Faculty, for which the Learned, in our Illustrious Age, have no manner of Occasion, who deal entirely with *Invention*,[1] and strike all Things out of themselves, or at least, by Collision, from each other: Upon which Account we think it highly Reasonable to produce our great Forgetfulness, as an Argument unanswerable for our great Wit. I ought in Method, to have informed the Reader about fifty Pages ago, of a Fancy *Lord Peter* took, and infused into his Brothers, to wear on their Coats whatever Trimmings came up in Fashion; never pulling off any, as they went out of the Mode, but keeping on all together; which amounted in time to a Medley, the most Antick you can possibly conceive; and this to a Degree, that upon the Time of their falling out there was hardly a Thread of the Original Coat to be seen,[2] but an infinite Quantity of *Lace*, and *Ribbands*, and *Fringe*, and *Embroidery*, and *Points*; (I mean, only those **tagg'd with Silver*, for the rest fell off.) Now, this material Circumstance, having been forgot in due Place; as good Fortune hath ordered, comes in very properly here, when the two Brothers are just going to reform their Vestures into the Primitive State, prescribed by their Father's *Will*.

THEY both unanimously entred upon this great Work, looking sometimes on their Coats, and sometimes on the *Will*. *Martin* laid the first Hand; at one

---

* *Points tagg'd with Silver, are those Doctrines that promote the Greatness and Wealth of the Church, which have been therefore woven deepest in*[3] *the Body of Popery.*

[1] Cf. p. 42, note 1.
[2] Ceremonys and Innovations multiplied to such a degree, that there was no more of the ancient primitive Christianity to be seen [1720].
[3] 'into' *Notes* 1711.

twitch brought off a large Handful of *Points*,[1] and with a second pull, stript away ten dozen Yards of *Fringe*.[2] But when He had gone thus far, he demurred a while: He knew very well, there yet remained a great deal more to be done; however, the first Heat being over, his Violence began to cool, and he resolved to proceed more moderately in the rest of the Work; having already very narrowly scap'd a swinging Rent in pulling off the *Points*, which being *tagged with Silver*[3] (as we have observed before) the judicious Workman had with much Sagacity, double sown, to preserve them from *falling*.[4] Resolving therefore to rid his Coat of a huge Quantity of *Gold Lace*; he pickt up the Stitches with much Caution, and diligently gleaned out all the loose Threads as he went, which proved to be a Work of Time. Then he fell about the embroidered *Indian* Figures of Men, Women and Children; against which, as you have heard in its due Place, their Father's Testament was extreamly exact and severe: These, with much Dexterity and Application, were after a while, quite eradicated, or utterly defaced.[5] For the rest, where he observed the Embroidery to be workt so close, as not to be got away without damaging the Cloth, or where it served to hide or strengthen any Flaw in the Body of the Coat, contracted by the perpetual tampering of Workmen upon it; he concluded the wisest Course was to let it remain, resolving in no Case whatsoever, that the Substance of the Stuff should suffer Injury; which he thought the best Method for serving the true Intent and Meaning

---

[1] Dogmas [*MS. Pate*]. Cf. p. 90.

[2] Alluding to the commencement of the Reformation in England, by seizing on the abbey lands [Scott].

[3] Points that bring in gain to the Clergy [*MS. Pate*].

[4] The dissolution of the monasteries occasioned several insurrections, and much convulsion, during the reign of Edward VI [Scott].

[5] The abolition of the worship of saints was the second grand step in English reformation [Scott].

Original Design

of his Father's *Will*. And this is the nearest Account I have been able to collect, of *Martin*'s Proceedings upon this great Revolution.

BUT his Brother *Jack*, whose Adventures will be so extraordinary, as to furnish a great Part in the Remainder of this Discourse; entred upon the Matter with other Thoughts, and a quite different Spirit. For, the Memory of *Lord Peter*'s Injuries, produced a Degree of Hatred and Spight, which had a much greater Share of inciting Him, than any Regards after his Father's Commands, since these appeared at best, only Secondary and Subservient to the other. However, for this Meddly of Humor, he made a Shift to find a very plausible Name, honoring it with the Title of *Zeal*; which is, perhaps, the most significant Word that hath been ever yet produced in any Language; As, I think, I have fully proved in my excellent *Analytical* Discourse upon that Subject; wherein I have deduced a *Histori-theo-physilogical* Account of *Zeal*,[1] shewing how it first proceeded from a *Notion* into a *Word*, and from thence in a hot Summer, ripned into a *tangible Substance*. This Work containing three large Volumes in Folio, I design very shortly to publish by the *Modern* way of *Subscription*,[2] not doubting but the Nobility and Gentry of the Land will give me all possible Encouragement, having already had such a Taste of what I am able to perform.

---

[1] See the Catalogue before the Title [1720].

[2] 'To print by subscription was, for some time, a practice peculiar to the English. The first considerable work for which this expedient was employed is said to have been Dryden's *Virgil*' (Johnson, 'Life of Pope', ed. Birkbeck Hill, iii. 109). Malone pointed out that Tonson's 1688 edition of *Paradise Lost* was published by subscription, and that in 1691 Wood similarly disposed of about 415 of the 500 copies of his *Athenæ Oxonienses* (Malone's *Dryden*, i. 233, 4).

Walton's *Polyglot Bible* (1654–7) and Somner's *Anglo-Saxon Dictionary* (1659) were published by subscription. The method was even earlier. John

I record therefore, that Brother *Jack*, brimful of this miraculous Compound, reflecting with Indignation upon *PETER*'s Tyranny, and farther provoked by the Despondency of *Martin*; prefaced his Resolutions to this purpose. *What*; said he; *A Rogue that lock'd up his Drink,*[1] *turned away our Wives, cheated us of our Fortunes; paumed his damned Crusts upon us for Mutton; and at last kickt us out of Doors; must we be in His Fashions with a Pox? a Rascal, besides, that all the Street cries out against.* Having thus kindled and enflamed himself as high as possible, and by Consequence, in a delicate Temper for beginning a Reformation, he set about the Work immediately, and in three Minutes, made more Dispatch than *Martin* had done in as many Hours. For, (Courteous Reader) you are given to understand, that *Zeal* is never so highly obliged, as when you set it a *Tearing*: and *Jack*, who doated on that Quality in himself, allowed it at this Time its full Swinge. Thus it happened, that stripping down a Parcel of *Gold Lace*, a little too hastily, he rent the *main Body* of his *Coat* from Top to Bottom;[2] and whereas his Talent was not of the happiest in *taking up a Stitch*, he knew no better way, than to dern it again with *Packthred* and a *Scewer*.[3] But the Matter was yet infinitely worse (I record it with Tears) when he proceeded to the *Embroidery*: For, being Clumsy by Nature, and of Temper, Impatient; withal, beholding Millions of Stitches, that required the nicest Hand, and sedatest Constitution, to extricate; in a great Rage, he

---

Taylor, the Water Poet, used it. Minsheu's *Guide into Tongues* (1617) has a list of purchasers. Swift's description of the method as 'modern' is explained by its vogue in his day.

[1] Denieth the cup to the laity; enjoined celibacy to the clergy; transubstantiation [*MS. Pate*].

[2] Removing Episcopacy, and setting up Presbytery in its room [*MS. Pate*].

[3] The reformers in Scotland left their established clergy in an almost beggarly condition, from the hasty violence with which they seized on all the possessions of the Romish church [Scott].

tore off the whole Piece, Cloth and all, and flung it into the Kennel,[1] and furiously thus continuing his Career; *Ah, Good Brother* Martin, said he, *do as I do, for the Love of God; Strip, Tear, Pull, Rent, Flay off all, that we may appear as unlike the Rogue* Peter, *as it is possible:*[2] *I would not for a hundred Pounds carry the least Mark about me, that might give Occasion to the Neighbours, of suspecting I was related to such a Rascal.* But *Martin,* who at this Time happened to be extremely flegmatick and sedate, *begged his Brother of all Love, not to damage his Coat by any Means; for he never would get such another:* Desired him *to consider, that it was not their Business to form their Actions by any Reflection upon* Peter's,[3] *but by observing the Rules prescribed in their Father's* Will. That *he should remember,* Peter *was still their Brother, whatever Faults or Injuries he had committed; and therefore they should by all means avoid such a Thought, as that of taking Measures for Good and Evil, from no other Rule, than of Opposition to him.* That *it was true, the Testament of their good Father was very exact in what related to the wearing of their* Coats; *yet was it no less penal and strict in prescribing Agreement, and Friendship, and Affection between them. And therefore, if straining a Point were at all dispensable,*[4] *it would certainly be so, rather to the Advance of Unity, than Increase of Contradiction.*

MARTIN had still proceeded as gravely as he began; and doubtless, would have delivered an admirable Lecture of Morality, which might have exceedingly

---

[1] The presbyterians, in discarding forms of prayers, and unnecessary church ceremonies, disused even those founded in scripture [Scott]. The *kennel* is the *gutter*.

[2] The presbyterians were particularly anxious to extend their church government into England. This was the bait held out by the English parliament, to prevail on the Scots to invade England in 1643, and it proved successful [Scott].   [3] 'Peter' edd. 4, 5.

[4] i.e. subject to dispensation, capable of being permitted.

contributed to my Reader's *Repose, both of Body and Mind:* (the true ultimate End of *Ethicks*;) But *Jack* was already gone a Flight-shot beyond his Patience. And as in Scholastick Disputes, nothing serves to rouze the Spleen of him that *Opposes*, so much as a kind of Pedantick affected Calmness in the *Respondent*; Disputants being for the most part like unequal Scales, where the *Gravity* of one Side advances the *Lightness* of the Other, and causes it to fly up and kick the Beam;[1] So it happened here, that the *Weight* of *Martin*'s Arguments[2] exalted *Jack*'s *Levity*, and made him fly out and spurn against his Brother's Moderation. In short, *Martin*'s *Patience* put *Jack* in a *Rage*; but that which most afflicted him was, to observe his Brother's Coat so well reduced into the State of Innocence; while his own was either wholly rent to his Shirt; or those Places which had scaped his cruel Clutches, were still in *Peter*'s Livery. So that he looked like a drunken *Beau*, half rifled by *Bullies*; Or like a fresh Tenant of *Newgate*, when he has refused the Payment of *Garnish*;[3] Or like a discovered *Shoplifter*, left to the Mercy of *Exchange-Women*;[4] Or like a *Bawd* in her old Velvet-Petticoat, resign'd into the

---

[1] Cf. *Paradise Lost,* iv. 1002–4.

[2] 'Argument' edd. 4,5,

[3] Money extorted from a new prisoner as a jailer's fee, or as drink-money. Cf. Gay, *Beggar's Opera* (1727), II. vii.

[4] The galleries over the piazzas in the *Royal Exchange* were formerly filled with shops, kept chiefly by women; the same use was made of a building called the *New Exchange* in the *Strand*; this edifice has been pulled down; the shopkeepers have removed from the *Royal Exchange* into *Cornhill*, and the adjacent streets; and there are now no remains of *Exchange women*, but in *Exeter-'change,* and they are no longer deemed the first ministers of fashion [Hawkesworth].

The New Exchange was a kind of bazaar on the south side of the Strand, near the site of the Adelphi, opened in 1609 and taken down in 1737. See Cunningham and Wheatley, *London Past and Present,* ii. 581–3. Cf. Steele's *Lying Lover,* II. ii and *The Spectator,* No. 155.

secular Hands of the *Mobile.*[1] Like any, or like all of these, a Meddley of *Rags*, and *Lace*, and *Rents*, and *Fringes*, unfortunate *Jack* did now appear: He would have been extremely glad to see his Coat in the Condition of *Martin*'s, but infinitely gladder to find that of *Martin*'s in the same Predicament with his. However, since neither of these was likely to come to pass, he thought fit to lend the whole Business another Turn, and to dress up Necessity into a Virtue. Therefore, after as many of the *Fox*'s Arguments,[2] as he could muster up, for bringing *Martin* to *Reason*, as he called it; or, as he meant it, into his own ragged, bobtail'd[3] Condition; and observing he said all to little purpose; what, alas, was left for the forlorn *Jack* to do, but after a Million of Scurrilities[4] against his Brother, to run mad with Spleen, and Spight, and Contradiction. To be short, here began a mortal Breach between these two. *Jack* went immediately to *New Lodgings*, and in a few Days it was for certain reported, that he had run out of his Wits. In a short time after, he appeared abroad, and confirmed the Report, by falling into the oddest Whimsies that ever a sick Brain conceived.

AND now the little Boys in the Streets began to salute him with several Names.[5] Sometimes they would call Him, **Jack the Bald*; sometimes, †*Jack with a Lan-*

---

* *That is* Calvin, *from* Calvus, *Bald.*
† *All those who pretend to Inward Light.*

---

[1] Mob (Latin *mobile vulgus*). Swift objected to the contraction which in these days was fast gaining currency. See his letter in *The Tatler*, No. 230; and cf. Addison, *The Spectator*, No. 135. Cf. also p. 13, note 3, and p. 41, note 3.

[2] In Æsop's fable of the Fox that lost his tail: cf. L'Estrange's *Fables of Æsop* (1692), ci.

[3] Short cloaks [*MS. Pate*].

[4] Cf. p. 122, l. 15.

[5] These different names allude to different sects of Calvinists and Enthousiasts [1720].

thorn;[1] sometimes, *Dutch Jack*; sometimes, †*French Hugh*;[2] sometimes, ‡*Tom the Beggar*;[3] and sometimes, ||*Knocking Jack of the North*.[4] And it was under one, or some, or all of these Appellations (which I leave the Learned Reader to determine) that he hath given Rise to the most Illustrious and Epidemick Sect of *Æolists*,[5] who with honourable Commemoration, do still acknowledge the Renowned *JACK* for their Author and Founder. Of whose Original, as well as Principles, I am now advancing to gratify the World with a very particular Account.

——*Mellæo contingens cuncta Lepore*.[6]

* Jack *of* Leyden, *who gave Rise to the* Anabaptists.
† *The* Hugonots.
‡ *The* Gueuses, *by which Name some Protestants in* Flanders *were call'd*.
|| John Knox, *the Reformer of* Scotland.

[1] Cf. *Hudibras*, i. i. 505:
'Tis a *dark-Lanthorn* of the spirit,
Which none see by but those that bear it.
[2] The Hugonots [*MS. Pate*].
[3] In the Low Countries, the first Protestants were by way of contempt called *Gueux*, that is Beggars [1734].

[4] From *John Knox*, a hot-headed Reformer in Scotland [1734].
[5] See p. 150.
[6] *Musæo contingens*, &c. Lucretius, i. 934: cf. 938 and 947, which show that Swift was quoting from memory. The wrong spelling of 'Melleo' disguises the false quantity.

SECT. VII.

A Digression in Praise of Digressions.

I HAVE sometimes *heard* of an *Iliad* in a *Nut-shell*;[1] but it hath been my Fortune to have much oftner *seen* a *Nut-shell* in an[2] *Iliad*. There is no doubt, that Human Life has received most wonderful Advantages from both; but to which of the two the World is chiefly indebted, I shall leave among the Curious, as a Problem worthy of their utmost Enquiry. For the Invention of the latter, I think the Commonwealth of Learning is chiefly obliged to the great *Modern* Improvement of *Digressions*: The late Refinements in Knowledge, running parallel to those of Dyet in our Nation, which among Men of a judicious Taste, are drest up in various Compounds, consisting in *Soups* and *Ollio's*, *Fricassées* and *Ragousts*.[3]

'TIS true, there is a sort of morose, detracting, ill-bred People, who pretend utterly to disrelish these polite Innovations: And as to the Similitude from Dyet, they allow the Parallel, but are so bold to pronounce the Example it self, a Corruption and Degeneracy of

---

[1] Pliny, *Natural History*, vii. 21, 85: 'in nuce inclusam Iliadem Homeri carmen in membrana scriptum tradit Cicero'. The passage is not found in Cicero's extant works.

Craik points out that the elder Scaliger refers to the passage in Pliny in his *De Subtilitate* (Exercitatio Prima, 1), which Swift knew: see p. 203. He also knew Rabelais—*Pantagruel* v. xx: 'en lettres aussi petites que dit Cicero avoir leu l'*Iliade* d'Homère, tellement qu'on la couvrait d'une coquille de noix'.

[2] 'a' edd. 3–5.

[3] *Ollio's* ('*Ollioes*' edd. 1, 2), mixed stews, of Portuguese or Spanish origin; cf. 'olla podrida'. Swift again couples the two French names for dishes in his *Modest Proposal*, 1729: 'will equally serve in a *Fricasie* or *Ragoust.*' Both are joined with 'olio', as here, in Burns's *Address to a Haggis*.

Taste. They tell us, that the Fashion of jumbling fifty Things together in a Dish, was at first introduced in Compliance to a depraved and *debauched Appetite*, as well as to a *crazy Constitution*; And to see a Man hunting thro' an *Ollio*, after the *Head* and *Brains* of a *Goose*, a *Wigeon*, or a *Woodcock*, is a Sign, he wants a Stomach and Digestion for more substantial Victuals. Farther, they affirm, that *Digressions* in a Book, are like *Forein Troops* in a *State*, which argue the Nation to want a *Heart* and *Hands* of its own, and often, either *subdue* the *Natives*, or drive them into the most *unfruitful Corners*.

BUT, after all that can be objected by these supercilious Censors; 'tis manifest, the Society of Writers would quickly be reduced to a very inconsiderable Number, if Men were put upon making Books, with the fatal Confinement of delivering nothing beyond what is to the Purpose. 'Tis acknowledged, that were the Case the same among Us, as with the *Greeks* and *Romans*, when Learning was in its *Cradle*, to be reared and fed, and cloathed by *Invention*; it would be an easy Task to fill up Volumes upon particular Occasions, without farther exspatiating from the Subject, than by moderate Excursions, helping to advance or clear the main Design. But with *Knowledge*, it has fared as with a numerous Army, encamped in a fruitful Country; which for a few Days maintains it self by the Product of the Soyl it is on; Till Provisions being spent, they send to forrage many a Mile, among Friends or Enemies it matters not. Mean while, the neighbouring Fields trampled and beaten down, become barren and dry, affording no Sustenance but Clouds of Dust.

THE whole Course of Things being thus entirely changed between *Us* and the *Antients*; and the *Moderns* wisely sensible of it, we of this Age have discovered a shorter, and more prudent Method, to become *Scholars* and *Wits*, without the Fatigue of *Reading* or of *Thinking*. The most accomplisht Way of using Books at present, is twofold: Either first, to serve them as some Men do *Lords*, learn their *Titles* exactly, and then brag of their Acquaintance. Or Secondly, which is indeed the choicer, the profounder, and politer Method, to get a thorough Insight into the *Index*,[1] by which the whole Book is governed and turned, like *Fishes* by the *Tail*.[2] For, to enter the Palace of Learning at the *great Gate*, requires an Expence of Time and Forms; therefore Men of much Haste and little Ceremony, are content to get in by the *Back-Door*. For, the Arts are all in a *flying* March, and therefore more easily subdued by attacking them in the *Rear*. Thus Physicians discover the State of the whole Body, by consulting only what comes from *Behind*. Thus Men catch Knowledge by throwing their *Wit* on the *Posteriors* of a book, as Boys do Sparrows with flinging *Salt* upon their *Tails*. Thus Human Life is best understood by the wise man's Rule of *Regarding the End*.[3] Thus are the Sciences found like *Hercules*'s Oxen, by *tracing them Backwards*. Thus are *old Sciences* unravelled like *old Stockings*,[4] by beginning at the *Foot*.

BESIDES all this, the Army of the Sciences hath been of late, with a world of Martial Discipline, drawn into its *close Order*, so that a View, or a Muster may be taken of it with abundance of Expedition. For this great Blessing we are wholly indebted to *Systems* and *Abstracts*, in which the *Modern* Fathers of Learning, like prudent Usurers, spent their Sweat for the Ease of

[1] In Boyle's *Examination* (1698) Bentley is repeatedly attacked for his knowledge of indexes and lexicons (e.g. pp. 68, 145, 197, 286). Cf. p. 43.
[2] Cf. *The Dunciad*, i, ll. 279–80:

How Index-learning turns no student pale,
Yet holds the eel of Science by the tail.

[3] Herodotus, i. 32, in the speech of Solon to Croesus.
[4] '*Stockins*' edd. 1, 2.

Us their Children. For *Labor* is the Seed of *Idleness*, and it is the peculiar Happiness of our Noble Age to gather the *Fruit*.

NOW the Method of growing Wise, Learned, and *Sublime*, having become so regular an Affair, and so established in all its Forms; the Number[1] of Writers must needs have encreased accordingly, and to a Pitch that has made it of absolute Necessity for them to interfere continually with each other. Besides, it is reckoned, that there is not at this present, a sufficient Quantity of new Matter left in Nature, to furnish and adorn any one particular Subject to the Extent of a Volume.[2] This I am told by a very skillful *Computer*, who hath given a full Demonstration of it from Rules of *Arithmetick*.

THIS, perhaps, may be objected against, by those, who maintain the Infinity of Matter, and therefore, will not allow that any *Species* of it can be exhausted. For Answer to which, let us examine the noblest Branch of *Modern* Wit or Invention, planted and cultivated by the present Age, and, which of all others, hath born the most, and the fairest Fruit. For tho' some Remains of it were left us by the *Antients*, yet have not any of those, as I remember, been translated or compiled into Systems for *Modern* Use. Therefore We may affirm, to our

[1] Edd. 1, 2; 'Numbers' edd. 3–5.

[2] Swift is thinking of what Wotton had said about the advance of scientific learning during 'this last age', *Reflections* (1697), pp. 410–11: 'such Swarms of Great Men, in evey Part of Natural and Mathematical Knowledge, have within these few Years appeared, that it may, perhaps, without Vanity, be believed, that if this Humour lasts much longer, and learned Men do not divert their Thoughts to Speculations of another kind, the next Age will not find much Work of this kind to do'. Wotton was doubtful 'whether Knowledge will improve in the next Age, proportionably as it has done in this', and saw reason 'to fear that it may decay' (p. 418).

own Honor, that it has in some sort, been both invented, and brought to a Perfection by the same Hands. What I mean, is that highly celebrated Talent among the *Modern* Wits, of deducing Similitudes, Allusions, and Applications, very Surprizing, Agreeable, and Apposite, from the *Pudenda*[1] of either Sex, together with *their proper Uses*. And truly, having observed how little Invention bears any Vogue, besides what is derived into these *Channels*, I have sometimes had a Thought, That the happy Genius of our Age and Country, was prophetically held forth by that antient *typical Description of the *Indian* Pygmies; *whose Stature did not exceed above* two Foot*; Sed quorum pudenda crassa, & ad talos usque pertingentia.*[2] Now, I have been very curious to inspect the late Productions, wherein the Beauties of this kind have most prominently appeared. And altho' this *Vein* hath bled so freely, and all Endeavours have been used in the Power of Human Breath, to dilate, extend, and keep it open: Like the Scythians, †*who had a Custom, and an Instrument, to blow up the Privities of their Mares, that they might yield the more Milk*;[3] Yet I am under an Apprehension, it is near growing dry, and past all Recovery; And that either some new *Fonde*[4] of Wit should, if possible, be provided, or else that we must e'en be content with Repetition here, as well as upon all other Occasions.

*   *Ctesiæ fragm. apud Photium.*

†   *Herodot. L.* 4.

THIS will stand as an uncontestable Argument, that our *Modern* Wits are not to reckon upon the Infinity of Matter, for a constant Supply. What remains therefore, but that our last Recourse must be had to large *Indexes*, and little *Compendiums*; *Quotations* must

[1] 'the *Genitals*' edd. 1–4.
[2] Photius, ed. Bekker (1824), p. 46.
[3] Herodotus, iv. 2.
[4] Stock, store. Cf. p. 105, note 2.

be plentifully gathered, and bookt in Alphabet; To this End, tho' Authors need be little consulted, yet *Criticks*, and *Commentators*, and *Lexicons* carefully must. But above all, those judicious Collectors of *bright Parts*, and *Flowers*, and *Observanda's*, are to be nicely dwelt on; by some called the *Sieves* and *Boulters* of Learning; tho' it is left undetermined, whether they dealt in *Pearls* or *Meal*; and consequently, whether we are more to value that which *passed thro'*, or what *staid behind*.

BY these Methods, in a few Weeks, there starts up many a Writer, capable of managing the profoundest, and most universal Subjects. For, what tho' his *Head* be empty, provided his *Common-place-Book* be full; And if you will bate him but the Circumstances of *Method*, and *Style*, and *Grammar*, and *Invention*; allow him but the common Priviledges of transcribing from others, and digressing from himself, as often as he shall see Occasion; He will desire no more Ingredients towards fitting up a Treatise, that shall make a very comely Figure on a Bookseller's Shelf, there to be preserved neat and clean, for a long Eternity, adorn'd with the Heraldry of its Title, fairly inscribed on a Label; never to be thumb'd or greas'd by Students, nor bound to everlasting Chains of Darkness in a Library:[1] But when the Fulness of time is come, shall haply[2] undergo the Tryal of Purgatory, in order *to ascend the Sky*.

WITHOUT these Allowances, how is it possible, we *Modern* Wits should ever have an Opportunity to introduce our Collections listed under so many thousand Heads of a different Nature? for want of which, the Learned World would be deprived of infinite Delight,

---

[1] It was still the habit in Swift's time to chain books in libraries. Cf. the *Battle of the Books*, p.223. In the Bodleian the removal of the chains began about 1757. See W. D. Macray, *Annals of the Bodleian* (1890), p. 161.

[2] 'haply' ed. 1; 'happily' edd. 2–5.

as well as Instruction, and we our selves buried beyond Redress in an inglorious and undistinguisht Oblivion.

FROM such Elements as these, I am alive to behold the Day, wherein the Corporation of Authors can out-vie all its Brethren in the *Field*.[1] A Happiness derived to us with a great many others, from our *Scythian* Ancestors;[2] among whom, the Number of *Pens* was so infinite, that the *Grecian Elo-quence[3] had no other way of expres-   * *Herodot.* L. 4. sing it, than by saying, *That in the Regions, far to the* North, *it was hardly possible for a Man to travel, the very Air was so replete with* Feathers.

THE Necessity of this Digression, will easily excuse the Length; and I have chosen for it as proper a Place as I could readily find. If the judicious Reader can assign a fitter, I do here empower him to remove it into any other Corner he pleases.[4] And so I return with great Alacrity to pursue a more important Concern.

[1] '*Yield*' edd. 1, 2; '*Field*' edd. 3–5; '*guild*' Hawkesworth.
[2] See p. 99, note 2.
[3] Herodotus, iv. 7 and 31.
[4] 'please' edd. 1, 2.

SECT. VIII.

A TALE of a TUB.

THE Learned **Æolists*,[1] maintain the Original Cause of all Things to be *Wind*, from which Principle this whole Universe was at first produced, and into which it must at last be resolved; that the same Breath which had kindled, and blew *up* the Flame of Nature, should one Day blow it *out*.

Quod procul à nobis flectat Fortuna gubernans.[2]

THIS is what the *Adepti* understand by their *Anima Mundi*;[3] that is to say, the *Spirit*, or *Breath*, or *Wind* of

* *All Pretenders to Inspiration whatsoever.*

---

[1] *Spirit* and *Wind* are here made synonimous terms; so *Æolists* may signify all those that believe spiritual Beings; or perhaps those that are called among the Godly, *Spiritualisers* or *Spiritually minded* [1720]. Spirit . . . Beings, or all those that pretend to Inspiration, or make any account of it [1734].

[2] Lucretius, v. 107.

[3] *Anima Mundi* is defined in Thomas Vaughan's *Anthroposophia Theomagica* (1650, pp. 38–39), in a passage which Swift had in mind when writing this section: '. . . *Anima Mundi*, commonly called *Anima media*, because the Influences of the *Divine Nature* are conveyed through *it* to the more material parts of the Creature, with which of themselves they have no proportion. By meanes of this *Anima Media*, or the *æthereal Nature: Man* is made subject to the Influence of Stars, and is partly dispos'd of by the *Cælestial harmony*. For this middle spirit (middle I mean between both Extreames, and not that which actually unites the whole together) aswell that which is in the outward Heaven, as that which is in Man, is of a fruitfull insinuating nature, and carried with a strong desire to multiply it self, so that the *Cælestiall Form* stirs up, and excites the Elementall. For this Spirit is in Man, in Beasts, in Vegetables, in Minerals: and in every thing it is the *mediate Cause* of Composition and Multiplication.' Cf. also Vaughan's *Anima Magica Abscondita* (1650, p. 10):

the World: Or¹ Examine the whole System by the
Particulars of Nature, and you will find it not to be
disputed. For, whether you please to call the *Forma
informans*² of Man, by the Name of *Spiritus*, *Animus*,
Afflatus, or *Anima*; What are all these but several Appellations for *Wind*? which is the ruling *Element* in
every Compound, and into which they all resolve upon
their Corruption. Farther, what is Life itself, but as
it is commonly call'd, the *Breath* of our Nostrils?³
Whence it is very justly observed by Naturalists, that
Wind still continues of great Emolument in *certain
Mysteries* not to be named, giving Occasion for those
happy Epithets of *Turgidus*, and *Inflatus*, apply'd either
to the *Emittent*, or *Recipient* Organs.

BY what I have gathered out of antient Records, I
find the *Compass* of their Doctrine took in two and thirty
Points,⁴ wherein it would be tedious to be very particular. However, a few of their most important Precepts,
deducible from it, are by no means to be omitted; among
which the following Maxim was of much Weight; That
since *Wind* had the Master-Share, as well as Operation
in every Compound, by Consequence, those Beings
must be of chief Excellence, wherein that *Primordium*
appears most prominently to abound; and therefore,
Man is in highest Perfection of all created Things,
as having by the great Bounty of Philosophers, been

'To be plaine then, this *Principle* is *Anima Mundi*, or the universall *spirit* of Nature.'

¹ 'Or' edd. 1–4; 'for' ed. 5.

² One of the scholastic distinc-tions of *Forma*, thus explained in *Celebriorum Distinctionum Philo-sophicarum Synopsis. Authore Henr. Ludov. Castanæo* (1657, p. 74): '*Forma Abstracta*, seu *separata à materia*, seu *forma per se* subsistens, seu *immaterialis*, ut Deus & Intelligentiæ. *Informans*, seu *forma perficiens materiam*, seu *forma intra rem*, ut forma substantialis ignis.'

Cf. p. 222, note 3.

³ See Genesis ii. 7 and vii. 22; Isaiah ii. 22.

⁴ Allusion aux 32 points du vent [Justus van Effen].

endued with three distinct *Anima's* or *Winds*, to which the
Sage *Æolists*, with much Liberality, have added a fourth
of equal Necessity, as well as Ornament with the other
three;[1] by this *quartum Principium*,[2] taking in the[3] four
Corners of the World; which gave Occasion to that Renowned *Cabbalist*.[4] *Bumbastus*, of placing the Body of
Man, in due position to the four *Cardinal* Points.[5]

IN Consequence of this, their next Principle was,
that *Man* brings with him into the World a peculiar
Portion or Grain of *Wind*, which may be called a *Quinta
essentia*, extracted from the other four.[5] This *Quintessence* is of a Catholick Use upon all Emergencies of
Life, is improvable into all Arts and Sciences, and may
be wonderfully refined, as well as enlarged by certain
Methods in Education. This, when *blown* up to its
Perfection, ought not to be covetously hoarded up,

* *This is one of the Names of* Paracelsus; *He was call'd* Christophorus,
Theophrastus, Paracelsus, Bumbastus.

[1] The three *Anima's* bestow'd
on Man by Philosophers are the
*Vegetativa, Sensitiva, and Ratio-
nalis,* and the fourth bestow'd by
the *Æolists* is the *Spiritualis*
[1720].

The scholastic conception of
'three distinct *Anima's*' is ex-
pounded by Aquinas, e.g. *Summa,*
i. 76. 3: 'Videtur quod praeter
animam intellectivam sint in ho-
mine aliae animae per essentiam
differentes, scilicet sensitiva et
nutritiva. Corruptibile enim et
incorruptibile non sunt unius sub-
stantiae. Sed anima intellectiva est
incorruptibilis; aliae vero animae,
scilicet sensitiva et nutritiva, sunt
corruptibiles.' It is based on Plato
and Aristotle, who are quoted by

Aquinas.

Cf. *Batman uppon Bartholome*
(1582), lib. iii, cap. 7: 'If we take
heed to the soule in comparison to
his working, wee finde three manner of vertues, *Vegetabilis*, that
giveth life, *Sensibilis*, that giveth
feeling, *Racionalis*, that giveth
reason.'

[2] 'Hoc nomen, *principium*, nihil
aliud significat quam id a quo
aliquid procedit. Omne enim a
quo aliquid procedit quocumque
modo, dicimus esse principium, et
e converso.' Aquinas, *Summa,* i.
33. 1.

[3] 'the' edd. 1–4; 'our' ed. 5.

[4] '*Cabalist*' edd. 1, 2; cf.
p. 127, note 3.

[5] See Appendix F, p. 358.

stifled, or hid under a Bushel,[1] but freely communicated to Mankind. Upon these Reasons, and others of equal Weight, the Wise *Æolists*, affirm the Gift of BELCH-ING,[2] to be the noblest Act of a Rational Creature. To cultivate which Art, and render it more serviceable to Mankind, they made Use of several Methods. At certain Seasons of the Year, you might behold the Priests amongst them in vast Numbers, with their *Mouths gaping wide against a Storm.* At other times were to be seen several Hundreds link'd together in a circular Chain, with every Man a Pair of Bellows applied to his Neighbour's Breech, by which they blew up each other to the Shape and Size of a *Tun*; and for that Reason, with great Propriety of Speech, did usually call their Bodies, their *Vessels*.[3] When, by these and the like Performances, they were grown sufficiently replete, they would immediately depart, and disembogue for the Publick Good, a plentiful Share of their Acquirements into their Disciples Chaps. For we must here observe, that all Learning was esteemed among them to be compounded from the same Principle. Because, First, it is generally affirmed, or confess'd that Learning *puffeth Men up*:[4] And Secondly, they proved it by the following Syllogism; *Words are but Wind; and Learning is nothing but Words*; Ergo, *Learning is nothing but Wind.* For this Reason, the Philosophers among them, did in their Schools, deliver to their Pupils, all their Doctrines and Opinions by *Eructation*, wherein they had acquired a wonderful Eloquence, and of incredible Variety. But the great Characteristick,

* *This is meant of those Seditious Preachers; who blow up the Seeds of Rebellion,* &c.

[1] Matt. v. 15 [1720].
[2] *Belching*, is in Latin called *eructatio*, a term used to express the action of the Priests in the Temples of the Oracles when they delivered their prophecies or inspirations among the Ancients [1720].
[3] Cf. Acts ix. 15 and Rom. ix 22.   [4] 1 Cor. viii. 1 [1720].

by which their chief Sages were best distinguished, was a certain Position of Countenance, which gave undoubted Intelligence to what Degree or Proportion, the Spirit agitated the inward Mass. For, after certain Gripings, the *Wind* and Vapours issuing forth; having first by their Turbulence and Convulsions within, caused an Earthquake in Man's little World;[1] distorted the Mouth, bloated the Cheeks, and gave the Eyes a terrible kind of *Relievo*.[2] At which Junctures, all their *Belches* were received for Sacred, the Sourer the better, and swallowed with infinite Consolation by their meager Devotees.[3] And to render these yet more compleat, because the Breath of Man's Life is in his Nostrils, therefore, the choicest, most edifying, and most enlivening *Belches*, were very wisely conveyed thro' that Vehicle, to give them a Tincture as they passed.

THEIR Gods were the four *Winds*, whom they worshipped, as the Spirits that pervade and enliven the Universe, and as those from whom alone all *Inspiration* can properly be said to proceed. However, the Chief of these, to whom they performed the Adoration of *Latria*,[4] was the *Almighty-North*.[5] An antient Deity, whom the Inhabitants of *Megalopolis* in *Greece*, had likewise in highest Reverence. **Omnium Deorum Boream maxime celebrant.*[6] This God, tho' endued with Ubiquity, was

* *Pausan.* L. 8.

---

[1] Microcosm; cf. p. 78.

[2] This alludes to the grimaces and contorsions usual among inspired Teachers, and their tone in speaking through the nose [1720].

[3] 'Devotes' edd. 1, 2.

[4] λατρεία, divine worship.

[5] The more zealous sectaries were the presbyterians of the Scottish discipline [Scott].

See Masson's note on *Paradise Lost*, v. 688–9: 'The notion of the north parts of Heaven as the seat of the angelic rebellion was a theologico-poetic tradition, founded perhaps on Isaiah xiv. 12, 13.' See also the *Jewish Encyclopaedia*, s.v. *Earth (Four Quarters)*.

[6] Pausanias, viii. xxxvi. 6.

yet supposed by the profounder *Æolists*, to possess one peculiar Habitation, or (to speak in Form) a *Cælum Empyræum*, wherein he was more intimately present. This was situated in a certain Region, well known to the Antient *Greeks*, by them called Σκοτία,[1] or the *Land of Darkness*. And altho' many Controversies have arisen upon that Matter; yet so much is undisputed, that from a Region of the *like Denomination*,[2] the most refined *Æolists* have borrowed their Original, from whence, in every Age, the zealous among their Priesthood, have brought over their choicest *Inspiration*, fetching it with their own Hands, from the Fountain Head, in certain *Bladders*, and disploding[3] it among the Sectaries in all Nations, who did, and do, and ever will, daily Gasp and Pant after it.

NOW, their Mysteries and Rites were performed in this Manner. 'Tis well known among the Learned, that the Virtuoso's of former Ages, had a Contrivance for carrying and preserving *Winds* in Casks or Barrels,[4] which was of great Assistance upon long Sea Voyages; and the Loss of so useful an Art at present, is very much to be lamented, tho' I know not how, with great Negligence omitted by *Pancirollus*.[5] It was an Inven-

---

* *An Author who writ* De Artibus Perditis, &c. *of Arts lost, and of Arts invented.*

[1] Diodorus Siculus, i. 96.
Darkness, or Scotland [*MS. Pate*].

[2] Our Dissenters in England, who pretend to a much larger share of the Spirit, than those of the establisht Church, own the Kirk of Scotland for their Mother Church, where the Gospel shines in its greatest purity and lustre [1720].
Our Dissenters . . . Gospel,

they say, shines . . . lustre. For this reason they send most of their young men to study there [1734].

[3] Cf. *Paradise Lost*, vi. 605:
In posture to displode their second tire
Of thunder.

[4] *Odyssey*, x. 19 sqq.

[5] Swift refers to Guido Panciroli (1523–99), who wrote *Rerum memorabilium jam olim deperditarum libri II* (1599). The first

tion ascribed to *Æolus* himself, from whom this Sect is denominated, and who in Honour of their Founder's Memory, have to this Day preserved great Numbers of those *Barrels*,[1] whereof they fix one in each of their Temples, first beating out the Top; into this *Barrel*, upon Solemn Days, the Priest enters; where, having before duly prepared himself by the methods already described, a secret Funnel[2] is also convey'd from his Posteriors, to the Bottom of the Barrel, which admits new Supplies of Inspiration from a *Northern* Chink or Crany. Whereupon, you behold him swell immediately to the Shape and Size of his *Vessel*. In this Posture he disembogues whole Tempests upon his Auditory, as the Spirit from beneath gives him Utterance; which issuing *ex adytis*, and *penetralibus*,[3] is not performed without much Pain and Gripings. And the *Wind* in breaking forth, *deals with his Face, as it does with that of the Sea; first *blackning*, then *wrinkling*, and at last, *bursting it into a Foam*. It is in this Guise, the Sacred *Æolist* delivers his oracular *Belches* to his panting Disciples; Of whom, some are greedily gaping after the sanctified Breath; others are all the while hymning out the Praises of the *Winds*; and gently wafted to and fro by their own Humming, do thus represent the soft Breezes of their Deities appeased.

I T is from this Custom of the Priests, that some Authors maintain these *Æolists*, to have been very

* *This is an exact Description of the Changes made in the Face by Enthusiastick Preachers.*

book deals with the arts and inventions known to the ancients but since lost; the second, with the inventions of the moderns.

[1] See Plate 2.

Many Dissenters, affecting extraordinary plainness and simplicity, have their Pulpits of a figure not unlike a barrel or tub [1720].

[2] Such funnels were formerly used in the Temple of Delphos, as is further explained in the following paragraph. [1720].

[3] Cf. Virgil, *Aen.* ii. 297.

antient in the World. Because, the Delivery of their Mysteries, which I have just now mention'd, appears exactly the same with that of other antient Oracles,[1] whose Inspirations were owing to certain subterraneous *Effluviums* of *Wind*, delivered with the *same*[2] Pain to the Priest, and much about the *same* Influence on the People. It is true indeed, that these were frequently managed and directed by *Female* Officers, whose Organs were understood to be better disposed for the Admission of those Oracular *Gusts*, as entring and passing up thro' a Receptacle of greater Capacity, and causing also a Pruriency by the Way, such as with due Management, hath been refined from a[3] Carnal, into a Spiritual Extasie. And to strengthen this profound Conjecture, it is farther insisted, that this Custom of *Female Priests is kept up still in certain refined Colleges of our *Modern Æolists*, who are agreed to receive their Inspiration, derived thro' the Receptacle aforesaid, like their Ancestors, the *Sibyls*.[4]

AND, whereas the mind of Man, when he gives the Spur and Bridle to his Thoughts, doth never stop, but naturally sallies out into both extreams of High and Low, of Good and Evil; His first Flight of Fancy, commonly transports Him to Idea's of what is most Perfect, finished, and exalted; till having soared out of his own Reach and Sight, not well perceiving how near the

* *Quakers who suffer their Women to preach and pray.*

[1] Cf. Temple, *Thoughts upon Reviewing the Essay of Antient and Modern Learning* (1701), pp. 218–19: 'In this they [the advocates of the moderns] discover their deep Knowledge of Antiquity, taking the Oracle of *Delphos* to have been managed by some frantick or fanatick Wenches; whereas the *Pythia's* there, were only Engines managed by the Priests of *Delphos*, who . . . were a Colledge or Society of wise and learned Men, in all sorts of Sciences.'

[2] '*same*' edd. 1, 2; 'same' edd. 3–5.

[3] 'a Carnal' ed. 1; 'Carnal' edd. 2–5.

[4] '*Sybils*' edd. 1, 2.

Frontiers of Height and Depth, border upon each
other; With the same Course and Wing, he falls down
plum into the lowest Bottom of Things; like one who
travels the *East* into the *West*; or like a strait Line
drawn by its own Length into a Circle.[1] Whether
a Tincture of Malice in our Natures, makes us fond of
furnishing every bright Idea with its Reverse; Or,
whether Reason reflecting upon the Sum of Things,
can, like the Sun, serve only to enlighten one half of
the Globe, leaving the other half, by Necessity, under
Shade and Darkness: Or, whether Fancy, flying up to
the imagination of what is Highest and Best, becomes
over-shot,[2] and spent, and weary, and suddenly falls
like a dead Bird of Paradise, to the Ground.[3] Or, whether
after all these *Metaphysical* Conjectures, I have not entirely missed the true Reason; The Proposition, however, which hath stood me in so much Circumstance, is
altogether true; That, as the most unciviliz'd Parts
of Mankind, have some way or other, climbed up into
the Conception of a *God*, or Supream Power, so they
have seldom forgot to provide their Fears with certain
ghastly Notions, which instead of better, have served
them pretty tolerably for a *Devil*. And this Proceeding
seems to be natural enough; For it is with Men, whose
Imaginations are lifted up very high, after the same
Rate, as with those, whose Bodies are so; that, as they
are delighted with the Advantage of a nearer Contemplation upwards, so they are equally terrified with
the dismal Prospect of the Precipice below. Thus, in

[1] Cf. Marvell, *The Rehearsal Transpros'd* (1672), p. 206: 'as a streight line continued grows a Circle'.

[2] 'over-shot' ed. 1; 'over-short' edd. 2–5.

[3] It was an ancient belief that birds of paradise had no feet, but always continued on the wing until their death [Scott].

The belief that they had no feet is said to have arisen from the way in which their skins were prepared for export.

the Choice of a *Devil*, it hath been the usual Method of Mankind, to single out some Being, either in Act, or in Vision, which was in most Antipathy to the God they had framed. Thus also the Sect of *Æolists*, possessed themselves with a Dread, and Horror, and Hatred of two Malignant Natures, betwixt whom, and the Deities they adored, perpetual Enmity was established. The first of these, was the **Camelion*, sworn Foe to *Inspiration*,[1] who in Scorn, devoured large Influences of their

* *I do not well understand what the Author aims at here, any more than by the terrible Monster, mention'd in the following Lines, called* Moulinavent, *which is the* French *Word for a Windmill.*

[1] The chameleon, according to the popular belief, lived on air. Cf. *Hamlet*, iii. ii. 98; and see Sir Thomas Browne, *Vulgar Errors*, bk. iii, chap. 21.

The author seems to mean latitudinarians, persons too indifferent to religion, either to object to, or to receive with interest, any modification of its doctrines [Scott].

The worshippers of wind or air found their evil spirits in the chameleon, by which it was eaten, and the windmill, Moulin-à-vent, by whose four hands it was beaten [Henry Morley].

Scott's interpretation is inadequate, and Morley's note avoids the allegory.

A resolute attempt to solve the problem was made by Barrett in his *Essay on the Earlier Part of the Life of Swift* (1808). What follows is the substance of his solution (pp. 34–35): 'By Camelion and Moulinavent are understood Church and State; that is, the Episcopal Church of England by law established, and the Monarchy. Against these two all Æolists (that is, sectaries of every description) have ever opposed themselves. Moulinavent has four arms; these are the four sceptres (of England, Scotland, France, and Ireland), issuing from the centre of the coin, and including the arms of those kingdoms. A windmill is a proper image of a State or Monarchy, whose condition is subject to many vicissitudes. An animal that lives upon air, and refunds no part of it by eructation, is the image of the Church of England, whose articles acknowledge the inspiration of the Holy Scripture, while its members make no pretences to inspiration in themselves; and having a set form of prayer they do not make use of extemporaneous praying and preaching, here called Eructations. Further the camelion would

God; without refunding the smallest Blast by *Eructa-tion*. The other was a huge terrible Monster, called *Moulinavent*, who with four strong Arms, waged eternal Battel with all their Divinities, dextrously turning to avoid their Blows, and repay them with Interest.

THUS furnisht, and set out with *Gods*, as well as *Devils*, was the renowned Sect of *Æolists*; which makes at this Day so illustrious a Figure in the World, and whereof, that Polite Nation of *Laplanders*, are beyond all Doubt, a most Authentick Branch; Of whom, I therefore cannot, without Injustice, here omit to make honourable Mention; since they appear to be so closely allied in Point of Interest, as well as Inclinations, with their Brother *Æolists* among Us, as not only to buy their *Winds* by wholesale from the *same* Merchants, but also to retail them after the *same* Rate and Method, and to Customers much alike.[1]

represent the ecclesiastics who exist on the promises of the great, and rise to power by complying with their variable humours.'

Yet the reader may still say 'I do not well understand what the Author aims at here'. This footnote, added in 1710, was in all probability written by Swift himself. See p. xxv.

In the second edition of his Swift (1824, vol. i, p. 84), after remarking that Swift's annotators have sometimes overstrained the allegory, Scott said that this passage appears to mean nothing more than that the fanatics 'spent their time in combating imaginary spiritual obstacles to their salvation, as the distempered imagination of Don Quixote converted windmills into giants'.

[1] See Olaus Magnus, *De Gentibus Septentrionalibus* (Rome, 1555), iii, chap. 16; *The History of Lapland* . . . by John Scheffer . . . Oxford, 1674, p. 58 (a translation from the Latin); and another translation of Scheffer's book, published in 1704, pp. 151–2.

Cf. *Hudibras*, ii. ii. 343–4:
And sell their blasts of wind as dear
As Lapland witches bottled air.
Cf. also Thomas Heywood, *The Hierarchie of the blessed Angells* (1635), bk. 8, p. 506:
The Finnes and Laplands are acquainted well
With such like Sp'rits, and Windes to Merchants sell, *etc.*

NOW, whether the System here delivered, was wholly compiled by *Jack*, or, as some Writers believe, rather copied from the Original at *Delphos*,[1] with certain Additions and Emendations suited to Times and Circumstances, I shall not absolutely determine. This I may affirm, that *Jack* gave it at least a new Turn, and formed it into the same Dress and Model, as it lies deduced by me.

I have long sought after this Opportunity, of doing Justice to a Society of Men, for whom I have a peculiar Honour, and whose Opinions, as well as Practices, have been extreamly misrepresented, and traduced by the Malice or Ignorance of their Adversaries. For, I think it one of the greatest, and best of humane Actions, to remove Prejudices, and place Things in their truest and fairest Light; which I therefore boldly undertake without any Regards of my own, beside the Conscience, the Honour, and the Thanks.

[1] i.e. Delphi: the form Delphos was the subject of much contention in the Phalaris controversy. Temple used it in his *Essay on Ancient and Modern Learning* (1690); Wotton corrected him in the second edition of his *Reflections* (1697), p. 59; Boyle defended Temple on the ground that *Delphos* is good English (*Examination*, 1698, pp. 96–97); Bentley replied in his *Dissertation* (1699, Preface, pp. xc–xciii), and proved that *Delphos* is a blunder.

Swift could not have used the correct form (even if he had wished to) without admitting that Temple was wrong.

In the course of the argument several English authors were quoted, but neither Shakespeare nor Milton was referred to, though both use the form *Delphos* (*Winter's Tale*, ii. i. 182; *Hymn on the Nativity*, 178; *Paradise Regained*, i. 458).

Similarly *Colchos* (p. 111, l. 1)—found also in Prior's poem 'On the Coronation'—is a late survival of the spelling in Chaucer and Gower, in Golding's *Ovid*, and in *The Merchant of Venice*, i. i. 171. Cooper's Latin dictionary (1565) has *Colchis*, as also Sandys's *Ovid*.

SECT. IX.

A Digression concerning the Original, the Use and Improvement of Madness *in a Commonwealth.*

NOR shall it any ways detract from the just Reputation of this famous Sect, that its Rise and Institution are owing to such an Author as I have described *Jack* to be; A Person whose Intellectuals were overturned, and his Brain shaken out of its Natural Position; which we commonly suppose to be a Distemper, and call by the Name of *Madness* or *Phrenzy.*[1] For, if we take a Survey of the greatest Actions that have been performed in the World, under the Influence of Single Men; which are, *The Establishment of New Empires by Conquest: The Advance and Progress of New Schemes in Philosophy; and the contriving, as well as the propagating of New Religions:* We shall find the Authors of them all, to have been Persons, whose natural Reason hath admitted great Revolutions from their Dyet, their Education, the Prevalency of some certain Temper, together with the particular Influence of Air and Climate. Besides, there is something Individual in human Minds, that easily kindles at the accidental Approach and Collision of certain Circumstances, which tho' of paltry and mean Appearance, do often flame out into the greatest Emergencies of Life. For great Turns are not always given by strong Hands, but by lucky Adaption, and at proper Seasons; and it is of no import, where the

---

[1] Credite mihi, anathymiasis si in cerebrum est [*lege* it], in toto corpore fluctum facit. Trimalchio apud Petronium.—ἀναθυμίασις vapor est & exhalatio, quae hic de ventris flatibus intelligenda [*MS. Pate*].

For the quotation see Petronius, cap. 47. The comment explaining ἀναθυμίασις is by Scheffer; see ed. Burman, 1709, p. 238.

Fire was kindled, if the Vapor has once got up into the Brain. For the *upper Region* of Man, is furnished like the *middle Region* of the Air; The Materials are formed from Causes of the widest Difference, yet produce at last the same Substance and Effect. Mists arise from the Earth, Steams from Dunghils, Exhalations from the Sea, and Smoak from Fire; yet all Clouds are the same in Composition, as well as Consequences: and the Fumes issuing from a Jakes, will furnish as comely and useful a Vapor, as Incense from an Altar. Thus far, I suppose will easily be granted me; and then it will follow, that as the Face of Nature never produces Rain, but when it is overcast and disturbed, so Human Understanding, seated in the Brain, must be troubled and overspread by Vapours, ascending from the lower Faculties, to water the Invention, and render it fruitful. Now, altho' these Vapours (as it hath been already said) are of as various Original, as those of the Skies, yet the Crop they produce, differs[1] both in Kind and Degree, meerly according to the Soil. I will produce two Instances to prove and Explain what I am now advancing.

*A certain Great Prince[2] raised a mighty Army, filled his Coffers with infinite Treasures, provided an invincible Fleet, and all this, without giving the least Part of his Design to his greatest Ministers, or his nearest Favourites. Immediately the whole World was alarmed; the neighbouring Crowns, in trembling Expectation,[3] towards what Point the Storm would burst; the small

* *This was* Harry *the Great of* France.

[1] 'differs' edd. 1–4; 'differ' ed. 5. Hawkesworth reads 'crops . . . differ'.

[2] K. Henry IV of France; who was assassinated by Ravillac [1720]. Swift based this passage on Mezeray's *Abrégé de l'histoire de France*, 1696, vi, pp. 368 ff. See H. Teerink, 'A Source-book . . . from Swift's own Library', *The Irish Book Lover*, October 1949, pp. 59–62.

[3] 'Expectation' edd. 1–3; 'Expectations' edd. 4, 5.

Politicians, every where forming profound Conjectures. Some believed he had laid a Scheme for Universal Monarchy: Others, after much Insight, determined the Matter to be a Project for pulling down the *Pope*, and setting up the *Reformed* Religion, which had once been his own. Some, again, of a deeper Sagacity, sent him into *Asia* to subdue the *Turk*, and recover *Palestine*. In the midst of all these Projects and Preparations; a certain *State-Surgeon*, gathering the Nature of the Disease by these Symptoms, attempted the Cure, at one Blow performed the Operation, broke the Bag, and out flew the *Vapour*; nor did any thing want to render it a compleat Remedy, only, that the Prince unfortunately happened to Die in the Performance. Now, is the Reader exceeding curious to learn, from whence this *Vapour* took its Rise, which had so long set the Nations at a Gaze? What secret Wheel, what hidden Spring could put into Motion so wonderful an Engine? It was afterwards discovered, that the Movement of this whole Machine had been directed by an absent *Female*, whose Eyes had raised a Protuberancy, and before Emission, she was removed into an Enemy's Country. What should an unhappy Prince do in such ticklish Circumstances as these? He tried in vain the Poet's neverfailing Receipt of *Corpora quæque*;[1] For,

> *Idque petit corpus mens unde est saucia amore;*
> *Unde feritur, eo tendit, gestitq; coire.* Lucr.[2]

HAVING to no purpose used all peaceable Endeavours, the collected part of the *Semen*, raised and enflamed, became adust, converted to Choler, turned head[3]

* Ravillac, *who stabb'd* Henry *the Great in his Coach.*

[1] Lucretius, iv. 1065.
[2] Lucretius, iv. 1048 and 1055.
[3] *To turn head*, to turn and face an enemy, opposite of *to turn tail*: cf. Shakespeare, *1 Henry IV*, iii. ii. 102.

upon the spinal Duct, and ascended to the Brain. The very same Principle that influences a *Bully* to break the Windows of a Whore, who has jilted him, naturally stirs up a Great Prince to raise mighty Armies, and dream nothing but Sieges, Battles, and Victories.

——*Teterrima belli*
   Causa ——————[1]

THE other *Instance is, what I have read some-where, in a very antient Author, of a mighty King,[2] who for the space of above thirty Years, amused him-self to take and lose[3] Towns; beat Armies, and be beaten; drive Princes out of their Dominions; fright Children from their Bread and Butter; burn, lay waste, plunder, dragoon,[4] massacre Subject and Stranger, Friend and Foe, Male and Female. 'Tis recorded, that the Philosophers of each Country were in grave Dispute, upon Causes Natural, Moral, and Political, to find out where they should assign an original Solution of this *Phænomenon*. At last the *Vapour* or *Spirit*, which ani-mated the Hero's Brain, being in perpetual Circulation, seized upon that Region of the[5] Human Body, so re-nown'd for furnishing the †*Zibeta Occidentalis*,[6] and gathering there into a Tumor, left the rest of the World for that Time in Peace. Of such mighty Consequence

* *This is meant of the Present French King.*

† *Paracelsus, who was so famous for Chymistry, try'd an Experiment upon human Excrement, to make a Perfume of it, which when he had brought to Perfection, he called* Zibeta Occidentalis, *or* Western-Civet, *the back Parts of Man (according to his Division mention'd by the Author, page 160[7],) being the* West.

[1] Horace, *Sat.* i. iii. 107. Edd. 1–4 read 'Cunnus teterrima belli Causa'.

[2] Lewis XIV [1720]. Lewis XIV was cut of a *Fistula in ano* [1734]. See Michelet, *Histoire de France*, vol. xv, ch. xxiv (1686).

[3] 'lose' ed. 1; 'loose' edd. 2–5.

[4] See p. 122, note 1.

[5] 'the' omitted edd. 1–5.

[6] See Appendix F, p. 358.

[7] Page 152 of this edition.

it is, where those Exhalations fix; and of so little, from whence they proceed. The same Spirits which in their superior Progress would conquer a Kingdom, descending upon the *Anus*, conclude in a *Fistula*.

LET us next examine the great Introducers of new Schemes in Philosophy, and search till we can find, from what Faculty of the Soul the Disposition arises in mortal Man, of taking it into his Head, to advance new Systems with such an eager Zeal, in things agreed on all hands impossible to be known: from what Seeds this Disposition springs, and to what Quality of human Nature these Grand Innovators have been indebted for their Number of Disciples. Because, it is plain, that several of the chief among them, both *Antient* and *Modern*, were usually mistaken by their Adversaries, and indeed, by all, except their own Followers, to have been Persons Crazed, or out of their Wits, having generally proceeded in the common Course of their Words and Actions, by a Method very different from the vulgar Dictates of *unrefined* Reason: agreeing for the most Part in their several Models, with their present undoubted Successors in the *Academy* of *Modern Bedlam* (whose Merits and Principles I shall farther examine in due Place.) Of this Kind were *Epicurus, Diogenes, Apollonius,*[1] *Lucretius, Paracelsus, Des Cartes,* and others; who, if they were now in the World, tied fast, and separate from their Followers, would in this our undistinguishing Age, incur manifest Danger of *Phlebotomy*, and *Whips*, and *Chains*, and *dark Chambers*, and *Straw*. For, what Man in the natural State, or Course of Thinking, did ever conceive it in his Power, to reduce the Notions of all Mankind, exactly to the same Length, and Breadth, and Height[2] of his own? Yet

---

[1] Apollonius of Tyana. Cf. *Hudibras*, ii. iii. 656.

[2] 'Height' edd. 1, 2; 'Heighth' edd. 3–5, an old spelling attributable to the printer, perhaps induced by 'Breadth'.

this is the first humble and civil Design of all Innovators in the Empire of Reason. *Epicurus* modestly hoped, that one Time or other, a certain Fortuitous Concourse of all Mens Opinions, after perpetual Justlings, the Sharp with the Smooth, the Light and the Heavy, the Round and the Square, would by certain *Clinamina*,[1] unite in the Notions of *Atoms* and *Void*, as these did in the Originals of all Things. *Cartesius* reckoned to see before he died, the Sentiments of all Philosophers, like so many lesser Stars in his *Romantick* System, rapt and drawn within his own *Vortex*. Now, I would gladly be informed, how it is possible to account for such Imaginations as these in particular Men, without Recourse to my *Phænomenon* of *Vapours*, ascending from the lower Faculties to over-shadow the Brain, and thence[2] distilling into Conceptions, for which the Narrowness of our Mother-Tongue has not yet assigned any other Name, besides that of *Madness* or *Phrenzy*. Let us therefore now conjecture how it comes to pass, that none of these great Prescribers, do ever fail providing themselves and their Notions, with a Number of implicite Disciples. And, I think, the Reason is easie to be assigned: For, there is a peculiar *String* in the Harmony of Human Understanding, which in several individuals is exactly of the same Tuning. This, if you can dexterously screw up to its right Key, and then strike gently upon it; Whenever you have the Good Fortune to light among those of the same Pitch, they will by a secret necessary Sympathy, strike exactly at the same time.[3] And in this one Circumstance, lies all the Skill

---

[1] *Clinamen* is the word used by Lucretius [ii. 292] to represent the κλίσις of Epicurus, the bias or deviation from a straight line which was supposed to explain the concourse of atoms.

[2] 'thence' ed. 1; 'their' edd. 2–4; 'there' ed. 5.

[3] Cf. Sir Thomas Browne, *Vulgar Errors*, bk. vii, chap. 18, *ad fin.*

or Luck of the Matter; for if you chance to jar the String among those who are either above or below your own Height, instead of subscribing to your Doctrine, they will tie you fast, call you Mad, and feed you with Bread and Water. It is therefore a Point of the nicest Conduct to distinguish and adapt this noble Talent, with respect to the Differences of Persons and of Times. *Cicero* understood this very well, when writing to a Friend in *England*, with a Caution, among other Matters, to beware of being cheated by our *Hackney-Coachmen* (who, it seems, in those days, were as arrant Rascals as they are now) has these remarkable Words. **Est quod gaudeas te in ista loca venisse, ubi aliquid sapere viderere.*[1] For, to speak a bold Truth, it is a fatal Miscarriage, so ill to order Affairs, as to pass for a *Fool* in one Company, when in another you might be treated as a *Philosopher*. Which I desire *some certain Gentlemen of my Acquain-*

* *Epist. ad Fam. Trebatio.*

[1] 'The excellent Translator of Cicero's Familiar Letters observes that Swift has applied a passage in them, *with more humour*, perhaps, *than it was at first conceived.* And yet half the application is founded on a false fact. "In the Tale of a Tub", he says, "*Cicero*, writing to his friend Trebatius in England, with a caution, among other matters, to beware of being cheated by our hackney-coachmen . . . has these very remarkable words, *Est quod gaudeas te in ista loca venisse, ubi aliquid sapere viderere.*" Ep. Fam. vii. 10. Would any one think now, that the very next words in *Cicero* shew, that Trebatius did NOT GO into England? And yet it follows, *With how much greater advantage would your*

noble talents have appeared, HAD YOU GONE *into* BRITAIN! W.B.'

This note appears in Nichols's edition of Swift's *Works* (1808), vol. ii, p. 326.

'W.B.' is William Bowyer, the printer, Nichols's senior partner; and the 'excellent Translator' is William Melmoth. The note to which Bowyer refers is in *The Letters of Cicero*, 1753, vol. i, pp. 149, 150.

Swift's 'Hackney-Coachmen' represent Cicero's 'charioteers' (*Ep. Fam.* vii. 6). The quotation is not from the same but from a subsequent letter (*Ep. Fam.* vii. 10). When Cicero wrote to him, Trebatius was not in England, but in Gaul.

tance, to lay up in their Hearts, as a very seasonable *Innuendo*.[1]

THIS, indeed, was the Fatal Mistake of that worthy Gentleman, my most ingenious Friend, Mr. *W-tt-n:* A Person, in appearance ordain'd for great Designs, as well as Performances; whether you will consider his *Notions* or his *Looks*. Surely, no Man ever advanced into the Publick, with fitter Qualifications of Body and Mind, for the Propagation of a new Religion. Oh, had those happy Talents misapplied to vain Philosophy, been turned into their proper Channels of *Dreams* and *Visions*, where *Distortion* of Mind and Countenance, are of such Sovereign Use; the base detracting World would not then have dared to report, that something is amiss, that his Brain hath undergone an unlucky Shake; which even his Brother *Modernists* themselves, like Ungrates, do whisper so loud, that it reaches up to the very Garret I am now writing in.[2]

LASTLY, Whoever[3] pleases to look into the Fountains of *Enthusiasm*, from whence, in all Ages, have eternally proceeded such fatning Streams, will find the Spring Head to have been as *troubled* and *muddy* as the Current; Of such great Emolument, is a Tincture of this *Vapour*, which the World calls *Madness*, that without its Help, the World would not only be deprived of those two great Blessings, *Conquests* and *Systems*, but even all Mankind would unhappily[4] be reduced to the same Belief in Things Invisible. Now, the former *Postulatum* being held, that it is of no Import from what Originals this *Vapour* proceeds, but either in what *Angles* it strikes and spreads over the Understanding, or upon what *Species* of Brain it ascends; It will be a very delicate Point, to cut the Feather,[5] and divide the

[1] See p. 114, note 2.

[2] '*Garrat* I am writing in' ed. 1.

[3] 'Whosoever' edd. 3–5.

[4] 'happily' edd. 4, 5.

[5] i.e. to make fine distinctions, to 'split hairs'.

several Reasons to a Nice and Curious Reader, how this numerical Difference in the Brain, can produce Effects of so vast a Difference from the same *Vapour*,[1] as to be the sole Point of Individuation[2] between *Alexander the Great*, *Jack of Leyden*,[3] and Monsieur *Des Cartes*. The present Argument is the most abstracted that ever I engaged in, it strains my Faculties to their highest Stretch; and I desire the Reader to attend with utmost Perpensity; For, I now proceed to unravel this knotty Point.

* THERE is in Mankind a certain*   *   *
*   *   *   *   *   *   *   *

Hic multa   *   *   *   *   *   *
desiderantur.
                *   *   *   *   *   *

*   *   *   *   *   *   *   *   *

*   *   *   And this I take to be a clear Solution of the Matter.

HAVING therefore so narrowly past thro' this intricate Difficulty, the Reader will, I am sure, agree with me in the Conclusion; that if the *Moderns* mean

* *Here is another Defect in the Manuscript, but I think the Author did wisely, and that the Matter which thus strained his Faculties, was not worth a Solution; and it were well if all Metaphysical Cobweb Problems were no otherwise answered.*

[1] How the same nerves are fashion'd to sustain
   The greatest pleasure, and the greatest pain.
                        GARTH. [*MS. Pate*].
The couplet is quoted from *The Dispensary*, canto I, ll. 38–39.
[2] In scholastic philosophy, *individuatio* is the process leading to individual existence, as distinct from that of the species.
[3] Johann Bockholdt, a tailor of Leyden, the leader in the final struggle of Anabaptist communism. In Münster, of which the Anabaptists gained complete possession, he was crowned king of the 'New Jerusalem', under the title of John of Leyden. The town was retaken on 24 June 1535, and in January 1536 'Jack of Leyden' was executed. See also the *Mechanical Operation of the Spirit*, p. 288.

by *Madness*, only a Disturbance or Transposition of the
Brain, by Force of certain *Vapours* issuing up from the
lower Faculties; Then has this *Madness* been the Parent
of all those mighty Revolutions, that have happened in
Empire, in *Philosophy*, and in *Religion*. For, the Brain,
in its natural Position and State of Serenity, disposeth
its Owner to pass his Life in the common Forms,
without any Thought of subduing Multitudes to his
own *Power*, his *Reasons* or his *Visions*; and the more
he shapes his Understanding by the Pattern of Human
Learning, the less he is inclined to form Parties after
his particular Notions; because that instructs him in his
private Infirmities, as well as in the stubborn Ignorance
of the People. But when a Man's Fancy gets *astride*
on his Reason, when Imagination is at Cuffs with the
Senses, and common Understanding, as well as common Sense, is Kickt out of Doors; the first Proselyte he
makes, is Himself, and when that is once compass'd,
the Difficulty is not so great in bringing over others;
A strong Delusion always operating from *without*, as
vigorously as from *within*. For, Cant[1] and Vision[2] are
to the Ear and the Eye, the same that Tickling is to
the Touch. Those Entertainments and Pleasures we
most value in Life, are such as *Dupe* and play the Wag
with the Senses. For, if we take an Examination of what
is generally understood by *Happiness*, as it has Respect,
either to the Understanding or the Senses, we shall find
all its Properties and Adjuncts will herd under this
short Definition: That, *it is a perpetual Possession of
being well Deceived.*[3] And first, with Relation to the

---

[1] See the passage on 'canting' in the *Mechanical Operation*, p. 280; and compare the definition and the popular (but erroneous) derivation given by Steele in *The Spectator*, No. 147.

[2] In *Thoughts on Various Subjects* Swift says that 'Vision is the art of seeing things invisible'.

[3] Swift is thought by Sir Henry Craik to have had in his mind the passage in Horace (*Ep.* ii. ii. 140)

Mind or Understanding; 'tis manifest, what mighty
Advantages Fiction has over Truth; and the Reason is
just at our Elbow; because Imagination can build nobler
Scenes, and produce more wonderful Revolutions than
Fortune or Nature will be at Expence to furnish.[1] Nor
is Mankind so much to blame in his Choice, thus deter-
mining him, if we consider that the Debate meerly lies
between *Things past*, and *Things conceived*; and so the
Question is only this; Whether Things that have Place
in the *Imagination*, may not as properly be said to *Exist*,
as those that are seated in the *Memory*; which may be
justly held in the Affirmative, and very much to the
Advantage of the former, since This is acknowledged to
be the *Womb* of Things, and the other allowed to be no
more than the *Grave*. Again, if we take this Definition
of Happiness, and examine it with Reference to the
Senses, it will be acknowledged wonderfully adapt. How
fade[2] and insipid do all Objects accost us that are not
convey'd in the Vehicle of *Delusion?* How shrunk is
every Thing, as it appears in the Glass of Nature? So,
that if it were not for the Assistance of Artificial *Mediums*,
false Lights, refracted Angles, Varnish, and Tinsel;
there would be a mighty Level in the Felicity and En-
joyments of Mortal Men.[3] If this were seriously considered by the World, as I have a certain Reason to
suspect it hardly will; Men would no longer reckon
among their high Points of Wisdom, the Art of exposing
weak Sides, and publishing Infirmities; an Employment
in my Opinion, neither better nor worse than that of

where the Argive citizen regrets
having been cured of his *mentis
gratissimus error*. But the idea was
too real to Swift to be derived
from any book. And it is common;
compare, for example, Prior's
verses 'To Charles Montague'.

[1] Cf. Bacon, *Advancement of
Learning*, bk. ii. iv. 2.
[2] 'fade' edd. 1, 2; 'fading' edd.
3–5. Cf. Swift's poem 'To Mr.
Congreve', l. 212.
[3] Cf. Bacon, *Essayes*, 'Of
Truth'.

Unmasking, which I think, has never been allowed fair
Usage, either in the *World* or the *Play-House*.

IN the Proportion that Credulity is a more peaceful
Possession of the Mind, than Curiosity, so far preferable
is that Wisdom, which converses about the Surface, to
that pretended Philosophy which enters into the Depth
of Things, and then comes gravely back with Informations and Discoveries, that in the inside they are good
for nothing. The two Senses, to which all Objects first
address themselves, are the Sight and the Touch; These
never examine farther than the Colour, the Shape, the
Size, and whatever other Qualities dwell, or are drawn
by Art upon the Outward of Bodies; and then comes
Reason officiously, with Tools for cutting, and opening,
and mangling, and piercing, offering to demonstrate,
that they are not of the same consistence quite thro'.
Now, I take all this to be the last Degree of perverting
Nature: one of whose Eternal Laws it is, to put her best
Furniture forward. And therefore, in order to save the
Charges of all such expensive Anatomy for the Time to
come; I do here think fit to inform the Reader, that in
such Conclusions as these, Reason is certainly in the
Right; and that in most Corporeal Beings, which have
fallen under my Cognizance, the *Outside* hath been
infinitely preferable to the *In:*[1] Whereof I have been
farther convinced from some late Experiments. Last
Week I saw a Woman *flay'd*, and you will hardly believe,
how much it altered her Person for the worse. Yesterday
I ordered the Carcass of a *Beau* to be stript in my
Presence; when we were all amazed to find so many
unsuspected Faults under one Suit of Cloaths: Then
I laid open his *Brain*, his *Heart*, and his *Spleen*; But,
I plainly perceived at every Operation, that the farther
we proceeded, we found the Defects encrease upon us

---

[1] '*Inn*' ed. 5.

in Number and Bulk: from all which, I justly formed this Conclusion to my self; That whatever Philosopher or Projector can find out an Art to sodder and patch up the Flaws and Imperfections of Nature, will deserve much better of Mankind, and teach us a more useful Science, than that so much in present Esteem, of widening and exposing them (like him who held *Anatomy* to be the ultimate End of *Physick*.) And he, whose Fortunes and Dispositions have placed him in a convenient Station to enjoy the Fruits of this noble Art; He that can with *Epicurus* content his Ideas with the *Films* and *Images* that fly off upon his Senses from the *Superficies* of Things; Such a Man truly wise, creams off Nature, leaving the Sower and the Dregs, for Philosophy and Reason to lap up. This is the sublime and refined Point of Felicity, called, *the Possession of being well deceived*; The Serene Peaceful State of being a Fool among Knaves.

BUT to return to *Madness*. It is certain, that according to the System I have above deduced; every *Species* thereof proceeds from a Redundancy of *Vapour*;[1] therefore, as some Kinds of *Phrenzy* give double Strength to the Sinews, so there are of other *Species*, which add Vigor, and Life, and Spirit to the Brain: Now, it usually happens, that these active Spirits, getting Possession of the Brain, resemble those that haunt other waste and empty Dwellings, which for want of Business, either vanish, and carry away a Piece of the House, or else stay at home and fling it all out of the Windows. By which are mystically display'd the two principal Branches of *Madness*, and which some Philosophers not considering so well as I, have mistook to be different in their Causes, over-hastily assigning the first to Deficiency, and the other to Redundance.

---

[1] *'Vapor'* edd. 1–3; *'Vapour'* ed. 4; *'Vapours'* ed. 5.

I think it therefore manifest, from what I have here advanced, that the main Point of Skill and Address, is to furnish Employment for this Redundancy of *Vapour*, and prudently to adjust the Seasons[1] of it; by which means it may certainly become of Cardinal and Catholick Emolument in a Commonwealth. Thus one Man chusing a proper Juncture, leaps into a Gulph,[2] from thence[3] proceeds a Hero, and is called the Saver of his Country; Another atchieves the same Enterprise,[4] but unluckily timing it, has left the Brand of *Madness*, fixt as a Reproach upon his Memory; Upon so nice a Distinction are we taught to repeat the Name of *Curtius* with Reverence and Love; that of *Empedocles*, with Hatred and Contempt. Thus, also it is usually conceived, that the Elder *Brutus* only personated the *Fool* and *Madman*, for the Good of the Publick: but this was nothing else, than a Redundancy of the same *Vapor*, long misapplied, called by the *Latins*, **In-*   * *Tacit.* *genium par negotiis*:[5] Or, (to translate it as nearly as I can) a sort of *Phrenzy*, never in its right Element, till you take it up in Business of the State.

UPON all which, and many other Reasons of equal Weight, though not equally curious; I do here gladly embrace an Opportunity I have long sought for, of Recommending it as a very noble Undertaking, to Sir E——d S——r, Sir C——r M——ve, Sir *J*——n B——ls, *J*——n H————w, Esq;[6] and other Patriots

---

[1] 'Season' ed. 5.
[2] Curtius [*MS. Pate*].
[3] 'whence' ed. 5.
[4] Empedocles [*MS. Pate*].
[5] Tacitus, *Annals*, vi. 39 and xvi. 18.
[6] '*H*—*w*' is printed '*H*—' in edd. 1–4. The names are printed 'Sir *Edward Seymour*. Sir *Christopher Musgrave*, Sir *John Bowls*,

John How, Esq;' in the *Miscellaneous Works* of 1720, with the footnote: 'These were at that time topping Members of the House of Commons.' Cf. p. 341.

They were leading Tories. Sir John Bowls, or Bolles, was member for Lincoln from 1690 to 1702. On 5 Aug. 1699 he was 'somewhat disordered on the

concerned, that they would move for Leave to bring in a Bill, for appointing Commissioners to Inspect into *Bedlam*, and the Parts adjacent; who shall be empowered to *send for Persons, Papers, and Records:* to examine into the Merits and Qualifications of every Student and Professor; to observe with utmost Exactness their several Dispositions and Behaviour; by which means, duly distinguishing and adapting their Talents, they might produce admirable Instruments for the several Offices in a State,[1] * * * * * * * *Civil* and *Military*; proceeding in such Methods as I shall here humbly propose. And, I hope the Gentle Reader will give some Allowance to my great Solicitudes in this important Affair, upon Account of that high Esteem I have ever born that honourable Society, whereof I had some Time the Happiness to be an unworthy Member.

IS any Student tearing his Straw in piece-meal,[2] Swearing and Blaspheming, biting his Grate, foaming at the Mouth, and emptying his Pispot in the Spectator's Faces? Let the Right Worshipful, the *Commissioners of Inspection*, give him a Regiment of Dragoons, and send him into *Flanders* among the *Rest*. Is another eternally talking, sputtering, gaping, bawling, in a Sound without Period or Article? What wonderful Talents are here mislaid! Let him be furnished immediately * *A Law-* with a green Bag and Papers, and *three yer's Coach-* *Pence*[3] in his Pocket, and away with Him to *hire.* *Westminster-Hall.* You will find a Third,

bench' at Lincoln assizes (Luttrell, Diary, iv, p. 545; cf. 592). Burnet says that in 1701 he 'was then disordered in his Senses, and soon after quite lost them' (*History*, ii, p. 271). For the others see *D.N.B.*

[1] 'For the principal Manage-

ment of affairs Ecclesiasticall,' [1720]. Hawkesworth in a note fills the gap with only the word '*Ecclesiasticall*'.

[2] For a similar description of Bedlam see Edward Ward's *London Spy*, part iii, January 1699.

[3] A lawyer's coach-hire, when

gravely taking the Dimensions of his Kennel; A Person of Foresight and Insight, tho' kept quite in the Dark; for why, like *Moses, Ecce *cornuta erat ejus facies*.[1] He walks duly in one Pace, intreats your Penny with due Gravity and Ceremony; talks much of hard Times, and Taxes, and the *Whore of Babylon*; Bars up the woodden Window[2] of his Cell constantly at eight a Clock: Dreams of *Fire*, and *Shop-lifters*, and *Court-Customers*, and *Priviledg'd Places*. Now, what a Figure would all these Acquirements amount to, if the Owner were sent into the *City* among his Brethren! Behold a Fourth, in much and deep Conversation with himself, biting his Thumbs at proper Junctures; His Countenance chequered with Business and Design; sometimes walking very fast, with his Eyes nailed to a Paper that he holds in his Hands: A great Saver of Time, somewhat thick of Hearing, very short of Sight, but more of Memory. A Man ever in Haste, a great Hatcher and Breeder of Business, and excellent at the Famous Art of *whispering Nothing*. A huge Idolater of Monosyllables and Pro-

* Cornutus, *is either Horned or Shining, and by this Term*, Moses *is described in the vulgar* Latin *of the Bible.*

four together, from any of the inns of court to *Westminster* [Hawkesworth].

Cf. *The Tatler*, No. 249: 'to treat a Templer at a Twelvepenny Ordinary, or carry him with Three Friends to *Westminster Hall*'; and Robert Lloyd, *The Law-Student*, ed. 1762, p. 135: 'To club your legal threepence for a coach.'

[1] Exod. xxxiv. 29, 30 [1720]. Cf. Sir Thomas Browne, *Vulgar Errors*, bk. v, chap. 9. 'In many pieces, and some of ancient Bibles, *Moses* is described with horns. . . . The ground of this absurdity was surely a mistake of the Hebrew Text, in the history of *Moses* when he descended from the Mount; upon the affinity of *Kæren* and *Karan*, that is, an horn, and to shine, which is one quality of horn: The Vulgar Translation conforming unto the former. *Ignorabat quod cornuta esset facies ejus. Qui videbant faciem Mosis esse cornutam.*'

[2] 'Window' omitted edd. 1–4.

crastination; so ready to *Give* his Word to every Body, that he never *keeps* it. One that has forgot the common *Meaning* of Words, but an admirable Retainer of the *Sound.* Extreamly subject to the *Loosness*, for his *Occasions* are perpetually *calling him away.* If you approach his Grate in his familiar Intervals; *Sir*, says he, *Give me a Penny, and I'll sing you a Song: But give me the Penny first.* (Hence comes the common Saying, and commoner Practice of parting with Money for a *Song.*) What a compleat System of *Court-Skill* is here described in every Branch of it, and all utterly lost with wrong Application? Accost the Hole of another Kennel, first stopping your Nose, you will behold a surley, gloomy, nasty, slovenly Mortal, raking in his own Dung, and dabling in his Urine. The best Part of his Diet, is the Reversion of his own Ordure, which exspiring into Steams, whirls perpetually about, and at last reinfunds. His Complexion is of a dirty Yellow, with a thin scattered Beard, exactly agreeable to that of his Dyet upon its first Declination; like other Insects, who having their Birth and Education in an Excrement, from thence borrow their Colour and their Smell. The Student of this Apartment is very sparing in his Words, but somewhat over-liberal of his Breath; He holds his Hand out ready to receive your Penny, and immediately upon Receipt, withdraws to his former Occupations. Now, is it not amazing to think, the Society of *Warwick-Lane*,[1] should have no more Concern, for the Recovery of so useful a Member, who, if one may judge from these Appearances, would become the greatest Ornament to that Illustrious Body?[2] Another Student struts up fiercely to your Teeth, puffing with his Lips, half squeezing out

[1] The Royal College of Physicians was in Warwick Lane from 1674 to 1825.

[2] This passage has much in common with the description of the Projector in the *Voyage to Laputa*, chap. v, paragraph 4.

his Eyes, and very graciously holds you out his Hand
to kiss. The *Keeper* desires you not to be afraid of this
Professor, for he will do you no Hurt: To him alone is
allowed the Liberty of the Anti-Chamber, and the *Orator* of the Place[1] gives you to understand, that this solemn
Person is a *Taylor* run mad with Pride. This considerable Student is adorned with many other Qualities, upon
which, at present, I shall not farther enlarge.   —   —
*Heark in your Ear   —   —   —   —   —   —   —
I am strangely mistaken, if all his Address, his Motions,
and his Airs, would not then be very natural, and in
their proper Element.

I shall not descend so minutely, as to insist upon the
vast Number of *Beaux, Fidlers, Poets,* and *Politicians,* that
the World might recover by such a Reformation; But
what is more material, besides the clear Gain redound-
ing to the Commonwealth, by so large an Acquisition
of Persons to employ, whose Talents and Acquirements,
if I may be so bold to affirm it, are now buried, or at
least misapplied: It would be a mighty Advantage ac-
cruing to the Publick from this Enquiry, that all these
would very much excel, and arrive at great Perfection
in their several Kinds; which, I think, is manifest from
what I have already shewn; and shall inforce by this

*I cannot conjecture what the Author means here, or how this Chasm
could be fill'd, tho' it is capable of more than one Interpretation.*

[1] Bedlam was regularly opened
to visitors and was a popular show.
Cf. *The Tatler,* No. 30, and *The
London Spy,* part iii; and see E. G.
O'Donoghue's *Story of Bethlehem
Hospital* (1914), chap. xxvi,
'Visiting Days'; also pp. 249–51
for Swift's connexion with Bed-
lam as governor.

In the *Journal to Stella* (13
Dec. 1710) Swift tells how he,
and Lady Kerry and her son, and
Lord Shelburne's children, spent
a day in visiting the Tower and
Bedlam, and ended the round at
the puppet-show. Cf. also Swift's
Legion Club (1736):

When I saw the keeper frown,
Tipping him with half-a-crown,
Now, said I, we are alone,
Name your heroes one by one.

one plain Instance; That even, I my self, the Author of
these momentous Truths, am a Person, whose Imaginations are hard-mouth'd, and exceedingly disposed to
run away with his *Reason*, which I have observed from
long Experience, to be a very light Rider, and easily
shook off; upon which Account, my Friends will never
trust me alone, without a solemn Promise, to vent my
Speculations in this, or the like manner, for the universal
Benefit of Human kind;[1] which, perhaps, the gentle,
courteous, and candid Reader, brimful of that *Modern*
Charity and Tenderness, usually annexed to his *Office*,
will be very hardly persuaded to believe.

[1] Cf. the title-page, and p. 184, l. 15.

SECT. X.

A ṬALE of a TUB.[1]

IT is an unanswerable Argument of a very refined Age, the wonderful Civilities that have passed of late Years, between the Nation of *Authors*, and that of *Readers*. There can hardly *pop out a *Play*, a *Pamphlet*, or a *Poem*, without a Preface full of Acknowledgements[2] to the World, for the general Reception and Applause they have given it, which the Lord knows where, or when, or how, or from whom it received. In due Deference to so laudable a Custom, I do here return my humble Thanks to *His Majesty*, and both Houses of *Parliament*; To the *Lords* of the King's most honourable Privy-Council, to the Reverend the *Judges:* To the *Clergy*, and *Gentry*, and *Yeomantry*[3] of this Land: But in a more especial manner, to my worthy Brethren and Friends at *Will*'s *Coffee-House*, and *Gresham-College*, and *Warwick-Lane*, and *Moor-Fields*,[4] and *Scotland-Yard*,[5] and *Westminster-Hall*, and *Guild-Hall*; In short, to all Inhabitants and Retainers whatsoever, either in Court, or Church, or Camp, or City, or Country; for their generous and universal Acceptance of this Divine

* *This is literally true, as we may observe in the Prefaces to most Plays, Poems, &c.*

[1] This section is headed 'The Authors Compliment to the Readers &c.' in ed. 1720; and 'A Further Digression' in ed. Hawkesworth.

[2] 'Acknowledgement' ed. 5.

[3] This spelling occurs in edd. 1–5 ('*Yeomanry*' edd. 1711, 1720, &c.); due to assimilation with *Gentry*, or to false analogy with 'infantry' and similar words.

[4] Bedlam was in Moorfields.

[5] Scotland Yard is perhaps mentioned because of Wells's Coffee-house, which was a popular resort there: see *The Flying Post* (printed by John Salusbury), 27–29 Oct. 1696.

Treatise.[1] I accept their Approbation, and good Opinion with extream Gratitude, and to the utmost of my poor Capacity, shall take hold of all Opportunities to return the Obligation.

I am also happy, that Fate has flung me into so blessed an Age for the mutual Felicity of *Booksellers* and *Authors,* whom I may safely affirm to be at this Day the two only satisfied Parties in *England.* Ask an *Author* how his last Piece hath succeeded; *Why, truly he thanks his Stars, the World has been very favourable, and he has not the least Reason to complain: And yet, By G——, He writ it in a Week at Bits and Starts, when he could steal an Hour from his urgent Affairs;*[2] as it is a hundred to one, you may see farther in the Preface, to which he refers you; and for the rest, to the Bookseller. There you go as a Customer, and make the same Question: *He blesses his God, the* Thing *takes wonderfully, he is just Printing a Second Edition, and has but three left in his Shop.*[3] *You beat down the* Price: *Sir, we shall not differ*; and in hopes of your Custom another Time, lets you have it as reasonable as you please; *And, pray send as many of your Acquaintance as you will, I shall upon your Account furnish them all at the same Rate.*

NOW, it is not well enough consider'd, to what Accidents and Occasions the World is indebted for the greatest Part of those noble Writings, which hourly

[1] Cf. p. 124, l. 19.

[2] See, for example, Blackmore's preface to *Prince Arthur* (1695): 'Poetry has been so far from being my *Business* and *Profession,* that it has imploy'd but a small part of my Time; and then, but as my *Recreation,* and the Entertainment of my idle hours'; also his Preface to *King Arthur* (1697): 'for the greatest part, that Poem [*Prince Arthur*] was written in *Coffee-houses,* and in passing up and down the streets.'

[3] Cf. *A short Review of the Controversy between Mr. Boyle, and Dr. Bentley* (1701), p. 12: 'A Bookseller will . . . tell you that the Impression is almost quite gone off, though he can hardly get into his Warehouse for the dead remnant of it that lyes there.'

start up to entertain it. If it were not for a *rainy Day*, *a drunken Vigil, a Fit of the Spleen, a Course of Physick, a sleepy Sunday, an ill Run at Dice, a long Taylor's Bill, a Beggar's Purse, a factious Head, a hot Sun, costive Dyet, Want of Books, and a just Contempt of Learning*. But for these Events, I say, and some Others too long to recite, (especially *a prudent Neglect of taking Brimstone inwardly*,) I doubt, the Number of *Authors*, and of *Writings* would dwindle away to a Degree most woful to behold. To confirm this Opinion, hear the Words of the famous *Troglodyte* Philosopher:[1] *'Tis certain* (said he) *some Grains of Folly are of course annexed, as Part of*[2] *the Composition of Human Nature, only the Choice is left us, whether we please to wear them* Inlaid *or* Embossed;[3] *And we need not go very far to seek how that is usually determined, when we remember it, it is with Human Faculties as with Liquors, the lightest will be ever at the Top.*

THERE is in this famous Island of *Britain* a certain paultry *Scribbler*, very voluminous, whose Character the Reader cannot wholly be a Stranger to. He deals in a pernicious Kind of Writings, called *Second Parts*, and usually passes under the Name of *The Author of the First*. I easily foresee, that as soon as I lay down my Pen, this nimble *Operator* will have stole it, and treat me as inhumanly as he hath already done Dr. *Bl——re*, *L——ge*,[4] and many others who shall here be nameless. I therefore fly for Justice and Relief, into the Hands of that great *Rectifier of Saddles*,[5] and *Lover of Mankind*,

---

[1] This still awaits explanation.

[2] '*Part in*' edd. 1–4.

[3] Cf. Sprat, *Life of Cowley*, 1668, d 2 v: 'His Learning ... sat exceeding close and handsomly upon him: it was not imbossed on his mind, but enamelled.'

[4] No 'second parts' appear to have been falsely attributed to Blackmore or L'Estrange. Swift satirizes the frequency of their publications.

[5] Alluding to the trite phrase *place the saddle on the right horse* [Hawkesworth].

Dr. *B——tly,* begging he will take this enormous Grievance into his most *Modern* Consideration: And if it should so happen, that the *Furniture of an Ass,*[1] in the Shape of a *Second Part,* must for my Sins by clapt by a Mistake upon my Back, that he will immediately please, in the Presence of the World, to lighten me of the Burthen, and take it home to *his own House,* till the *true Beast* thinks fit to call for it.

I N the mean time I do here give this publick Notice, that my Resolutions are, to circumscribe within this Discourse the whole Stock of Matter I have been so many Years providing. Since my *Vein* is once opened, I am content to exhaust it all at a Running, for the peculiar Advantage of my dear Country, and for the universal Benefit of Mankind.[2] Therefore hospitably considering the Number of my Guests, they shall have my whole Entertainment at a Meal; And I scorn to set up the *Leavings* in the Cupboard. What the *Guests* cannot eat may be given to the *Poor,* and the *Dogs under the Table may gnaw the *Bones;* This I understand for a more generous Proceeding, than to turn the Company's Stomachs[3] by inviting them again to morrow to a scurvy Meal of *Scraps.*

I F the Reader fairly considers the Strength of what I have advanced in the foregoing Section, I am convinced it will produce a wonderful Revolution in his Notions and Opinions; And he will be abundantly better prepared to receive and to relish the concluding Part of this miraculous Treatise. Readers may be divided into three Classes, the *Superficial,* the *Ignorant,* and the

---

* *By Dogs, the Author means common injudicious Criticks, as he explains it himself before in his* Digression upon Criticks, (*Page* 96.[4])

[1] Alluding to Bentley's use of the Greek proverb, that 'Leucon carries one thing, and his Ass quite another'. See p. 233, note 4.

[2] Cf. p. 108, l. 8.

[3] 'Stomach' ed. 5.

[4] Pp. 103–4 of this edition.

Learned: And I have with much Felicity fitted my Pen to the Genius and Advantage of each. The *Superficial* Reader will be strangely provoked to *Laughter*; which clears the Breast and the Lungs, is Soverain against the *Spleen*, and the most innocent of all *Diureticks*. The *Ignorant* Reader (between whom and the former, the Distinction is extreamly nice) will find himself disposed to *Stare*; which is an admirable Remedy for ill Eyes, serves to raise and enliven the Spirits, and wonderfully helps *Perspiration*. But the Reader truly *Learned*, chiefly for whose Benefit I wake, when others sleep, and sleep when others wake, will here find sufficient Matter to employ his Speculations for the rest of his Life. It were much to be wisht, and I do here humbly propose for an Experiment, that every Prince in *Christendom* will take seven of the *deepest Scholars* in his Dominions, and shut them up close for *seven* Years, in *seven* Chambers, with a Command to write *seven* ample Commentaries on this comprehensive Discourse.[1] I shall venture to affirm, that whatever Difference may be found in their several Conjectures, they will be all, without the least Distortion, manifestly deduceable from the Text. Mean time, it is my earnest Request, that so useful an Undertaking may be entered upon (if their Majesties[2] please) with all convenient speed; because I have a strong Inclination, before I leave the World, to taste a Blessing, which we *mysterious* Writers can seldom reach, till we have got into our Graves. Whether it is, that *Fame* being a Fruit grafted on the Body, can hardly grow, and much less ripen, till the *Stock* is in the Earth:

---

[1] This alludes to the story of the seventy Interpreters [1720].

According to the story, which is told in the spurious Letter of Aristeas to Philocrates, the Septuagint was the work of seventy-two Jewish scholars, who were shut up in seventy-two cells, and in seventy-two days produced versions that agreed in all details.

[2] i.e. 'every Prince in Christendom'.

Or, whether she be a Bird of Prey, and is lured among the rest, to pursue after the Scent of a *Carcass:* Or, whether she conceives, her Trumpet sounds best and farthest, when she stands on a *Tomb*, by the Advantage of a rising Ground, and the Echo of a hollow Vault.

'TIS true, indeed, the Republick of *dark* Authors, after they once found out this excellent Expedient of *Dying*, have been peculiarly happy in the Variety, as well as Extent of their Reputation. For, *Night* being the universal Mother of Things, wise Philosophers hold all Writings to be *fruitful* in the Proportion they are *dark*; And therefore, the **true illuminated*[1] (that is to say, the *Darkest* of all) have met with such numberless Commentators, whose *Scholiastick* Midwifry hath deliver'd them of Meanings, that the Authors themselves, perhaps, never conceived, and yet may very justly be allowed the Lawful Parents of them: †The Words of such Writers being like Seed, which, however scattered at random, when they light upon a fruitful Ground, will multiply far beyond either the Hopes or Imagination of the Sower.

* A Name of the Rosycrucians.

AND therefore in order to promote so useful a Work, I will here take Leave to glance a few *Innuendo*'s,[2] that may be of great Assistance to those sublime Spirits, who shall be appointed to labor in a universal Comment upon this wonderful Discourse. And First, ‡I have couched

† *Nothing is more frequent than for* Commentators *to force Interpretation, which the Author never meant.*

‡ *This is what the* Cabbalists *among the* Jews *have done with the* Bible, *and pretend to find wonderful Mysteries by it.*

[1] 'Illuminati' (φωτιζόμενοι) was a name given to the baptized in the early church; and it was assumed by two sects of enthusiasts—the *Alumbrados* in Spain, and the *Guérinets* in France—as well as the Rosicrucians. See A. E. Waite, *The Real History of the Rosicrucians,* 1887, passim.

[2] See p. 114, note 2.

a very profound Mystery in the Number of O's multiply'd by *Seven*, and divided by *Nine*.[1] Also, if a devout
Brother of the *Rosy Cross* will pray fervently for sixty
three Mornings, with a lively Faith, and then transpose
certain Letters and Syllables according to Prescription,
in the second and fifth Section; they will certainly reveal
into a full Receit of the *Opus Magnum*. Lastly, Whoever will be at the Pains to calculate the whole Number
of each Letter in this Treatise, and sum up the Difference exactly between the several Numbers, assigning
the true natural Cause for every such Difference; the
Discoveries in the Product, will plentifully reward his
Labour. But then he must beware of *Bythus and *Sigè*,
and be sure not to forget the Qualities of *Acamoth; A
cujus lacrymis humecta prodit Substantia, à risu lucida, à
tristitiâ solida, & à timore mobilis*, wherein   † *Vid. A-*
†*Eugenius Philalethes* hath committed an un-   *nima magica*
pardonable Mistake.[2]   *abscondita.*

    * *I was told by an Eminent Divine, whom I consulted on this Point,
that these two Barbarous Words, with that of* Acamoth *and its Qualities,
as here set down, are quoted from* Irenæus. *This he discover'd by searching
that Antient Writer for another Quotation of our Author, which he has
placed in the Title Page, and refers to the Book and Chapter; the Curious
were very Inquisitive, whether those Barbarous Words,* Basima Eacabasa,
&c. are[3] really in Irenæus, *and upon enquiry 'twas found they were a sort
of Cant or Jargon of certain Hereticks, and therefore very properly prefix'd
to such a Book as this of our Author.*

    † *To the abovementioned Treatise, called* Anthroposophia Theo-
magica, *there is another annexed, called* Anima Magica Abscondita,
written by the same Author Vaughan, *under the Name of* Eugenius
Philalethes, *but in neither of those Treatises is there any mention of* Acamoth *or its Qualities, so that this is nothing but Amusement, and a Ridicule
of dark, unintelligible Writers; only the Words,* A cujus lacrymis, *&c.
are as we have said, transcribed from* Irenæus, *tho' I know not from what
part. I believe one of the Authors Designs was to set curious Men a hunting
thro' Indexes, and enquiring for Books out of the common Road.*

    [1] See p. 58, note 1.   [2] See Appendix F, p. 359.
          [3] 'were' *Notes* 1711.

SECT. XI.

A TALE of a TUB.

AFTER so wide a Compass as I have wandred, I do now gladly overtake, and close in with my Subject, and shall henceforth hold on with it an even Pace to the End of my Journey, except some beautiful Prospect appears within sight of my Way; whereof, tho' at present I have neither Warning nor Expectation, yet upon such an Accident, come when it will, I shall beg my Readers Favour and Company, allowing me to conduct him thro' it along with my self. For in *Writing*, it is as in *Travelling:* If a Man is in haste to be at home, (which I acknowledge to be none of my Case, having never so little Business, as when I am there) if his *Horse* be tired with long Riding, and ill Ways, or be naturally a Jade, I advise him clearly to make the straitest and the commonest Road, be it ever so dirty; But, then surely, we must own such a Man to be a scurvy Companion at best; He *spatters* himself and his Fellow-Travellers at every Step: All their Thoughts, and Wishes, and Conversation turn entirely upon the Subject of their Journey's End; and at every Splash, and Plunge, and Stumble, they heartily wish one another at the Devil.

ON the other side, when a Traveller and his *Horse* are in Heart and Plight, when his Purse is full, and the Day before him; he takes the Road only where it is clean or convenient; entertains his Company there as agreeably as he can; but upon the first Occasion, carries them along with him to every delightful Scene in View, whether of Art, of Nature, or of both; and if they chance to refuse out of Stupidity or Weariness; let them jog on by themselves, and be d—n'd; He'll overtake them at the next Town; at which arriving, he Rides furiously thro', the Men, Women, and Children run out to gaze, a hundred *noisy Curs run barking* after him, of which, if he honors the boldest with a *Lash of his Whip*, it is rather out of Sport than Revenge: But should some *sourer Mungrel* dare too near an Approach, he receives a *Salute* on the Chaps by an accidental Stroak from the Courser's Heels, (nor is any Ground lost by the Blow) which sends him yelping and limping home.

I now proceed to sum up the singular Adventures of my renowened *Jack*; the State of whose Dispositions and Fortunes, the careful Reader does, no doubt, most exactly remember, as I last parted with them in the Conclusion of a former Section. Therefore, his next Care must be from two of the foregoing, to extract a Scheme of Notions, that may best fit his Understanding for a true Relish of what is to ensue.

J A C K had not only calculated the first Revolutions[1] of his Brain so prudently, as to give Rise to that Epidemick Sect of *Æolists*, but succeeding also into a new and strange Variety of Conceptions, the Fruitfulness of his Imagination led him into certain Notions, which, altho' in Appearance very unaccountable, were not without their Mysteries and their Meanings, nor wanted Followers to countenance and improve them. I shall therefore be extreamly careful and exact in recounting such material Passages of this Nature, as I have been able to collect, either from undoubted Tradition, or indefatigable Reading; and shall describe them as graphically as it is possible, and as far as Notions of that Height and Latitude can be brought within the Compass of a Pen. Nor do I at all question, but they will furnish Plenty of noble Matter for such, whose converting

---

* *By these are meant what the Author calls,* The *True* Criticks, *Page* 96.[2]

[1] 'Revolution' edd. 2–5.   [2] Pp. 103–4 of this edition.

Imaginations dispose them to reduce all Things into
Types; who can make *Shadows*, no thanks to the Sun;
and then mold them into Substances, no thanks to
Philosophy; whose peculiar Talent lies in fixing Tropes
and Allegories to the *Letter*, and refining what is Literal
into Figure and Mystery.

J A C K had provided a fair Copy of his Father's *Will*,
engrossed in Form upon a large Skin of Parchment;
and resolving to act the Part of a most dutiful Son, he became the fondest Creature of it imaginable. For, altho',
as I have often told the Reader, it consisted wholly in
certain plain, easy Directions about the management
and wearing of their Coats, with Legacies and Penalties,
in case of Obedience or Neglect; yet he began to entertain a Fancy, that the Matter was *deeper* and *darker*,
and therefore must needs have a great deal more of
Mystery at the Bottom. *Gentlemen*, said he, *I will prove
this very Skin of Parchment to be Meat, Drink, and Cloth,
to be the Philosopher's Stone, and the Universal Medicine.**[1]
In consequence of which Raptures, he resolved to make
use of it in the most necessary, as well as the most paltry
Occasions of Life. He had a Way of working it into any
Shape he pleased; so that it served him for a Night-cap
when he went to Bed, and for an Umbrello in rainy
Weather.[2] He would lap a Piece of it about a sore Toe,
or when he had Fits, burn two Inches under his Nose;
or if any Thing lay heavy on his Stomach, scrape off,

* *The Author here lashes those Pretenders to Purity, who place so much
Merit in using Scripture Phrase[s] on all Occasions.*

[1] This is a just banter on the superstitious veneration for the Bible, that most Dissenters show on all occasions [1720].

[2] The original sense of a protection against the sun was being replaced at this time by the sense of a protection against rain. Cf. Gay, *Trivia* (1716), i, ll. 213–18:

Let *Persian* Dames the *Umbrella's* Ribs display,
To guard their Beauties from
the sunny Ray; . . .
Britain in Winter only knows

and swallow as much of the Powder as would lie on a
silver Penny, they were all infallible Remedies. With
Analogy to these Refinements, his common Talk and
Conversation* ran wholly in the Phrase of his Will, and
he circumscribed the utmost of his Eloquence within
that Compass, not daring to let slip a Syllable without
Authority from thence. Once at a strange House, he
was suddenly taken short, upon an urgent Juncture,
whereon it may not be allowed too particularly to dilate;
and being not able to call to mind, with that Sudden-
ness, the Occasion required, an Authentick Phrase for
demanding the Way to the Backside; he chose rather
as the more prudent Course, to incur the Penalty in
such Cases usually annexed. Neither was it possible for
the united Rhetorick of Mankind to prevail with him
to make himself clean again: Because having consulted
the Will upon this Emergency, he met with a † Passage
near the Bottom¹ (whether foisted in by the Tran-
scriber, is not known) which seemed to forbid it.²

HE made it a Part of his Religion, never to say

---

* *The* Protestant Dissenters *use* Scripture Phrases *in their serious
Discourses, and Composures more than the* Church of England-Men,
accordingly Jack *is introduced making his common Talk and Conversation
to run wholly in the Phrase of his WILL.* W. Wotton.

† *I cannot guess the Author's meaning here, which I would be very glad
to know, because it seems to be of Importance.*

its Aid,
   To guard from chilly Show'rs
      the walking Maid.
Also Swift's *Description of a City
Shower* (*The Tatler*, No. 238,
17 Oct. 1710), ll. 37–38:
   The tuck'd-up Sempstress
      walks with hasty Strides,
   While Streams run down her
      oil'd Umbrella's Sides.
It did not become the habit for
men to carry umbrellas till the

latter part of the century.
   ¹ The passage referred to is in
Rev. xxii. 11: 'he which is filthy,
let him be filthy still'. This clause
(καὶ ὁ ῥυπαρὸς ῥυπανθήτω ἔτι)
is omitted by the Codex Alexan-
drinus and six cursive MSS.
   ² See *Math. XV. 17, 18, 19, &
Mark VII. 15.* These or such like
passages being foolishly applied,
might give occasion to this banter
[1734].

*Grace to his Meat, nor could all the World persuade him, as the common Phrase is, to †eat his Victuals *like a Christian*.[1]

H E bore a strange kind of Appetite to ‖*Snap-Dragon*, and to the livid Snuffs of a burning Candle, which he would catch and swallow with an Agility, wonderful to conceive; and by this Procedure, maintained a perpetual Flame in his Belly, which issuing in a glowing Steam from both his Eyes, as well as his Nostrils, and his Mouth; made his Head appear in a dark Night, like the Scull of an Ass, wherein a roguish Boy hath conveyed a Farthing Candle, *to the Terror of His Majesty's Liege Subjects*. Therefore, he made use of no other Expedient to light himself home, but was wont to say, That *a Wise Man was his own Lanthorn*.[2]

H E would shut his Eyes as he walked along the Streets, and if he happened to bounce his Head against a Post, or fall into the Kennel (as he seldom missed either to do one or both) he would tell the gibing Prentices, who looked on, that *he submitted with entire Resignation, as to a Trip, or a Blow of Fate, with whom he found, by long Experience, how vain it was either to wrestle or to cuff; and whoever durst undertake to do either, would be sure to come off with a swinging Fall, or a bloody Nose*. It

* *The slovenly way of Receiving the Sacrament among the Fanaticks.*

† *This is a common Phrase to express Eating cleanlily,[3] and is meant for an Invective against that undecent Manner among some People in Receiving the Sacrament, so in the Lines before* ['*tis said, *Jack* would never say Grace to his Meat[4]], *which is to be understood of the Dissenters refusing to kneel at the Sacrament.*

‖ *I cannot well find the Author's meaning here, unless it be the hot, untimely, blind Zeal of Enthusiasts.*

[1] The Quakers never say Grace to their meat, but call it a superstitious and useless custom [1720].
[2] Probably Swift's coinage, but cf. *Hudibras*, II. ii. 219–20.
[3] 'cleanly' *Notes* 1711.
[4] ''tis . . . Meat' *Notes* 1711.

was ordained,[1] *said he, some few Days before the Creation, that my Nose and this very Post should have a Rencounter; and therefore, Nature*[2] *thought fit to send us both into the World in the same Age, and to make us Country-men and Fellow-Citizens. Now, had my Eyes been open, it is very likely, the Business might have been a great deal worse; For, how many a confounded Slip is daily got by Man, with all his Foresight about him? Besides, the Eyes of the Under-standing see best, when those of the Senses are out of the way; and therefore, blind Men are observed to tread their Steps with much more Caution, and Conduct, and Judg-ment, than those who rely with too much Confidence, upon the Virtue of the visual Nerve, which every little Accident shakes out of Order, and a Drop, or a Film, can wholly disconcert; like a Lanthorn among a Pack of roaring Bullies,*[3] *when they scower the Streets; exposing its Owner, and it self, to outward Kicks and Buffets, which both might have escaped, if the Vanity of Appearing would have suffered them to walk in the Dark. But, farther; if we examine the* Conduct *of these boasted Lights, it will prove yet a great deal worse than their* Fortune: '*Tis true, I have broke my Nose against this Post, because Fortune*[2] *either forgot, or did not think it convenient to twitch me by the Elbow, and give me notice to avoid it. But, let not this encourage either the present Age or Posterity, to trust their* Noses *into the keeping of their* Eyes, *which may prove the fairest Way of losing them for good and all. For, O ye Eyes, Ye blind Guides; miserable Guardians are Ye of our frail Noses; Ye, I say, who fasten upon the first Precipice in view, and then tow our wretched willing Bodies after You, to the very Brink of Destruction: But, alas, that Brink is rotten, our Feet slip,*

---

[1] Predestination [*MS. Pate*].

Predestination, the favorite doctrine of most Dissenters, is here exposed. *Dr. Wotton* calls this a direct profanation of the Majesty of God [1700].

[2] Instead of '*Nature*' (l. 3) and '*Fortune*' (l. 22) edd. 1–4 read '*Providence*'.

[3] Cf. *Paradise Lost*, i. 500–2.

and we tumble down prone into a Gulph, without one hos-
pitable Shrub in the Way to break the Fall; a Fall, to which
not any Nose of mortal Make is equal, except
Vide Don   *that of the Giant** Laurcalco,[1] *who was*
Quixot.   *Lord of the* Silver Bridge. *Most properly,*
therefore, O Eyes, and with great Justice, may You be com-
pared to those foolish Lights, which conduct Men thro' Dirt
and Darkness, till they fall into a deep Pit, or a noisom Bog.

THIS I have produced, as a Scantling of *Jack*'s
great Eloquence, and the Force of his Reasoning upon
such abstruse Matters.

HE was besides, a Person of great Design and Improvement in Affairs of *Devotion*, having introduced a
new Deity, who hath since met with a vast Number of
Worshippers; by some called *Babel*, by others, *Chaos*;[2]
who had an antient Temple of *Gothick* Structure upon
Salisbury-Plain; famous for its Shrine, and Celebration
by Pilgrims.[3]

† WHEN he had some Roguish Trick to play, he
would down with his Knees, up with his Eyes, and fall
to Prayers, tho' in the midst of the Kennel. Then it was
that those who understood his Pranks, would be sure
to get far enough out of his Way; And whenever

† *The Villanies and Cruelties committed by Enthusiasts and Phana-*
ticks among us, were all performed under the Disguise of Religion and long
Prayers.

[1] *Don Quixote,* i. 18 (or iii. 4).
[2] The Dissenters are accused
by those of our establisht Church,
as utter Enemys to what we call
order and regularity in matters of
Worship [1720].

Perhaps suggested by the title
of Andreas Libavius's book, *Turris*
Babel sive Judiciorum de Frater-
nitate Rosaceæ Crucis Chaos.
Argentorati, M.DC.XIX.

[3] Swift adopts the view that
Stonehenge was a druidical temple,
'Gothick' being used in the sense
of rude and barbarous. This was
Aubrey's view in *Monumenta*
Britannica. In the treatises of
Inigo Jones (1655, written 1620)
and John Webb (1665) it was
said to be Roman; and Walter
Charleton (1663) said it was
Danish.

Curiosity attracted Strangers to Laugh, or to Listen;
he would of a sudden, with one Hand out with his *Gear*,
and piss full in their Eyes, and with the other, all to-
bespatter[1] them with Mud.

*IN Winter he went always loose and unbuttoned,
and clad as thin as possible, to let *in* the ambient Heat;
and in Summer, lapt himself close and thick to keep it *out*.[2]

†IN all Revolutions of Government, he would make
his Court for the Office of *Hangman* General; and in
the Exercise of that Dignity, wherein he was very dex-
trous, would make use of ‖no other *Vizard* than a *long
Prayer*.[3]

HE had a Tongue so Musculous and Subtil, that he
could twist it up into his Nose, and deliver a strange
Kind of Speech from thence. He was also the first in
these Kingdoms, who began to improve the *Spanish*
Accomplishment of *Braying*;[4] and having large Ears,
perpetually exposed and arrect,[5] he carried his Art to
such a Perfection, that it was a Point of great Difficulty
to distinguish either by the View or the Sound, between
the *Original* and the *Copy*.

HE was troubled with a Disease, reverse to that

* *They affect Differences in Habit and Behaviour.*
† *They are severe Persecutors, and all in a Form of Cant and Devotion.*
‖ Cromwell *and his Confederates went, as they called it,* to seek God,
when they resolved to murther the King.

[1] 'to bespatter' edd. 4, 5.
[2] Cf. Joseph Hall, *Mundus
Alter et Idem, Sive Terra Australis
antehac semper Incognita* (1605),
III, Moronia, ii, p. 116: 'Media
hyeme aperto incedunt pectore, et
reliquo corpore leviter amicto, ut
eo facilius intret calor, frigus exeat;
æstate autem induunt endromida,
et superinduunt pallium, et quot
habent vestes, ne qua forte calor
intrare possit.' (*Works of Hall*, ed.

Wynter (1863), vol. x, p. 454.
This parallel was pointed out by
Henry Morley.
[3] 'long' edd. 4, 5.
[4] See *Don Quixote*, second part,
chaps. 25 and 27, where the two
aldermen bray to recover the lost
ass, and where Sancho shows his
proficiency in braying, which, 'like
swimming, once learnt is never
forgotten'.
[5] 'arrected' edd. 2–5.

called the Stinging of the *Tarantula*;[1] and would *run Dog-mad, at the Noise of *Musick*, especially a *Pair of Bag-Pipes*. But he would cure himself again, by taking two or three Turns in *Westminster-Hall*, or *Billingsgate*, or in a *Boarding-School*, or the *Royal-Exchange*, or a *State Coffee-House*.

HE was a Person that †*feared* no *Colours*,[2] but mortally *hated* all, and upon that Account, bore a cruel Aversion to *Painters*, insomuch, that in his Paroxysms, as he walked the Streets, he would have his Pockets loaden with Stones, to pelt at the *Signs*.

HAVING from this manner of Living, frequent Occasions[3] to *wash* himself, he would often leap over Head and Ears into the Water,[4] tho' it were in the midst of the Winter, but was always observed to come out again much *dirtier*, if possible, than he went in.

HE was the first that ever found out the Secret of contriving a ||*Soporiferous* Medicine to be convey'd in at the *Ears*;[5] It was a Compound of *Sulphur* and *Balm of Gilead*, with a little *Pilgrim's Salve*.[6]

* *This is to expose our Dissenters Aversion to Instrumental Musick in Churches.* W. Wotton.

† *They quarrel at the most Innocent Decency and Ornament, and defaced the Statues and Paintings on all the Churches in* England.

|| *Fanatick Preaching, composed either of Hell and Damnation, or a fulsome Description of the Joys of Heaven, both in such a dirty, nauseous Style, as to be well resembled to Pilgrims Salve.*

[1] Calvin was against church musick [*MS. Pate*].

Cf. Sir Thomas Browne, *Vulgar Errors*, bk. iii, chap. 27: 'Surely he that is bit with a *Tarantula*, shall never be cured by this Musick [i.e. the song of the swan].'

[2] He would suffer no paintings in churches [*MS. Pate*].

'To fear no colours' is 'to fear no foe'. Cf. *Twelfth Night*, i. v. 10.

[3] 'Occasion' ed. 5.

[4] Immersion in baptism [*MS. Pate*].

[5] Nothing conduceth more powerfully to sleep than long insipid Sermons, as may be seen by daily experience, as well among *Martins* followers as *Jacks*. So they are all obliged to the Author of so usefull an Invention [1720].

[6] 'An old ointment, made

HE wore a large Plaister of artificial *Causticks* on his Stomach, with the Fervor of which, he could set himself a *groaning*, like the famous *Board* upon Application of a red-hot Iron.[1]

*HE would stand in the Turning of a Street, and calling to those who passed by, would cry to One; *Worthy Sir, do me the Honour of a good Slap in the Chaps:* To another, *Honest Friend, pray, favour me with a handsom Kick on the Arse: Madam, shall I entreat a small Box on*[2] *the Ear, from your Ladyship's fair Hands? Noble Captain, Lend a reasonable Thwack, for the Love of God, with that Cane of yours, over these poor Shoulders.* And when he had by such earnest Sollicitations, made a shift to

---

* *The Fanaticks have always had a way of affecting to run into Persecution, and count vast Merit upon every little Hardship they suffer.*

---

chiefly of swine's grease and isinglass' (Halliwell).

[1] Cf. Evelyn, *Silva*, ed. Hunter (1776), p. 633: 'I must not pass by the *Groaning-Board* which they kept for a while in Southwark, drawing abundance of people to see the wonder.'

In illustration of a passage in *The Tatler*, No. 257, mentioning a 'groaning-board', Nichols gives this note: 'At the sign of the Woolsack in Newgate Merket, is to be seen a strange and wonderful thing, which is, an *elm*-BOARD; being touched with a hot iron, it doth express itself, as if it were a man dying with *groans* and trembling, to the great admiration of all hearers. It hath been presented before the king and his nobles, and hath given great satisfaction.' This is said to

'an advertisement in 1682, at the top of which are the king's arms, and C.R. Sloan MSS. 4to, 958, Brit. Museum'. (*The Tatler* (1786), vi, p. 336.) Nichols's reference is at fault. Sloane MS. 958 does not contain this advertisement.

Cf. Grew, *Anatomy of Plants* (1682), III. 2. vii, § 7, p. 138: 'The *Planks* commonly called *Groaning-Boards*, lately exposed, as a kind of *Prodigy* . . . were of *Elm*. The *Aer-Vessels* of this *Wood*, being . . . more ample, than in any other *Timber*. So that upon the application of the *Red-hot Iron* . . . every *Vessel* became, as it were a little *Wind-Pipe* . . . a great many of these *Pipes* playing together, might make a kind of big or groaning noyse.'

[2] '*in*' edd. 1–3.

procure a Basting sufficient to swell up his Fancy and his Sides, He would return home extremely comforted, and full of terrible Accounts of what he had undergone for the *Publick Good. Observe this Stroak,* (said he, shewing his bare Shoulders) *a plaguy* Janisary *gave it me this very Morning at seven a Clock, as, with much ado, I was driving off the* Great Turk. *Neighbours mine, this broken Head deserves a Plaister; had poor* Jack *been tender of his Noddle, you would have seen the* Pope, *and the* French King, *long before this time of Day, among your Wives and your Warehouses. Dear* Christians, *the* Great Mogul *was come as far as* White-Chappel, *and you may thank these poor Sides that he hath not (God bless us) already swallowed up Man, Woman, and Child.*

*I T was highly worth observing, the singular Effects of that Aversion, or Antipathy, which *Jack* and his Brother *Peter* seemed, even to an Affectation, to bear toward[1] each other. *Peter* had lately done *some Rogueries,* that forced him to abscond; and he seldom ventured to stir out before Night, for fear of Bayliffs. Their Lodgings were at the two most distant Parts of the Town, from each other; and whenever their Occasions, or Humors called them abroad, they would make Choice of the oddest unlikely Times, and most uncouth Rounds they could invent; that they might be sure to avoid one another: Yet after all this, it was their perpetual Fortune to meet. The Reason of which, is easy enough to

---

* *The Papists and Fanaticks, tho' they appear the most Averse to each other, yet bear a near Resemblance in many things, as has[2] been observed by Learned Men.*

Ibid. *The Agreement of our Dissenters and the Papists in that which Bishop* Stillingfleet *called,* The Fanaticism of the Church of *Rome, is ludicrously described for several Pages together by* Jack's *Likeness to* Peter, *and their being often mistaken for each other, and their frequent Meeting, when they least intended it.* W. Wotton.

[1] 'towards' edd. 1–4.   [2] 'hath' *Notes* 1711.

apprehend: For, the Phrenzy and the Spleen of both, having the same Foundation, we may look upon them as two Pair of Compasses, equally extended, and the fixed Foot of each, remaining in the same Center; which, tho' moving contrary Ways at first, will be sure to encounter somewhere or other in the Circumference. Besides, it was among the great Misfortunes of *Jack*, to bear a huge Personal Resemblance with his Brother *Peter*. Their Humours[1] and Dispositions were not only the same, but there was a close Analogy in their Shape, their Size, and[2] their Mien. Insomuch, as nothing was more frequent than for a Bayliff to seize *Jack* by the Shoulders, and cry, *Mr.* Peter, *You are the King's Prisoner*. Or, at other Times, for one of *Peter's* nearest Friends, to accost *Jack* with open Arms, *Dear* Peter, *I am glad to see thee, pray send me one of your best Medicines for the Worms*. This we may suppose, was a mortifying Return of those Pains and Proceedings, *Jack* had laboured in so long; And finding, how directly opposite all his Endeavours had answered to the sole End and Intention, which he had proposed to himself; How could it avoid having terrible Effects upon a Head and Heart so furnished as his? However, the poor Remainders of his *Coat* bore all the Punishment; The orient Sun never entred upon his diurnal Progress, without missing a Piece of it. He hired a Taylor to stitch up the Collar so close, that it was ready to choak him, and squeezed out his Eyes at such a Rate, as one could see nothing but the White. What little was left of the main Substance of the Coat, he rubbed every day for two hours, against a rough-cast Wall, in order to grind away the Remnants of *Lace* and *Embroidery*; but at the same time went on with so much Violence, that he proceeded a *Heathen*

---

[1] 'Humours' ed. 1; 'Humour' edd. 2–5.
[2] 'their Size, and' edd. 1–4; 'and Size and' ed. 5.

Philosopher. Yet after all he could do of this kind, the
Success continued still to disappoint his Expectation.
For, as it is the Nature of Rags, to bear a kind of mock
Resemblance to Finery; there being a sort of fluttering
Appearance in both, which is not to be distinguished
at a Distance, in the Dark, or by short-sighted Eyes:
So, in those Junctures, it fared with *Jack* and his Tat-
ters, that they offered to the first View a ridiculous
Flanting, which assisting the Resemblance in Person
and Air, thwarted all his Projects of Separation, and
left so near a Similitude between them, as frequently
deceived the very Disciples and Followers of both. *

*   *   *   *   *   *   *   *   *
                    *   *   *   *   *   *   *
Desunt non- *   *   *   *   *   *   *
nulla.   *   *   *   *   *   *   *
*   *   *   *   *   *   *   *   *

THE old *Sclavonian* Proverb said well, That *it is
with* Men, *as with* Asses; *whoever would keep them fast,
may[1] find a very good Hold at their Ears.*[2] Yet, I think,
we may affirm, and[3] it hath been verified by repeated
Experience, that,

   Effugiet tamen hæc sceleratus vincula Proteus.[4]

IT is good therefore, to read the Maxims of our
Ancestors, with great Allowances to Times and Persons: For, if we look into Primitive Records, we shall
find, that no Revolutions have been so great, or so frequent, as those of human *Ears.* In former Days, there
was a curious Invention to catch and keep them; which,
I think, we may justly reckon among the *Artes Perditæ:*[5]

---

[1] '*may*' ed. 1; '*must*' edd. 2–5.
[2] This proverb may be accepted
as Swift's own. His description
of it as 'Sclavonian' is 'nothing
but amusement'.

[3] 'and' edd. 1–4; 'that' ed. 5.
[4] Horace, *Sat.* ii. iii. 71.
[5] Cf. the note on Panciroli,
p. 155.

And how can it be otherwise, when in these latter Centuries, the very Species is not only diminished to a very lamentable Degree, but the poor Remainder is also degenerated so far, as to mock our skilfullest *Tenure?* For, if the only slitting of one *Ear* in a Stag, hath been found sufficient to propagate the Defect thro' a whole Forest;[1] Why should we wonder at the greatest Consequences, from so many Loppings and Mutilations, to which the *Ears* of our Fathers and our own, have been of late so much exposed: 'Tis true, indeed, that while this *Island* of ours, was under the *Dominion of Grace*, many Endeavours were made to improve the Growth of *Ears* once more among us. The Proportion of Largeness, was not only lookt upon as an Ornament of the *Outward* Man, but as a Type of Grace in the *Inward*.[2] Besides, it is held by Naturalists, that if there be a Protuberancy of Parts in the *Superiour* Region of the Body, as in the *Ears* and *Nose*, there must be a Parity also in the *Inferior*: And therefore in that truly pious Age, the *Males* in every Assembly, according as they were gifted, appeared very forward in exposing their *Ears* to view, and

* *Lib. de aëre locis & aquis.*

the Regions about them; because *Hippocrates tells us, that *when the Vein behind the Ear happens to be cut, a Man becomes a Eunuch*:[3] And the *Females* were nothing backwarder in beholding and edifying by them: Whereof those who

---

[1] Cf. Sir Thomas Browne, *Vulgar Errors*, bk. vi, chap. 10: 'Thus, as *Aristotle* observeth, the Deers of *Arginusa* had their ears divided; occasioned at first by slitting the ears of Deers.' See *Historia Animalium*, bk. vi. 29 (578 *b*).

[2] By cutting their hair close, the Puritans made their ears prominent. Cf. *The Character of*

a Roundhead (1641):

> What Creature's this with his short hairs,
> His little band and huge long ears.

(*The Rump*, i. p. 42; cf. pp. 46, 140, &c.) Cf. also *The Spectator*, No. 125.

[3] *De Genitura*, 3. Also *De Aere, Aquis, et Locis*, 50, 51.

had already *used the Means*, lookt about them with great Concern, in hopes of conceiving a suitable Offspring by such a Prospect: Others, who stood Candidates for *Benevolence*, found there a plentiful Choice, and were sure to fix upon such as discovered the largest *Ears*, that the Breed might not dwindle between them. Lastly, the devouter Sisters, who lookt upon all extraordinary Dilatations of that Member, as Protrusions of Zeal, or spiritual Excrescencies, were sure to honor every Head they sat upon, as if they had been *Marks of Grace*;[1] but, especially, that of the Preacher, whose *Ears* were usually of the prime Magnitude; which upon that Account, he was very frequent and exact in exposing with all Advantages to the People: in his Rhetorical *Paroxysms*, turning sometimes to *hold forth* the one, and sometimes to *hold forth* the other: From which Custom, the whole Operation of Preaching is to this very Day among their Professors, styled by the Phrase of *Holding forth*.

SUCH was the Progress of the *Saints*, for advancing the Size of that Member; And it is thought, the Success would have been every way answerable, if in Process of time, a *cruel King had not arose, who raised a bloody Persecution against all *Ears*, above a certain Standard: Upon which, some were glad to hide their flourishing Sprouts in a black Border, others crept wholly under a Perewig: some were slit, others cropt, and a great Number sliced off to the Stumps. But of this, more hereafter, in my *general History of Ears*;[2] which I design very speedily to bestow upon the Publick.

* *This was King* Charles *the Second, who at his Restauration, turned out all the Dissenting Teachers that would not conform.*

[1] Edd. 1–4 read 'as if they had been *cloven Tongues*'. See Acts ii. 9 and cf. the *Mechanical Operation*, p. 270, l. 35 and p. 275, l. 19.
[2] See the Catalogue, before the Title [1720].

FROM this brief Survey of the falling State of *Ears*, in the last Age, and the small Care had to advance their antient Growth in the present, it is manifest, how little Reason we can have to rely upon a Hold so short, so weak, and so slippery; and that, whoever desires to catch Mankind fast, must have Recourse to some other Methods. Now, he that will examine Human Nature with Circumspection enough, may discover several *Handles*, whereof the *Six Senses afford one apiece, beside a great Number that are screw'd to the Passions, and some few

* *Including Scaliger's.*[1]

riveted to the Intellect. Among these last, *Curiosity* is one, and of all others, affords the firmest Grasp: *Curiosity*, that Spur in the side, that Bridle in the Mouth, that Ring in the Nose, of a lazy, an impatient, and a grunting Reader. By this *Handle* it is, that an Author should seize upon his Readers; which as soon as he hath once compast, all Resistance and struggling are in vain; and they become his Prisoners as close as he pleases, till Weariness or Dullness force him to let go his Gripe.

AND therefore, I the Author of this miraculous Treatise, having[2] hitherto, beyond Expectation, maintained by the aforesaid *Handle*, a firm Hold upon my gentle Readers; It is with great Reluctance, that I am at length compelled to remit my Grasp; leaving them in the Perusal of what remains, to that natural *Oscitancy*[3] inherent in the Tribe. I can only assure thee, Courteous Reader, for both our Comforts, that my Concern is altogether equal to thine, for my Unhappiness in losing, or mislaying among my Papers the remaining Part of

[1] J. C. Scaliger, *De Subtilitate* (1557), p. 358, Exercitatio cclxxxvi. There is a reference to 'Scaliger's sixth Sense of Titillation' in Burton's *Anatomy of Melancholy*, I. i. ii. vi.

[2] 'having' edd. 1–4; 'have' ed. 5.

[3] See p. 124, note 1.

these Memoirs; which consisted of Accidents, Turns, and Adventures, both New, Agreeable, and Surprizing; and therefore, calculated in all due Points, to the delicate Taste of this our noble Age. But, alas, with my utmost Endeavours, I have been able only to retain a few of the Heads. Under which, there was a full Account, how *Peter* got a *Protection* out of the *King's-Bench*; and of a *Reconcilement between *Jack* and Him, upon a Design they had in a certain *rainy Night*, to trepan Brother *Martin* into a *Spunging-house*, and there strip him to the Skin. How *Martin*, with much ado, shew'd them both a fair pair of Heels.[1] How a *new Warrant* came out against *Peter*: upon which, how *Jack* left him in the lurch, *stole his Protection, and made use of it himself.* How *Jack's* Tatters came into Fashion in *Court* and *City*;[2] How he †*got upon a great Horse, and eat*

* *In the Reign of King* James *the Second, the Presbyterians by the King's Invitation, joined with the Papists, against the Church of* England, *and Address him for Repeal of the Penal-Laws and Test. The King by his Dispensing Power, gave Liberty of Conscience, which both Papists and Presbyterians made use of, but upon the Revolution, the Papists being down of Course, the Presbyterians freely continued their Assemblies, by Virtue of King* James's *Indulgence, before they had a Toleration by Law; this I believe the Author means by* Jack's *stealing* Peter's *Protection, and making use of it himself.*

† *Sir* Humphry Edwyn, *a Presbyterian, was some Years ago Lord-Mayor of* London, *and had the Insolence to go in his Formalities to a Conventicle, with the Ensigns of his Office.*

[1] This alludes to K. *James's* dispensing with the penal Laws against Papists & Protestant Dissenters, & granting full liberty to both; which made the Church of England turn against him, & joyn with K. *William*; after which the Rom. Catholicks were restrained again, but a Tolleration [was] granted to the Protestant Dissenters, to the great regret & offence of many Church-men. [1720.]

This alludes . . . regret of the High Church party, who were extremly offended to see a Presbiterian (Sir *Humphry Edwin*) Lord Mayor of London [1734].

[2] i.e. under William III.

Custard.[1] But the Particulars of all these, with several others, which have now slid out of my Memory, are lost beyond all Hopes of Recovery. For which Misfortune, leaving my Readers to condole with each other, as far as they shall find it to agree with their several Constitutions; but conjuring them by all the Friendship that hath passed between Us, from the Title-Page to this, not to proceed so far as to injure their Healths, for an Accident past Remedy; I now go on to the Ceremonial Part of an accomplish'd Writer, and therefore, by a Courtly *Modern*, least of all others to be omitted.

* *Custard is a famous Dish at a Lord-Mayors Feast.*[2]

[1] Sir Humphrey Edwin was elected Lord Mayor in September, 1697. His indiscretion was the occasion of several pamphlets, notably Defoe's *Enquiry into the Occasional Conformity of Dissenters in Cases of Preferment* (1697). See W. Wilson, *Memoirs of Defoe* (1830), i, pp. 270–6, and *D.N.B.*

Till the reign of George I the Lord Mayor rode on horseback in the annual procession. *A New and Compleat Survey of London* (1742), ii, p. 966, says that 'the Custom of riding being laid aside in the year 1714, the Procession at present is perform'd by Coaches'. In 1714, according to the brief report in *The Post Boy* for 28–30 October, the Lord Mayor 'made his Cavalcade with the usual Ceremonies';

but *The Political State of Great Britain* for 1718 (xvi, p. 378) says that the Lord Mayor and aldermen 'went in their Coaches'. The 'great Horse' was retained for other occasions. The account of the Lord Mayor in *The True State of England* (1726), p. 186, has this passage: 'When he appears abroad on Horse-back, 'tis with rich Caparisons, and always in long Robes; sometimes Purple, sometimes Scarlet, with a great Chain of Gold, . . . he is also attended by several Officers, walking before, and on both sides of him.' Cf. p. 79, ll. 8–10, where the addition of 'a white Rod' anticipates the satire on the 'sticks' in *Gulliver's Travels*, i. iii.

[2] 'Table' *Notes* 1711.

THE
CONCLUSION.

GOING *too long* is a Cause of Abortion as effectual, tho' not so frequent, as *Going too short*; and holds true especially in the *Labors* of the Brain. Well fare the Heart of that Noble *_Jesuit_,[1] who first adventur'd to confess in Print, that Books must be suited to their several Seasons, like Dress, and Dyet, and Diversions; And better fare our noble Nation,[2] for refining upon this, among other *French* Modes. I am living fast, to see the Time, when a *Book* that misses its Tide, shall be neglected, as the *Moon* by Day, or like *Mackarel* a Week after the Season. No Man hath more nicely observed our Climate, than the Bookseller who bought the Copy of this Work;[3] He knows to a Tittle what Subjects will best go off in a *dry Year*, and which it is proper to expose foremost, when the Weather-glass is fallen to *much Rain*. When he had seen this Treatise, and consulted his *Almanack* upon it; he gave me to understand, that he had maturely[4] considered the two Principal Things, which were the *Bulk*, and the *Subject*; and found, it would never *take*, but

* *Pere d'Orleans.*

---

[1] Swift refers to a passage in the *Avertissement* to the *Histoire de M. Constance . . . Par le Pere d'Orleans, de la Compagnie de Jesus* (1690): 'Les livres, comme les fruits, ont leur saison, hors de laquelle, sans cesser d'estre beaux & utiles, ils ne sont plus recherchez. Tandis qu'on parle d'une affaire, ou d'un evenement dans le monde; que c'est la nouvelle du jour; qu'on s'en entretient dans les compagnies: tout livre qui en traite, quelque mediocre qu'il soit, est favorablement receu.'

The *Histoire de M. Constance* is one of the books which Swift read in 1697.

[2] 'Notion' edd. 2–4.
[3] See p. 28.
[4] 'maturely' ed. 1; 'manifestly' edd. 2–5.

after a long Vacation, and then only, in case it should happen to be a hard Year for Turnips. Upon which I desired to know, *considering my urgent Necessities*, what he thought might be acceptable this Month. He lookt *Westward*, and said, *I doubt we shall have a Fit of bad Weather; However, if you could prepare some pretty little* Banter[1] (but not in Verse) *or a small Treatise upon the ―― it would run like Wild-Fire. But*, if it hold up, *I have already hired an Author to write something against* Dr. B–tl–y, *which, I am sure, will turn to Account.*[2]

AT length we agreed upon this Expedient; That when a Customer comes for one of these, and desires in Confidence to know the Author; he will tell him very privately, as a Friend, naming which ever of the Wits shall happen to be that Week in the Vogue; and if *Durfy*'s last Play should be in Course, I had as lieve he may be the Person as *Congreve*. This I mention, because I am wonderfully well acquainted with the present Relish of Courteous Readers; and have often observed, with singular Pleasure, that a *Fly* driven from a *Honey-pot*, will immediately, with very good Appetite alight, and finish his Meal on an *Excrement*.

I have one Word to say upon the Subject of *Profound Writers*, who are grown very numerous of late; And, I know very well, the judicious World is resolved to list me in that Number. I conceive therefore, as to the Business of being *Profound*, that it is with *Writers*, as with *Wells*; A Person with good Eyes may see to the Bottom of the deepest, provided any *Water* be there; and, that often, when there is nothing in the World at the Bottom, besides *Dryness* and *Dirt*, tho' it be but a Yard and

---

[1] See p. 13, note 3.
[2] When Dr. *Prideaux* brought the copy of his connexion of the Old and New Testament to the bookseller, he told him, it was a *dry subject*, and the printing could not safely be ventured unless he could *enliven it with a little humour* [Hawkesworth].

half under Ground, it shall pass, however, for wondrous *Deep*, upon no wiser a Reason than because it is wondrous *Dark*.

I am now trying an Experiment very frequent among Modern Authors; which is, to *write upon Nothing*;[1] When the Subject is utterly exhausted, to let the Pen still move on; by some called, the Ghost of Wit, delighting to walk after the Death of its Body. And to say the Truth, there seems to be no Part of Knowledge in fewer Hands, than That of Discerning *when to have Done*. By the Time that an Author has writ out a Book, he and his Readers are become old Acquaintance,[2] and grow very loth to part: So that I have sometimes known it to be in Writing, as in Visiting, where the Ceremony of taking Leave, has employ'd more Time than the whole Conversation before. The Conclusion of a Treatise, resembles the Conclusion of Human Life, which hath sometimes been compared to the End of a Feast; where few are satisfied to depart, *ut plenus vitæ conviva*:[3] For Men will sit down after the fullest Meal, tho' it be only to *doze*, or to *sleep* out the rest of the Day. But, in this latter, I differ extreamly from other Writers; and shall be too proud, if by all my Labors, I can have any ways contributed to the *Repose* of Mankind in *Times so turbulent and unquiet as these. Neither

* *This was writ before the Peace of* Riswick.

[1] 'The strongest effort of his [Rochester's] Muse is his poem upon *Nothing*. He is not the first who has chosen this barren topick for the boast of his fertility. There is a poem called *Nihil* in Latin by Passerat, a poet and critick of the sixteenth century in France.' (Johnson, *Lives of the Poets,* ed. Birkbeck Hill, i. 224.)

Cf. also Fielding's *Essay on Nothing,* in which it is said that 'except a hardy wit in the reign of Charles II, none ever hath dared to write on this subject'. There is a poem on *Nothing* by William of Poitiers, c. 1100.

[2] 'Acquaintance' edd. 1–3; 'Acquaintants' edd. 4, 5.

[3] Lucretius, iii. 938.

do I think such an Employment so very alien from the Office of a *Wit*, as some would suppose. For among a very Polite Nation in *Greece*,[1] there were the *same* Temples built and consecrated to *Sleep* and the *Muses*, between which two Deities, they believed the strictest Friendship was established.

* *Trezenii Pausan.* l. 2.

I have one concluding Favour, to request of my Reader; that he will not expect to be equally diverted and informed by every Line, or every Page of this Discourse; but give some Allowance to the Author's Spleen, and short Fits or Intervals of Dullness, as well as his own; And lay it seriously to his Conscience, whether, if he were walking the Streets, in dirty Weather, or a rainy Day; he would allow it fair Dealing in Folks at their Ease from a Window, to Critick[2] his Gate, and ridicule his Dress at such a Juncture.

IN my Disposure of Employments of the Brain, I have thought fit to make *Invention* the *Master*, and to give[3] *Method* and *Reason*, the Office of its *Lacquays*. The Cause of this Distribution was, from observing it my peculiar Case, to be often under a Temptation of being *Witty*, upon Occasions,[4] where I could be neither *Wise* nor *Sound*, nor any thing to the Matter in hand. And, I am too much a Servant of the *Modern* Way, to neglect any such Opportunities, whatever Pains or Improprieties I may be at, to introduce them. For, I have observed, that from a laborious Collection of Seven Hundred Thirty Eight *Flowers*, and *shining Hints* of the best *Modern* Authors, digested with great Reading, into my Book of *Common-places*; I have not been able after five Years to draw, hook, or force into common

---

[1] Pausanias, ii. 31. 5.

[2] Cf. Dryden, *Virgil* (1697), Life, p. 20: 'those who can Critick his *Poetry*, can never find a blem-ish in his *Manners*'.

[3] 'to give' edd. 1–4; 'give' ed. 5.

[4] 'Occasions' ed. 1; 'Occasion' edd. 2–5.

Conversation, any more than a Dozen. Of which Dozen, the one Moiety failed of Success, by being dropt among unsuitable Company; and the other cost me so many Strains, and Traps, and *Ambages* to introduce, that I at length resolved to give it over. Now, this Disappointment, (to discover a Secret) I must own, gave me the first Hint of setting up for an *Author*; and, I have since found among some particular Friends, that it is become a very general Complaint, and has produced the same Effects upon many others. For, I have remarked many a *towardly Word*, to be wholly neglected or despised in *Discourse*, which hath passed very smoothly, with some Consideration and Esteem, after its Preferment and Sanction in *Print*. But now, since by the Liberty and Encouragement of the Press, I am grown absolute Master of the Occasions and Opportunities, to expose the Talents I have acquired; I already discover, that the *Issues* of my *Observanda* begin to grow too large for the *Receipts*. Therefore, I shall here pause awhile, till I find, by feeling the World's Pulse, and my own, that it will be of absolute Necessity for us both, to resume my Pen.

F I N I S.

A

Full and True Account

OF THE

BATTEL

Fought laſt *FRIDAY*,

Between the

Antient and the *Modern*

BOOKS

IN

St. *JAMES*'s

LIBRARY.

LONDON:

Printed in the Year, MDCCX.

THE
BOOKSELLER
TO THE
READER.[1]

THE following Discourse, as it is unquestionably of the same Author, so it seems to have been written about the same time with the former, I mean, the Year 1697,[2] when the famous Dispute was on Foot, about *Antient and Modern Learning*. The Controversy took its Rise from an Essay of Sir *William Temple*'s,[3]

[1] This account of the Ancient and Modern Learning Controversy appears to have been written just before the *Battle of the Books* was published in 1704. Charles Boyle became Earl of Orrery in August 1703. In the *Battle* itself the account of the Controversy ends with Boyle's attack on Bentley and Wotton in 1698.

[2] As the dates of the pamphlets show, the years 1698 and 1699, quite as much as 1697, were those in which the 'dispute was on foot'.

[3] The Essay of Sir William Temple's is that on *Ancient and Modern Learning*, which appeared in the second part of his *Miscellanea* in 1690. The answer by W. Wotton is his *Reflections upon Ancient and Modern Learning* (first edition 1694; second edition with

Bentley's *Dissertations upon the Epistles of Phalaris . . . And the Fables of Æsop*, 1697, third edition with Wotton's *Defense of the Reflections upon Ancient and Modern Learning*, 1705). The 'Appendix by Dr. Bentley' is the *Dissertation* just mentioned as having appeared in the second edition of Wotton's book. The 'new edition of Phalaris' is that published by Charles Boyle in 1695. 'Boyle replied at large' in *Dr. Bentley's Dissertations . . . Examin'd by the Honourable Charles Boyle, Esq.* (first edition 1698; second edition with the addition of 'A Short Account of Dr. Bentley, by way of Index', same year; third edition with the addition of four pages of remarks occasioned by John Milner's *View of the Dissertation upon*

upon that Subject; which was answer'd by *W. Wotton*,
B.D. with an Appendix by Dr. *Bently*, endeavouring to
destroy the Credit of *Æsop* and *Phalaris*, for Authors,
whom Sir *William Temple* had in the Essay before-
mentioned, highly commended. In that Appendix, the
Doctor falls hard upon a new Edition of *Phalaris*, put
out by the Honourable *Charles Boyle* (now *Earl* of
Orrery) to which, Mr. *Boyle* replyed at large, with great
Learning and Wit; and the Doctor, voluminously, re-
joyned. In this Dispute, the Town highly resented to
see a Person of Sir *William Temple*'s Character and
Merits, roughly used by the two Reverend Gentlemen
aforesaid, and without any manner of Provocation. At
length, there appearing no End of the Quarrel, our
Author tells us, that the BOOKS in St. *James*'s
Library,[1] looking upon themselves as Parties principally
concerned, took up the Controversie, and came to a
decisive Battel; But, the Manuscript, by the Injury of
Fortune, or Weather, being in several Places imperfect,
we cannot learn to which side the Victory fell.

I must warn the Reader, to beware of applying to
Persons what is here meant, only of Books in the most
literal Sense. So, when *Virgil* is mentioned, we are not
to understand the Person of a famous Poet, call'd by
that Name, but only certain Sheets of Paper, bound up
in Leather, containing in Print, the Works of the said
Poet, and so of the rest.

the Epistles of Phalaris, 1699).
Bentley 'voluminously rejoined'
in his *Dissertation upon the Epistles
of Phalaris. With An Answer to the
Objections of the Honourable
Charles Boyle, Esquire* . . . 1699.

[1] The Royal Library in St.
James's Palace. Bentley was nom-
inated librarian in succession to
Henry de Justel in December
1693, and the patent constituting
him keeper of all the king's
libraries was dated 12 April 1694.
See the Preface to his *Dissertation*
(1699), pp. xiv–xix.

THE

PREFACE

OF THE

AUTHOR.

S*ATYR is a sort of* Glass, *wherein Beholders do generally*
discover every body's Face but their Own; which is the
chief Reason for that kind of [1] *Reception it meets in the World,*
and that so very few are offended with it. But *if it should*
happen otherwise, the Danger is not great; and, I have
learned from long Experience, never to apprehend Mischief
from those Understandings, I have been able to provoke;
For, Anger and Fury, though they add Strength to the
Sinews *of the* Body, *yet are found to relax those of the*
Mind, *and to render all its Efforts feeble and impotent.*

THERE is a Brain *that will endure but one* Scum-
ming: [2] *Let the Owner gather it with Discretion, and*
manage his little Stock with Husbandry; but of all things,
let him beware of bringing it under the Lash *of his* Betters;
because, That will make it all bubble up into Impertinence,
and he will find no new Supply: Wit, *without knowledge,*
being a Sort of Cream, [3] *which gathers in a Night to the*

---

[1] 'of' omitted edd. 4, 5.

[2] This seems to refer to Wotton, but *wit without knowledge* is
far from applicable to him. It may

be a sarcasm on the mass of general
information in his *Reflections*.

[3] There is a similar metaphor
in the *Histoire Poëtique* of François

Top, and by a skilful Hand, may be soon whipt *into* Froth; *but once scumm'd away, what appears underneath will be fit for nothing, but to be thrown to the Hogs.*

de Callières (1688), p. 74: 'tous les discours de cet Auteur [Balzac] ressembloient à de la crême foüettée qui a beaucoup d'apparence & peu de substance'. See above, p. 14, note 2.

Original Design

A Full and True

ACCOUNT

OF THE

BATTEL

Fought last *FRIDAY*, &c.

WHOEVER examines with due Circumspection into the *Annual Records of Time,[1] will find it remarked, that *War is the Child of Pride*, and *Pride the Daughter of Riches*; The former of which Assertions may be soon granted; but one cannot so easily subscribe to the latter: For *Pride* is nearly related to Beggary and *Want*, either by Father or Mother, and sometimes by both; And, to

> * *Riches produ-ceth Pride; Pride is War's Ground, &c.* Vid. Ephem. de *Mary Clarke;* opt. Edit.

---

[1] The reference to the 'Ephem. de Mary Clarke' was thus explained by Hawkesworth—'now called *Wing's* sheet almanack, and printed by *J. Roberts* for the Company of *Stationers*'. In Swift's days the sheet almanack issued under the name of Vincent Wing was 'printed by Mary Clark, for the Company of Stationers'. It contained in columns the calendar for the year, with weather prognostications, and other entries. In the top left hand corner there was a figure showing the signs of the Zodiac, and beside it was the following rhyme:
> War begets Poverty,
>   Poverty Peace:
> Peace maketh Riches flow,
>   (Fate ne'er doth cease:)
> Riches produceth Pride,
>   Pride is War's ground,
> War begets Poverty, &c.
>   (The World) goes round.

The contraction *Ephem.* stands for *Ephemeris* or *Ephemerides. Opt. Edit.,* i.e. *Optima Editio,* is a

speak naturally, it very seldom happens among Men to
fall out, when all have enough: Invasions usually travelling from *North* to *South*, that is to say, from Poverty
upon[1] Plenty. The most antient and natural Grounds
of Quarrels, are *Lust* and *Avarice*; which, tho' we may
allow to be Brethren or collateral Branches of *Pride*, are
certainly the Issues of *Want*. For, to speak in the Phrase
of Writers upon the Politicks,[2] we may observe in the
Republick of *Dogs*, (which in its Original seems to be
an Institution of the *Many*) that the whole State is ever
in the profoundest Peace, after a full Meal; and, that
Civil Broils arise among them, when it happens for one
great *Bone* to be seized on by some *leading Dog*, who
either divides it among the *Few*, and then it falls to an
Oligarchy, or keeps it to Himself, and then it runs up to
a *Tyranny*. The same Reasoning also, holds Place among

humorous description of the current issue of a popular sheet.

Cf. the *Lettere storiche di Luigi
da Porto* (Florence, 1857, p. 26):
'Perciocchè io sempre ho udito
dire, che la pace fa ricchezza; la
ricchezza fa superbia; la superbia
fa ira; la ira fa guerra; la guerra fa
povertà; la povertà fa umanità; la
umanità fa pace; e la pace, come
dissi, fa ricchezza: e così girano
le cose del mondo (Da Vicenza,
7 marzo 1509).' In Puttenham's
Arte of English Poesie (1588) the
verses are attributed to 'Ihean de
Mehune the French poet' (ed.
Arber, p. 217).

Many other instances might be
cited, e.g. Denham's *Cooper's Hill*,
ll. 33–34:
    While luxury, and wealth, like
        war and peace,
    Are each the others ruine, and

increase.

Others are given in the correspondence on the subject in *The
Times Literary Supplement*, 17
February–30 March 1916. It is
found in English as early as the
fifteenth century.

In his Essay *Of Poetry*, ed.
1696, p. 357, Temple says that
'Plenty begets Wantonness and
Pride'.

And the rhyme was no doubt
still in Swift's mind when he said
in *Gulliver's Travels*, iv, chap. v,
that '*Poor* Nations are *hungry*, and
rich Nations are *proud*; and Pride
and Hunger will ever be at
Variance'.

[1] 'to' Hawkesworth.

[2] Cf. Hobbes, *Leviathan*, part
ii, chap. 17, where Aristotle is
cited as numbering Bees and Ants
'amongst Politicall creatures'.

them, in those Dissensions we behold upon a Turges-
cency in any of their Females. For, the Right of Possession lying in common (it being impossible to establish
a Property in so delicate a Case) Jealousies and Suspi-
cions do so abound, that the whole Commonwealth of
that Street, is reduced to a manifest *State of War*,
of every *Citizen* against every *Citizen*; till some One of
more Courage, Conduct, or Fortune than the rest, seizes
and enjoys the Prize; Upon which, naturally arises
Plenty of Heartburning, and Envy, and Snarling against
the *Happy Dog*. Again, if we look upon any of these
Republicks engaged in a Forein War, either of Invasion
or Defence, we shall find, the same Reasoning will serve,
as to the Grounds and Occasions of each; and, that
Poverty, or *Want*, in some Degree or other, (whether
Real, or in Opinion, which makes no Alteration in the
Case) has a great Share, as well as *Pride*, on the Part of
the Aggressor.

NOW, whoever will please to take this Scheme, and
either reduce or adapt it to an Intellectual State, or
Commonwealth of Learning, will soon discover the first
Ground of Disagreement between the two great Parties
at this Time in Arms; and may form just Conclusions
upon the Merits of either Cause. But the Issue or
Events of this War are not so easie to conjecture at:
For, the present Quarrel is so enflamed by the warm
Heads of either Faction, and the Pretensions *somewhere
or other* so exorbitant, as not to admit the least Overtures
of Accommodation: This Quarrel first began (as I have
heard it affirmed by an old Dweller in the Neighbourhood) about a small Spot of Ground, *lying* and *being*
upon one of the two Tops of the Hill *Parnassus*; the
highest and largest of which had, it seems, been time
out of Mind, in quiet Possession of certain Tenants,
call'd the *Antients*; And the other was held by the
Moderns. But, these disliking their present Station, sent

certain Ambassadors to the *Antients*, complaining of a great Nuisance, how the Height of that Part of *Parnassus*, quite spoiled the Prospect of theirs, especially towards the *East*;[1] and therefore, to avoid a War, offered them the Choice of this Alternative; either that the *Antients* would please to remove themselves and their Effects down to the lower Summity,[2] which the *Moderns* would graciously surrender to them, and advance in their Place; or else, that the said *Antients* will give leave to the *Moderns* to come with Shovels and Mattocks, and level the said Hill, as low as they shall think it convenient. To which, the *Antients* made Answer: How little they expected such a Message as this, from a Colony, whom they had admitted out of their own Free Grace, to so near a Neighbourhood. That, as to their own Seat, they were *Aborigines* of it, and therefore, to talk with them of a Removal or Surrender, was a Language they did not understand. That, if the Height of the Hill, on their side, shortned the Prospect of the *Moderns*, it was a Disadvantage they could not help, but desired them to consider, whether that Injury (if it be any) were not largely recompenced by the *Shade* and *Shelter* it afforded them. That, as to levelling[3] or digging down, it was either Folly or Ignorance to propose it, if they did, or did not know, how that side of the Hill was an entire Rock, which would break their Tools and Hearts; without any Damage to itself. That they would therefore advise the *Moderns*, rather to raise their own

[1] Whence we derive all learning [*MS. Pate*].

Sir William Temple affects to trace the progress of arts and sciences from east to west. Thus the moderns had only such knowledge of the learning of Chaldæa and Egypt as was conveyed to them through the medium of Grecian and Roman writers [Scott]. See Temple's Essay on *Ancient and Modern Learning*, ed. 1696, pp. 7 ff.

[2] An old form of *summit*, common in the sixteenth and seventeenth centuries, but not given in Johnson's *Dictionary*.

[3] 'the levelling' edd. 4, 5.

side of the Hill, than dream of pulling down that of the
Antients, to the former of which, they would not only
give Licence, but also largely contribute. All this was
rejected by the *Moderns*, with much Indignation, who
still insisted upon one of the two Expedients; And so
this Difference broke out into a long and obstinate War,
maintain'd on the one Part, by Resolution, and by the
Courage of certain Leaders and Allies; but, on the
other, by the greatness of their Number, upon all De-
feats, affording continual Recruits. In this Quarrel,
whole Rivulets of *Ink* have been exhausted, and the
Virulence of both Parties enormously augmented. Now,
it must here be understood, that *Ink* is the great mis-
sive Weapon, in all Battels of the *Learned*, which, convey'd thro' a sort of Engine, call'd a *Quill*, infinite Numbers of these are darted at the Enemy, by the Valiant on
each side, with equal Skill and Violence, as if it were an
Engagement of *Porcupines*. This malignant Liquor was
compounded by the Engineer, who invented it, of two
Ingredients, which are *Gall* and *Copperas*, by its Bitterness and Venom, to *Suit* in some Degree, as well as to
Foment the Genius of the Combatants. And as the *Grecians*, after an Engagement, when they could not *agree*
about the Victory, were wont to set up Trophies on
both sides,[1] the beaten Party being content to be at the
same Expence, to keep it self in Countenance (A laudable and antient Custom, happily reviv'd of late, in the
Art of War[2]) so the *Learned*, after a sharp and bloody
Dispute, do on both sides hang out their Trophies too,
which-ever comes by the worst. These Trophies have
largely inscribed on them the Merits of the Cause; a
full impartial Account of such a Battel, and how the
Victory fell clearly to the Party that set them up. They

[1] Cf. Thucydides, i. 54 (Battle
of Sybota), ii. 92, &c. Swift read
Hobbes's translation in 1697.

[2] Perhaps an allusion to the
Catholic celebrations on the supposed victory at the Boyne.

are known to the World under several Names: As, *Disputes*, *Arguments*, *Rejoynders*, *Brief Considerations*, *Answers*, *Replies*, *Remarks*, *Reflexions*, *Objections*, *Confutations*. For a very few Days they are fixed up in all Publick Places, either by themselves or their *Representatives, for Passengers to gaze at:[1] From whence the chiefest and largest are removed to certain Magazines, they call, *Libraries*, there to remain in a Quarter purposely assign'd them, and from thenceforth, begin to be called, *Books of Controversie*.

* *Their Title-Pages.*

IN these Books, is wonderfully instilled and preserved, the Spirit of each Warrier, while he is alive;[2] and after his Death, his Soul transmigrates there, to inform them.[3] This, at least, is the more common Opinion; But, I believe, it is with Libraries, as with other Cemeteries,[4] where some Philosophers affirm, that a certain Spirit, which they call *Brutum hominis*,[5] hovers

[1] Cf. p. 34, note 2.

[2] Cf. Milton, *Areopagitica*, par. 2: 'Books . . . do preserve as in a violl the purest efficacie and extraction of that living intellect that bred them.'

[3] i.e. to animate, to imbue with spirit or character: from scholastic Latin *informare* (cf. p. 151). Cf. Sir Thomas Browne, *Religio Medici*, i, sect. 12: 'if one soule were so perfect as to informe three distinct bodies, that were a petty Trinity'; and *Absalom and Achitophel*, ll. 156–8:
A fiery Soul, which working out its way,
Fretted the Pigmy Body to decay:
And o'r informed the Tenement of Clay.

[4] 'Cœmeteries' edd. 4, 5.

[5] Swift appears to have taken this phrase from Thomas Vaughan's *Anthroposophia Theomagica* (1650), p. 58: 'This Vanish, or ascent of the inward *Ethereall* Principles doth not presently follow their separation: For that part of man which *Paracelsus* calls *Homo Sydereus*, and more appositly *Brutum hominis*: but *Agrippa Idolum*, and *Virgil*
Æthereum sensum atq; Aurai Simplicis Ignē;
This Part I say, which is the *Astral Man*, hovers sometimes about the *Dormitories* of the Dead.' Cf. Sir Thomas Browne, *Religio Medici*, i. 36, and Sir Kenelm Digby, *Observations upon Religio Medici*.

over the Monument, till the Body is corrupted, and turns to *Dust*, or to *Worms*, but then vanishes or dissolves: So, we may say, a restless Spirit haunts over every *Book*, till *Dust* or *Worms* have seized upon it; which to some, may happen in a few Days, but to others, later; And therefore, *Books* of Controversy, being of all others, haunted by the most disorderly Spirits, have always been confined in a separate Lodge from the rest; and for fear of mutual violence against each other, it was thought Prudent by our Ancestors, to bind them to the Peace[1] with strong Iron Chains. Of which Invention, the original Occasion was this:[2] When the Works of *Scotus* first came out, they were carried to a certain great Library, and had Lodgings appointed them; But this Author was no sooner settled, than he went to visit his Master *Aristotle*, and there both concerted together to seize *Plato* by main Force, and turn him out from his antient Station among the *Divines*, where he had peaceably dwelt near Eight Hundred Years. The Attempt succeeded, and the two Usurpers have reigned ever since in his stead: But to maintain Quiet for the future, it was decreed, that all *Polemicks* of the larger Size, should be held fast with a Chain.

BY this Expedient, the publick Peace of Libraries, might certainly have been preserved, if a new Species of controversial Books had not arose of late Years, instinct with a most malignant Spirit, from the War abovementioned, between the *Learned*, about the higher Summity of *Parnassus*.

WHEN these Books were first admitted into the

[1] Cf. Swift's *Legion Club*:
When you walk among your
books,
They reproach you with their
looks;
Bind them fast, or from their
shelves
They will come and right themselves.
Cf. also p. 148, note 1.

[2] Plato had been deposed by the theologians in favour of Aristotle long before the time of Duns Scotus.

Publick Libraries, I remember to have said upon Occasion, to several Persons concerned, how I was sure, they would create Broyls wherever they came, unless a World of Care were taken: And therefore, I advised, that the Champions of each side should be coupled together, or otherwise mixt, that like the blending of contrary Poysons, their Malignity might be employ'd among themselves. And it seems, I was neither an ill Prophet, nor an ill Counsellor; for it was nothing else but the Neglect of this Caution, which gave Occasion to the terrible Fight that happened on *Friday* last between the *Antient* and *Modern Books* in the *King's Library*. Now, because the Talk of this Battel is so fresh in every body's Mouth, and the Expectation of the Town so great to be informed in the Particulars; I, being possessed of all Qualifications requisite in an *Historian*, and retained by neither Party; have resolved to comply with the urgent *Importunity of my Friends*, by writing down a full impartial Account thereof.

THE *Guardian* of the *Regal Library*,[1] a Person of great Valor, but chiefly renowned for his *Humanity*,[2] had been a fierce Champion for the *Moderns*, and in an Engagement upon *Parnassus*, had vowed, with his own

* *The Honourable Mr.* Boyle, *in the Preface to his Edition of* Phalaris, *says, he was refus'd a Manuscript by the Library-Keeper*, pro solita Humanitate suâ.

[1] Bentley. See p. 214, note 1.
[2] In the last paragraph of the Preface to his edition of the *Letters of Phalaris* Boyle had spoken of Bentley's lack of courtesy: 'Epistolas ipsas cum duobus MSS Bodleianis è Cantuariensi & Seldeni Musæo contuli, collatas etiam curavi usque ad Epist. 40 cum MSᵒ in Bibliothecâ Regiâ, cujus mihi copiam ulteriorem Biblio-thecarius pro singulari suâ humanitate negavit.' Bentley referred to this passage in his *Dissertation* of 1697, pp. 66 ff., rendering the allusion to his lack of courtesy as 'out of his singular Humanity'. Boyle in turn adopted this translation, and spoke of Bentley's 'Humanity' in his *Examination* (1698), p. 15.

Hands, to knock down two of the *Antient* Chiefs,[1] who
guarded a small Pass on the superior Rock; but endeavouring to climb up, was cruelly obstructed by his
own unhappy Weight, and tendency towards his Center; a Quality, to which, those of the *Modern* Party, are
extreme subject; For, being lightheaded, they have
in Speculation, a wonderful Agility, and conceive
nothing too high for them to mount; but in reducing
to Practice, discover a mighty Pressure about their
Posteriors and their Heels. Having thus failed in his
Design, the disappointed Champion bore a cruel Ran-
cour to the *Antients*, which he resolved to gratifie, by
shewing all Marks of his Favour to the *Books* of their
Adversaries, and lodging them in the fairest Apart-
ments; when at the same time, whatever *Book* had the
boldness to own it self for an Advocate of the *Antients*,
was buried alive in some obscure Corner, and threatned
upon the least Displeasure, to be turned out of Doors.
Besides, it so happened, that about this time, there was
a strange Confusion of Place among all the *Books* in the
Library;[2] for which several Reasons were assigned.

---

[1] Phalaris and Æsop.

[2] Boyle wrote in the *Examination* (1698), p. 14: 'Another
[learned man] that was desirous
to have a sight of the *Alexandrian*
MS, and apply'd himself to Dr
Bentley very earnestly for it, met
with no other Answer to his Request, but that *the Library was not
fit to be seen.*'

To the latter part of this accusation Bentley replied in his *Dissertation* (1699), pp. lxv–lxvi: 'I
will own, that I have often said
and lamented, *That the Library
was not fit to be seen.* . . . If the
Room be too mean, and too little
for the Books; if it be much out
of Repair; if the Situation be in-
convenient; if the Access to it be
dishonourable; is the Library-
keeper to answer for 't?'

Cf. *Misson's Memoirs* (trans.
Ozell, 1719), p. 175: 'The King's
Library at St. *James's* is also in a
miserable State: I am told, that Dr.
Bently, who has the keeping of it,
in the room of the late Mr. *Justel,*
does all he can to restore it; but
his Endeavours will be to no Purpose, until the Master of it has
Leisure and Will to have an Eye

Some imputed it to a great heap of *learned Dust*, which a perverse Wind blew off from a Shelf of *Moderns* into the *Keeper*'s Eyes. Others affirmed, He had a Humour to pick the *Worms* out of the *Schoolmen*, and swallow them fresh and fasting; whereof some fell upon his *Spleen*, and some climbed up into his Head, to the great Perturbation of both. And lastly, others maintained, that by walking much in the dark about the Library, he had quite lost the Situation of it out of his Head; And therefore, in replacing his *Books*, he was apt to mistake, and clap *Des-Cartes* next to *Aristotle*; Poor *Plato* had got between *Hobbes* and the *Seven Wise Masters*,[1] and *Virgil* was hemm'd in with *Dryden* on one side, and *Withers* on the other.[2]

MEAN while, those *Books* that were Advocates for the *Moderns*, chose out one from among them, to make a Progress thro' the whole Library, examine the Number and Strength of their Party, and concert their Affairs.

to it himself. There have been Books in Pawn in the Hands of the Binders I know not how many Years. King *Charles* II. did but laugh at it. It is nevertheless a Pity that so many good Books, and so well bound, should be given up to the Mould and Moisture of the Air, to Moths and to Dust.' The French original was published at The Hague in 1698.

[1] For an account of the book see *The Seven Sages of Rome*, ed. Killis Campbell (1907). Swift probably mentions the *Seven Wise Masters* as a sort of modern equivalent to the Seven Sages of the Ancients; cf. Temple, *Ancient and Modern Learning*, ed. 1696, p. 28.

[2] The common spelling of the name of George Wither (1588–1667) at this time: cf. Dryden, *Essay of Dramatic Poesy, ad init.*, and Pope, *The Dunciad*, i, l. 296. Wither was then regarded as a typically bad poet, by reason of his later work. The rare merits of his earlier work were not duly recognized till Lamb made the *Shepherd's Hunting* and *Philarete* the subject of an essay.

Here, as in the *Tale*, Swift shows his resentment towards Dryden for having said 'Cousin Swift, you will never be a poet' (Johnson, *Life of Swift, ad init.*). He mentions Dryden with a writer whom he was known to have despised.

This Messenger performed all things very industriously, and brought back with him a List of their Forces, in all Fifty Thousand, consisting chiefly of *light Horse, heavy-armed Foot,* and *Mercenaries*;[1] Whereof the *Foot* were in general but sorrily armed, and worse clad; Their *Horses* large, but extremely out of Case and Heart; However, some few by trading among the *Antients,* had furnisht themselves tolerably enough.

WHILE Things were in this Ferment; *Discord* grew extremely high, hot Words passed on both sides, and ill blood was plentifully bred. Here a solitary *Antient,* squeezed up among a whole Shelf of *Moderns,* offered fairly to dispute the Case, and to prove by manifest Reasons, that the Priority was due to them, from long Possession, and in regard of their Prudence, Antiquity, and above all, their great Merits towards the *Moderns.* But these denied the Premises, and seemed very much to wonder, how the *Antients* could pretend to insist upon their Antiquity, when it was so plain (if they went to that) the *Moderns* were much the more **Antient* of the two.[2] As for any Obligations they owed to the *Antients,* they renounced them all. *'Tis true,* said they, *we are informed, some few of our Party*

* *According to the Modern Paradox.*

---

[1] Cf. the fuller account given below, from which it appears that the *light Horse* are poets, and the *heavy-armed Foot* are historians.

[2] Cf. Bacon, *Advancement of Learning,* I. v. i: 'And to speak truly, *Antiquitas sæculi juventus mundi.* These times are the ancient times, when the world is ancient, and not those which we account ancient *ordine retrogrado,* by a computation backward from ourselves'; Hobbes, *Leviathan,* Con-

clusion: 'Though I reverence those men of Ancient time, that either have written Truth perspicuously, or set us in a better way to find it out our selves; yet to the Antiquity it self I think nothing due: For if we will reverence the Age, the Present is the Oldest' (cited in *MS. Pate*); Collier, *Essays,* pt. ii, p. 159: 'the present Age is really the Oldest'; Fontenelle, *Pluralité des Mondes,* ed. 1686, p. 350: 'les anciens

*have been so mean to borrow their Subsistence from You;
But the rest, infinitely the greater number (and especially,
we* French *and* English) *were so far from stooping to so
base an Example, that there never passed, till this very
hour, six Words between us. For, our* Horses *are of our
own breeding, our* Arms *of our own forging, and our* Cloaths
of our own cutting out and sowing. Plato *was by chance*
upon the next Shelf, and observing those that spoke to
be in the ragged Plight, mentioned a while ago; their
Jades lean and foundred, their *Weapons* of rotten Wood,
their *Armour* rusty, and nothing but Raggs underneath;
he laugh'd loud, and in his pleasant way, swore, *By
G——, he believ'd them.*

NOW, the *Moderns* had not proceeded in their late
Negotiation, with Secrecy enough to escape the Notice
of the Enemy. For, those Advocates, who had begun
the Quarrel, by setting first on Foot the Dispute of
Precedency, talkt so loud of coming to a Battel, that
Temple[1] happened to over-hear them, and gave immediate Intelligence to the *Antients*; who thereupon drew
up their scattered Troops together, resolving to act upon
the defensive; Upon which, several of the *Moderns* fled
over to their Party, and among the rest, *Temple* himself.
This *Temple* having been educated and long conversed[2]
among the *Antients*, was, of all the *Moderns*, their greatest
Favorite, and became their greatest Champion.

THINGS were at this Crisis, when a material Accident fell out. For, upon the highest Corner of a large
Window, there dwelt a certain *Spider*, swollen up to
the first Magnitude, by the Destruction of infinite Num-

étaient jeunes auprès de nous'; and
Perrault, *Parallèles*, dialogue i:
'notre siècle est postérieur à tous
les autres et par conséquent le
plus ancien de tous.' See also
p. 125, note 1.

[1] The Controversy was introduced into England from France
by Temple's essay on *Ancient and
Modern Learning.*
[2] i.e. conversant: an obsoles-
cent form in Swift's day.

bers of *Flies*, whose Spoils lay scattered before the Gates of his Palace, like human Bones before the Cave of some Giant. The Avenues to his Castle were guarded with Turn-pikes,[1] and Palissadoes, after all the *Modern* way of Fortification.[2] After you had passed several Courts, you came to the Center, wherein you might behold the *Constable* himself in his own Lodgings, which had Windows fronting to each Avenue, and Ports to sally out upon all Occasions of Prey or Defence. In this Mansion he had for some Time dwelt in Peace and Plenty, without Danger to his *Person* by *Swallows* from above, or to his *Palace* by *Brooms* from below: When it was the Pleasure of Fortune to conduct thither a wandring *Bee*, to whose Curiosity a broken Pane in the Glass had discovered it self; and in he went, where expatiating a while, he at last happened to alight upon one of the outward Walls of the *Spider*'s Cittadel; which yielding to the unequal Weight, sunk down to the very Foundation. Thrice he endeavoured to force his Passage, and Thrice the Center shook. The *Spider* within, feeling the terrible Convulsion, supposed at first, that *Nature* was approaching to her final Dissolution; or else, that *Beelzebub*[3] with all his Legions, was come to revenge the Death of many thousands[4] of his Subjects, whom this[5] Enemy had slain and devoured. However, he at length valiantly resolved to issue forth, and meet his Fate. Mean while, the *Bee* had acquitted himself of his Toils, and posted securely at some Distance, was employed in cleansing his Wings, and disengaging them from the ragged Remnants of the Cobweb. By this time the *Spider* was adventured out, when beholding the Chasms, and Ruins,

---

[1] 'Turk-pikes' ed. 5.
[2] The advocates of the Moderns claimed that in this art the Ancients had been excelled: cf. the fifth dialogue of Perrault's

Parallèles.
[3] The Hebrew god of flies [*MS. Pate*].
[4] 'thousand' ed. 1.
[5] 'this' edd. 1–4; 'his' ed. 5.

and Dilapidations of his Fortress, he was very near at his Wit's end, he stormed and swore like a Mad-man, and swelled till he was ready to burst. At length, casting his Eye upon the *Bee*, and wisely gathering Causes from Events, (for they knew each other by Sight) *A Plague split you*, said he, *for a giddy Son of a Whore; Is it you, with a Vengeance, that have made this Litter here? Could you not[1] look before you, and be d————n'd? Do you think I have nothing else to do (in the Devil's Name) but to Mend and Repair after your Arse? Good Words, Friend*, said the *Bee*, (having now pruned himself, and being disposed to drole) *I'll give you my Hand and Word to come near your Kennel no more; I was never in such a confounded Pickle since I was born. Sirrah*, replied the *Spider, if it were not for breaking an old Custom in our Family, never to stir abroad against an Enemy, I should come and teach you better Manners. I pray, have Patience*, said the *Bee, or you will spend your Substance, and for ought I see, you may stand in need of it all, towards the Repair of your House. Rogue, Rogue*, replied the *Spider, yet, methinks, you should have more Respect to a Person, whom all the World allows to be so much your Betters.[2] By my Troth*, said the *Bee, the Comparison will amount to a very good Jest, and you will do me a Favour, to let me know the Reasons, that all the World is pleased to use in so hopeful a Dispute.* At this, the *Spider* having swelled himself into the Size and Posture of a Disputant, began his Argument in the true Spirit of Controversy, with a Resolution to be heartily scurrilous and angry, to urge *on* his own Reasons, without the least Regard to the Answers or Objections of his Opposite;[3] and fully predetermined in his Mind against all Conviction.

---

[1] 'Could not you' edd. 4, 5.

[2] The plural form 'Betters' was commonly applied to a single person at this time. Cf. *The Spectator*, No. 266: 'a Squire or a Gentleman, or one that was her Betters'.

[3] Opponent. Cf. *Hamlet*, v. ii. 62.

NOT to disparage my self, said he, *by the Comparison with such a Rascal; What art thou but a Vagabond without House or Home, without Stock or Inheritance; Born to no Possession of your own, but a Pair of Wings, and a Drone-Pipe. Your Livelihood is an universal Plunder upon Nature; a Freebooter over Fields and Gardens; and for the sake of Stealing, will rob a Nettle as readily as a Violet. Whereas I am a domestick Animal, furnisht with a Native Stock within my self. This large Castle (to shew my Improvements in the Mathematicks)*[1] *is all built with my own Hands, and the Materials extracted altogether out of my own Person.*[2]

I am glad, answered the *Bee, to hear you grant at least, that I am come honestly by my Wings and my Voice, for then, it seems, I am obliged to Heaven alone for my Flights and my Musick; and Providence would never have bestowed on me*[3] *two such Gifts, without designing them for the noblest Ends. I visit, indeed, all the Flowers and Blossoms of the Field and the Garden, but whatever I collect from thence, enriches my self, without the least Injury to their Beauty, their Smell, or their Taste.*[4] *Now, for you and your Skill*

---

[1] Mathematics was a subject in which it was claimed that the Moderns had excelled the Ancients. Cf. Wotton's *Reflections*, chap. xiv. Improvements in fortification were supposed to be a result of increased mathematical knowledge. But Temple had cited ancient architecture as showing 'at what Heights the Mathematicks were among the Ancients' (*Ancient and Modern Learning*, ed. 1696, p. 45).

Swift disliked mathematics and lost no opportunity of deriding the pedantry of mathematicians: see for example *Gulliver's Travels*, part iii, chap. ii.

See also Appendix F, p. 360.

[2] Cf. Descartes, *Discours de la Méthode*, end of first chapter.

[3] 'bestowed me' edd. 1–3.

[4] The bee's answer bears some resemblance to the following passage in Temple's Essay *Of Poetry* (ed. 1696, p. 323): '[Bees] must range through Fields, as well as Gardens, chuse such flowers as they please, and by Properties and Scents they only know and distinguish: They must work up their Cells with Admirable Art, extract their Honey with infinite Labour, and sever it from the Wax, with such Distinction and Choice, as belongs to none but

*in Architecture, and other Mathematicks, I have little to
say: In that Building of yours, there might, for ought I know,
have been Labor and Method enough, but by woful Experience for us both, 'tis too plain, the Materials are nought, and
I hope, you will henceforth take Warning, and consider
Duration and matter, as well as method and Art. You,
boast, indeed, of being obliged to no other Creature, but of
drawing, and spinning out all from your self; That is to say,
if we may judge of the Liquor in the Vessel by what issues
out, You possess a good plentiful Store of Dirt and Poison
in your Breast; And, tho' I would by no means, lessen or
disparage your genuine Stock of either, yet, I doubt you are
somewhat obliged for an Encrease of both, to a little foreign
Assistance. Your inherent Portion of Dirt, does not fail of
Acquisitions, by Sweepings exhaled from below: and one
Insect furnishes you with a share of Poison to destroy another.
So that in short, the Question comes all to this; Whether is
the nobler Being of the two, That which by a lazy Contemplation of four Inches round; by an over-weening Pride,
which*[1] *feeding and engendering on it self, turns all into
Excrement and Venom; producing nothing at last,*[2] *but Fly-
bane and a Cobweb: Or That, which, by an universal
Range, with long Search, much Study, true Judgment, and
Distinction of Things, brings home Honey and Wax.*

THIS Dispute was managed with such Eagerness,
Clamor, and Warmth, that the two Parties of *Books* in
Arms below, stood Silent a while, waiting in Suspense
what would be the Issue; which was not long undetermined: For the *Bee* grown impatient at so much loss
of Time, fled strait away to a bed of Roses, without

---

themselves to perform or to judge.'
There is some resemblance also to
Bacon, *Novum Organum,* xcv.

[1] Hawkesworth omitted this
'which', and his alteration has
been generally adopted, but is not

convincing. Perhaps 'producing
should be 'produces', corresponding to 'brings home'.

[2] 'at last' ed. 1; 'at all' edd.
2–5.

looking for a Reply; and left the *Spider* like an Orator, *collected* in himself, and just prepared to burst out.

I T happened upon this Emergency, that *Æsop* broke silence first. He had been of late most barbarously treated by a strange Effect of the *Regent*'s *Humanity*,[1] who had tore off his Title-page,[2] sorely defaced one half of his Leaves, and chained him fast among a Shelf of *Moderns*. Where soon discovering how high the Quarrel was like to proceed, He tried all his Arts, and turned himself to a thousand Forms:[3] At length in the borrowed Shape of an *Ass*,[4] the *Regent* mistook him for a *Modern*; by which means, he had Time and Opportunity to escape to the *Antients*, just when the *Spider* and the *Bee* were entring into their Contest; to which He gave His Attention with a world of Pleasure; and when it was ended, swore in the loudest Key, that in all his Life, he had never known two Cases so parallel and adapt to each other, as That in the Window, and this upon the Shelves. The *Disputants*, said he, *have admirably managed the Dispute between them, have taken in the full Strength of all that is to be said on both sides, and exhausted the Substance of every Argument* pro *and* con. *It is but to adjust the Reasonings of both to the present Quarrel, then to compare and apply the Labors and Fruits of each, as the* Bee *has learnedly deduced them; and we shall*

---

[1] See above, p. 224, note 2.

[2] An allusion to Bentley's views on the genuineness of the Fables attributed to Æsop.

[3] Cf. *Georgics*, iv. 440–2.

[4] Bentley was supposed to have called Boyle an *Ass*. So at least Boyle complained in his *Examination*, pp. 219, 220. But Bentley had only quoted 'the old *Greek* Proverb, *That* Leucon *carries one thing, and his Ass quite another*'

(*Dissertation*, p. 74); and Boyle —'voluntarily', as Bentley said— had taken this to imply that 'the Writer of the Greek Epistle means differently from the *Ass* his Editor'. See also *Dissertation* (1699), pp. lxxv–lxxxiii. Accordingly Swift credits Bentley with a propensity to mistake Asses for Moderns—a happy stroke of satire as Bentley is himself a leader of the Moderns.

find the Conclusion[1] *fall plain and close upon the* Moderns *and* Us. *For, pray Gentlemen, was ever any thing so* Modern *as the* Spider *in his Air, his Turns, and his Paradoxes? He argues in the Behalf of* You *his Brethren, and Himself, with many Boastings of his native Stock, and great Genius; that he Spins and Spits wholly from himself, and scorns to own any Obligation or Assistance from without. Then he displays to you his great Skill in Architecture, and Improvement in the Mathematicks. To all this, the* Bee, *as an Advocate, retained by us the* Antients, *thinks fit to Answer; That if one may judge of the great Genius or Inventions of the* Moderns, *by what they have produced, you will hardly have Countenance to bear you out in boasting of either. Erect your Schemes with as much Method and Skill as you please; yet, if the materials be nothing but Dirt, spun out of your own Entrails (the Guts of* Modern *Brains) the Edifice will conclude at last in a* Cobweb: *The Duration of which, like that of other* Spiders *Webs, may be imputed to their being forgotten, or neglected, or hid in a Corner. For any Thing else of Genuine, that the* Moderns *may pretend to, I cannot recollect; unless it be a large Vein of* Wrangling *and* Satyr,[2] *much of a Nature and Substance with the* Spider's *Poison; which, however, they*[3] *pretend to spit wholly out of themselves, is improved by the same Arts, by feeding upon the* Insects *and* Vermin *of the Age. As for* Us, *the* Antients, *We are content with the* Bee, *to pretend to Nothing of our own, beyond our* Wings *and our* Voice: *that is to say, our* Flights *and our* Language; *For the rest, whatever we have got, has been by infinite Labor, and search, and ranging thro' every Corner of Nature: The Difference is, that instead of* Dirt *and* Poison, *we have rather chose to fill our Hives with* Honey *and* Wax, *thus*

---

[1] 'Conclusions' edd. 1, 2.
[2] Cf. Temple on 'the Vein of Ridiculing all that is serious and good', *Ancient and Modern Learning, ad fin.*; also p. 48, ll. 1–9.
[3] '*to pretend to*' ed. 5.

*furnishing Mankind with the two Noblest of Things, which
are* Sweetness *and* Light.[1]

'TIS wonderful to conceive the Tumult arisen among
the *Books*, upon the close of this long Descant of *Æsop*;
Both Parties took the Hint, and heightened their Ani-
mosities so on a sudden, that they resolved it should
come to a Battel. Immediately, the two main Bodies
withdrew under their several Ensigns, to the farther
Parts of the Library, and there entred into Cabals, and
Consults[2] upon the present Emergency. The *Moderns*
were in very warm Debates upon the Choice of their
Leaders, and nothing less than the Fear impending from
their Enemies, could have kept them from Mutinies
upon this Occasion. The Difference was greatest among
the *Horse*, where every private *Trooper* pretended to the
chief Command, from *Tasso* and *Milton*, to *Dryden* and
Withers. The *Light-Horse* were Commanded by *Cowly*
and *Despreaux*.[3] There, came the *Bowmen*[4] under their
valiant Leaders, *Des-Cartes*, *Gassendi*, and *Hobbes*,[5] whose

[1] A phrase familiar to later times from its use by Matthew Arnold, *Culture and Anarchy*, chap. i, &c. The advice given in Lucian's *Lexiphanes*, § 23, about 'Sacrificing to the Graces, and to Perspicuity'—μάλιστα δὲ θῦε Χάρισι καὶ Σαφηνείᾳ—had been quoted in Boyle's *Examination*, p. 288. But an exact anticipation of Swift's words occurs in the Latin translation of Philo Judaeus (*Opera* 1640, p. 470 B): 'Haec praecepta diuina Israeliticae, id est perspicaci animae afferunt lucem simul & dulcedinem' (φωτίζει . . . καὶ γλυκαίνει). See W. S. Walsh, *Literary Curiosities*, 1893, p. 1043. Swift need not be supposed

to have borrowed the phrase.

[2] Consultations. Cf. p. 251, l. 13; also *Paradise Lost*, book i, last line.

[3] Nicolas Boileau Despréaux. Boileau was one of the strongest supporters of the Ancients, and the chief antagonist of Perrault: see in particular his *Réflexions critiques sur Longin*. Like Milton and Cowley he is here named, without satirical purpose, as a representative modern poet.

[4] The philosophers.

[5] Descartes, Gassendi, and Hobbes are mentioned together in Wotton's *Reflections*, chap. xx. They differed widely in their views, and are here cited in a

Strength was such, that they could shoot their Arrows beyond the *Atmosphere*, never to fall down again, but turn like that of *Evander*[1] into *Meteors*, or like the *Canonball* into *Stars*. *Paracelsus* brought a *Squadron* of *Stink-Pot-Flingers*[2] from the snowy Mountains of *Rhætia*. There, came a vast Body of *Dragoons*,[3] of different Nations, under the leading of *Harvey*,[4] their great *Aga*:[5] Part armed with *Scythes*, the Weapons of Death; Part with *Launces* and long *Knives*, all steept in *Poison*; Part shot *Bullets* of a most malignant Nature, and used *white Powder* which infallibly killed without *Report*.[6] There, came several Bodies of *heavy-armed Foot*, all *Mercenaries*,[7] under the Ensigns of *Guiccardine*,[8] *Davila*,[9] *Polydore*

group as representative leaders in modern philosophy.

[1] A lapse of memory. Swift is referring to the arrow, not of Evander, but of Acestes. See *Aeneid*, v. 525–8.

[2] A reference to the chemical experiments of the Paracelsians. Paracelsus was a native of Switzerland.

[3] Writers on medical subjects.

[4] 'Hervey' ed. 1. William Harvey (1578–1657), the discoverer of the circulation of the blood. Temple had thrown doubt on the discovery, *Ancient and Modern Learning*, ed. 1696, p. 42: 'There is nothing new in *Astronomy*, to vye with the Ancients, unless it be the *Copernican* System; nor in *Physick*, unless Hervy's Circulation of the blood. But whether either of these be modern discoveries, or derived from old Fountains, is disputed: Nay, it is so too, whether they are true or no. . . .' Wotton had re-

plied in his *Reflections*, chap. xviii.

[5] A commander or chief officer in the Ottoman Empire. The word 'Agah' occurs several times in Bernier's *Grand Mogol*, which Swift read in 1697.

[6] Cf. Sir Thomas Browne, *Vulgar Errors*, book ii, chap. v. 5: 'Of white powder and such as is discharged without report, there is no small noise in the World.' Also John Cleveland, *Rupertismus*, ll. 39, 40:

For Beauty, like white Powder,
  makes no noise,
And yet the silent Hypocrite
  destroys.

[7] The historians. Cf. p. 227, l. 4.

[8] Francesco Guicciardini (1483–1540), Florentine historian. His *Historia d'Italia* (1561) was rendered into English by Fenton (1579). 'Guicciardine' or 'Guicciardin' is the English form of the name.

[9] Enrico Caterino Davila (1576–1631), author of the *His-*

Virgil,[1] *Buchanan,*[2] *Mariana,*[3] *Cambden,*[4] and others.
The *Engineers*[5] were commanded by *Regiomontanus*[6] and
Wilkins.[7] The rest were a confused Multitude, led by
Scotus, Aquinas, and *Bellarmine;*[8] of mighty Bulk and

toria delle Guerre Civili di Francia
(1630), translated by Aylesbury
and Cotterell (1647–8). Cf.
Temple, *Ancient and Modern
Learning,* p. 55: 'Are *D'avila's*
and *Strada's* Histories beyond
those of *Herodotus* and *Livy?*'
Also Wotton's reply to this,
Reflections, chap. iii *ad fin.*

[1] Polydore Vergil (1470–
1555), an Italian by birth, sent to
England by the Pope in 1501 as
sub-collector of Peter's Pence, and
naturalized as an Englishman in
1510. He wrote *Anglicae Histo-
riae libri xxvi* (1534).

[2] George Buchanan (1506–
82), the great Scottish humanist.
He had a European reputation for
his Latin plays and his skill in
Latin verse, but is here mentioned
for his *Rerum Scoticarum Historia*
(1582).

[3] Juan de Mariana (1537–
1624), the greatest of Spanish
historians. He wrote in Latin a
History of Spain (1592), 'to let
Europe know what Spain had
accomplished', and then rewrote
it in Spanish—*Historia de España*
(1601). He defended tyrannicide
in certain circumstances in his *De
Rege* (1599).

[4] William Camden (1551–
1623), the English antiquary and
historian.

[5] The mathematicians.

[6] Johann Müller (1436–76),

mathematician and astronomer.
His Latin name, Regiomontanus,
was taken from his birthplace,
Königsberg.

[7] John Wilkins (1614–72),
Bishop of Chester (1668), and
one of the founders of the Royal
Society during his tenure of the
Wardenship of Wadham College,
Oxford. He wrote *The Discovery
of a World in the Moone; or, a
Discourse tending to prove, that
'tis probable there may be another
Habitable World in that Planet*
(1638), with an addition in 1640
of a *Discourse concerning the
Possibility of a Passage to the
Moon.* In 1668 he produced *An
Essay towards a Real Character,
and a Philosophical Language.*
Both these books are referred to
slightingly by Temple in his
*Thoughts upon Reviewing the Essay
of Ancient and Modern Learning,*
ed. 1701, pp. 282–3: 'An Universal Language, which may serve
all Mens Turn, when they have
forgot their own . . . Discoveries
of new Worlds in the Planets, and
Voyages between this and that in
the Moon, to be made as frequently as between *York and
London.*' Cf. also *Ancient and
Modern Learning,* ed. 1696, p. 55.
But the *Real Character* is praised
by Bentley, *Dissertation* (1699),
Preface, p. xciii.

[8] Roberto Francesco Romolo

Stature, but without either Arms, Courage, or Discipline. In the last Place, came infinite Swarms of *Calones*,[1] a disorderly Rout led by *Lestrange*; Rogues and Raggamuffins, that follow the Camp for nothing but the Plunder; All without *Coats* to cover them.

THE Army of the *Antients* was much fewer in Number; *Homer* led the *Horse*, and *Pindar* the *Light-Horse*; *Euclid* was chief *Engineer*: *Plato* and *Aristotle* commanded the *Bow men*, *Herodotus* and *Livy* the *Foot*, *Hippocrates* the *Dragoons*. The *Allies*, led by *Vossius*[2] and *Temple*, brought up the Rear.

ALL things violently tending to a decisive Battel; *Fame*, who much frequented, and had a large Apartment formerly assigned her in the *Regal Library*, fled up strait to *Jupiter*, to whom she delivered a faithful account of all that passed between the two Parties below. (For, among the Gods, she always tells Truth.) *Jove* in great concern, convokes a Council in the *Milky-Way*. The Senate assembled, he declares the Occasion of convening them; a bloody Battel just impendent between two mighty Armies of *Antient* and *Modern* Creatures, call'd *Books*, wherein the Celestial Interest was but too

* *These are Pamphlets, which are not bound or cover'd.*[3]

Bellarmino (1542–1621), the famous apologist for Roman Catholicism against Protestantism. He is named with the two great Schoolmen as a representative theologian of the Catholic Church.

[1] By calling this disorderly rout *calones* the author points both his satyr and contempt against all sorts of mercenary scriblers, who write as they are commanded by the leaders and patrons of sedition, faction, corruption, and every evil

work: they are stiled *calones* because they are the meanest and most despicable of all writers, as the *calones*, whether belonging to the army or private families, were the meanest of all slaves or servants whatsoever [Hawkesworth].

[2] Possibly Gerrard John Vos or Vossius (1577–1649), but more probably his son Isaac (1618–89), whose book *De Sibyllinis* Swift read in the year 1698.

[3] Note omitted in *Notes* 1711.

deeply concerned. *Momus*, the Patron of the *Moderns*,[1] made an Excellent Speech in their Favor, which was answered by *Pallas* the Protectress of the *Antients*. The Assembly was divided in their affections; when *Jupiter* commanded the Book of Fate to be laid before Him. Immediately were brought by *Mercury*, three large Volumes in Folio, containing Memoirs of all Things past, present, and to come.[2] The Clasps were of Silver, double Gilt; the Covers, of Celestial Turky-leather, and the Paper such as here on Earth might almost pass for Vellum. *Jupiter* having silently read the Decree, would communicate the Import to none, but presently shut up the Book.

WITHOUT the Doors of this Assembly, there attended a vast Number of light, nimble Gods, menial Servants to *Jupiter*:[3] These are his ministring Instruments in all Affairs below. They travel in a Caravan, more or less together, and are fastened to each other like a Link of Gally-slaves, by a light Chain, which passes from them to *Jupiter*'s great Toe: And yet in receiving or delivering a Message, they may never approach above the lowest Step of his Throne, where he and they whisper to each other thro' a long hollow Trunk. These Deities are call'd by mortal Men, *Accidents*, or *Events*; but the Gods call them, *Second Causes*. *Jupiter* having delivered his Message to a certain Number of these Divinities, they flew immediately down to the Pinnacle of the Regal Library, and consulting a few Minutes, entered unseen, and disposed the Parties according to their Orders.

---

[1] Scott suggested that *Momus* is 'named as the presiding deity of the Moderns', probably on account of the superiority claimed for them in works of 'humour'. But it is more probable that Momus is named as the typical carping critic, the direct ancestor of the modern critics: see the *Tale of a Tub*, p. 94.

[2] Cf. *Iliad*, i. 70.

[3] Cf. *Iliad*, viii. 19.

MEAN while, *Momus* fearing the worst, and calling
to mind an antient Prophecy, which bore no very good
Face to his Children the *Moderns*; bent his Flight to
the Region of a malignant Deity, call'd *Criticism*. She
dwelt on the Top of a snowy Mountain in *Nova Zembla*;
there *Momus* found her extended in her Den, upon the
Spoils of numberless Volumes half devoured. At her
right Hand sat *Ignorance*,[1] her Father and Husband,[2]
blind with Age; at her left, *Pride* her Mother, dressing
her up in the Scraps of Paper herself had torn. There,
was *Opinion* her Sister, light of Foot, hoodwinkt, and[3]
headstrong, yet giddy and perpetually turning. About
her play'd her Children, *Noise* and *Impudence*, *Dullness*
and *Vanity*, *Positiveness*, *Pedantry*, and *Ill-Manners*. The
Goddess herself had Claws like a Cat: Her Head, and
Ears, and Voice, resembled those of an *Ass*; Her Teeth
fallen out before; Her Eyes turned inward, as if she
lookt only upon herself:[4] Her Diet was the overflowing
of her own *Gall:* Her *Spleen* was so large, as to stand
prominent like a Dug of the first Rate, nor wanted
Excrescencies in form of Teats, at which a Crew of ugly
Monsters were greedily sucking; and, what is wonderful to conceive, the bulk of Spleen encreased faster than
the Sucking could diminish it. *Goddess*, said *Momus*,

[1] Cf. Temple, *Ancient and
Modern Learning*, p. 3: 'Sufficiency, the worst composition out
of the pride and ignorance of
mankind'; and p. 53: 'his Pride
is greater than his Ignorance; and
what he wants in Knowledge, he
supplies by Sufficiency'. These
phrases had won Wotton's attention in his *Reflections*, chaps. i and
iv. See also Boyle's *Examination*,
p. 286.
    Cf. the *Tale of a Tub*, p. 94,
where the 'true critic' is the de-
scendant of Momus and Hybris.

[2] Perhaps a reminiscence of
Milton's description of 'Sin' and
the 'yelling Monsters' which are
her progeny, *Paradise Lost*,
ii, ll. 781–802.

[3] 'an' edd. 1–3.

[4] The inhabitants of Laputa
(*Gulliver's Travels*, part iii, chap.
ii) have 'one of their Eyes turned
inward, and the other directly up
to the Zenith'.

can you sit idly here, while our devout Worshippers, the
Moderns, *are this Minute entring into a cruel Battel, and,
perhaps, now lying under the Swords of their Enemies;
Who then hereafter, will ever sacrifice, or build Altars to
our Divinities?*[1] *Haste therefore to the* British Isle, *and,
if possible, prevent their Destruction, while I make Factions among the Gods, and gain them over to our Party.*

MOMUS *having thus delivered himself, staid not for
an answer,*[2] *but left the Goddess to her own Resentment;*[3] Up she rose in a Rage, and as it is the Form
upon such Occasions, began a Soliloquy. *'Tis I* (said
she) *who give Wisdom to Infants and Idiots; By Me,
Children grow wiser than their Parents. By Me,* Beaux[4]
become Politicians; and School-boys, *Judges of Philosophy.*[5] *By Me, Sophisters debate, and conclude upon the
Depths of Knowledge; and Coffee-house Wits instinct by
Me, can correct an Author's Style, and display his minutest
Errors, without understanding a Syllable of his Matter or his
Language. By Me, Striplings spend their Judgment, as they
do their Estate, before it comes into their Hands. 'Tis I,
who have deposed Wit and Knowledge from their Empire
over* Poetry, *and advanced my self in their stead. And
shall a few* upstart Antients *dare to*[6] *oppose me?*——*But,
come, my aged Parents, and you, my Children dear, and
thou my beauteous Sister; let us ascend my Chariot, and hast
to assist our devout* Moderns, *who are now sacrificing to us
a* Hecatomb, *as I perceive by that grateful Smell, which
from thence reaches my Nostrils.*

[1] Cf. *Aeneid,* i. 48–49.
[2] Cf. the opening of Bacon's
Essay 'Of Truth': 'What is Truth,
said jesting Pilate; and would not
stay for an Answer.'
[3] 'Resentments' edd. 1–4.
[4] '*Beaus*' edd. 1, 2.
[5] Cf. Temple, *Ancient and
Modern Learning,* p. 54: 'A Boy
of fifteen is wiser than his Father
at forty, the meanest Subject than
his Prince or Governors; and the
modern Scholars, because they
have for a Hundred Years past
learned their Lesson pretty well,
are much more knowing than the
Ancients their Masters.'
[6] '*dare oppose*' ed. 5.

THE Goddess and her Train having mounted the Chariot, which was drawn by *tame Geese*, flew over infinite Regions, shedding her Influence in due Places, till at length, she arrived at her beloved Island of *Britain*; but in hovering over its *Metropolis*, what Blessings did she not let fall upon her Seminaries of *Gresham* and *Covent-Garden*?[1] And now she reach'd the fatal Plain of St. *James*'s Library, at what time the two Armies were upon the Point to engage; where entring with all her Caravan, unseen, and landing upon a Case of Shelves, now desart, but once inhabited by a Colony of *Virtuoso's*[2] she staid a while to observe the Posture of both Armies.

BUT here, the tender Cares of a Mother began to fill her Thoughts, and move in her Breast. For, at the Head of a Troop of *Modern Bow-men*, she cast her Eyes upon her Son *W--tt--n*; to whom the Fates had assigned a very short Thread. *W--tt--n*, a young Hero, whom an unknown Father of mortal Race, begot by stollen Embraces with this Goddess. He was the Darling of his Mother, above all her Children, and she resolved to go and comfort Him. But first, according to the good old Custom of Deities, she cast about to change her Shape; for fear the Divinity of her Countenance might dazzle his Mortal Sight, and over-charge the rest of his Senses. She therefore gathered up her Person into an *Octavo* Compass:[3] Her Body grew white and arid, and split in pieces with Driness; the thick turned into Pastboard, and the thin into Paper, upon which, her Parents and Children, artfully strowed a Black Juice, or Decoction of Gall and Soot, in Form of

---

[1] The Royal Society met at this time in Gresham College; see p. 64. By *Covent-Garden* is meant the haunt of the wits; cf. p. 43. Will's Coffee-house was in Bow Street, Covent Garden.

[2] Presumably they were fighting for the Moderns. See p. 105, l. 21.

[3] Wotton's *Reflections* and Bentley's *Dissertations* were published in octavo.

Letters; her Head, and Voice, and Spleen, kept their primitive Form, and that which before, was a Cover of Skin, did still continue so. In which Guise, she march'd on towards the *Moderns*, undistinguishable in Shape and Dress from the *Divine Bn--tl--y, W--tt--n's* dearest Friend. *Brave W--tt--n,* said the Goddess, *Why do our Troops stand idle here, to spend their present Vigour and Opportunity of this[1] Day? Away, let us haste to the Generals, and advise to give the Onset immediately.* Having spoke thus, she took the ugliest of her Monsters, full glutted from her Spleen, and flung it invisibly into his Mouth; which flying strait up into his Head, squeez'd out his Eye-Balls, gave him a distorted Look, and half over-turned his Brain. Then she privately ordered two of her beloved Children, *Dulness* and *Ill-Manners*, closely to attend his Person in all Encounters. Having thus ac-coutred him, she vanished in a Mist,[2] and the *Hero* perceived it was the Goddess, his Mother.

THE destined Hour of Fate, being now arrived, the Fight began; whereof, before I dare adventure to make a particular Description, I must, after the Example of other Authors, petition for a hundred Tongues, and Mouths, and Hands, and Pens;[3] which would all be too little to perform so immense a Work. Say, Goddess, that presidest over History; who it was that first ad-vanced in the Field of Battel. *Paracelsus*, at the Head of his *Dragoons*, observing *Galen*[4] in the adverse Wing,

---

[1] '*the*' edd. 1–4.

[2] Cf. *Aeneid*, i. 412.

[3] Cf. *Iliad*, ii. 489, and *Aeneid*, vi. 625.

[4] The single combat between these authors may have been sug-gested by the following passage in Temple's *Thoughts upon Re-viewing the Essay of Antient and Modern Learning* (1701), pp. 205–6: 'till the new Philosophy had gotten Ground in these Parts of the World, which is about fifty or sixty Years date, there were but few that ever pretended to exceed or equal the Antients; those that did, were only some Physicians, as *Paracelsus* and His Disciples,

darted his Javelin with a mighty Force, which the brave *Antient* received upon his Shield, the Point breaking in the second fold.[1] *   *   *   *

Hic pauca desunt.   *   *   *   *   *   *   *

  *   *   *   *   *   *   *

They bore the wounded *Aga*,[2] on their Shields to his Chariot *   *   *   *   *   *   *

  *   *   *   *   *   *   *

Desunt non-nulla.   *   *   *   *   *   *   *

  *   *   *   *   *   *   *

*   *   *   *   *   *   *   *   *   *

THEN *Aristotle* observing *Bacon*[3] advance with a furious Mien, drew his Bow to the Head, and let fly his Arrow, which miss'd[4] the valiant *Modern*, and went hizzing over his Head; but *Des-Cartes* it hit; The Steel Point quickly found a *Defect* in his *Head-piece*; it pierced the Leather and the Past-board, and went in at his Right Eye. The Torture of the Pain, whirled the valiant *Bow-man* round, till Death, like a Star of superior Influence, drew him into his own *Vortex*.[5] *   *

*   *   *   *   *   *   *

*   *   *   *   *   *   *   *Ingens hiatus hic in MS.*

*   *   *   *   *   *   *

when *Homer* appeared at the Head of the Cavalry, mounted on a furious Horse, with Difficulty managed

who introduced new Notions in Physick, and new Methods of Practice, in opposition to the Galenical.' Cf. *Hudibras*, iii. iii. 475–6.

[1] The blank is left probably because Swift neither felt inclined nor qualified to discuss the relations between the different medical authorities of recent times [Craik].

[2] Cf. p. 236, note 4. Swift follows Temple in his treatment of Harvey.

[3] Temple had named Bacon as one of the greatest of the Moderns, *Ancient and Modern Learning*, p. 61. It is noticeable that he is not wounded.

[4] 'mist' edd. 4, 5.

[5] Cf. the allusion to Descartes' theory of vortices in the *Tale*, p. 167, ll. 8–11.

by the Rider himself, but which no other Mortal durst approach; He rode among the Enemies Ranks, and bore down all before him. Say, Goddess, whom he slew first, and whom he slew last. First, *Gondibert*[1] advanced against Him, clad in heavy Armour, and mounted on a staid sober Gelding, not so famed for his Speed as his Docility in kneeling,[2] whenever his Rider would mount or alight. He had made a Vow to *Pallas*, that he would never leave the Field, till he had spoiled **Homer* of his Armour; Madman, who had   * *Vid. Homer* never once *seen* the Wearer, nor under- stood his Strength. Him *Homer* overthrew, Horse and Man to the Ground, there to be trampled and choak'd in the Dirt. Then, with a long Spear, he slew *Denham*, a stout *Modern*, who from his† Father's side, derived his Lineage from *Apollo*, but his Mother was of Mortal Race. He fell, and bit the Earth. The Celestial Part *Apollo* took, and made it a Star, but the Terrestrial lay

† *Sir* John Denham's *Poems are very Unequal, extremely Good, and very Indifferent, so that his Detractor's said, he was not the real Author of* Coopers-Hill.[3]

[1] Sir William Davenant [*MS. Pate*]. His *Gondibert* (1650) had met with lavish praises. Great claims were made for it in his preface; and Hobbes in his 'Answer' to the Preface gave his testimony briefly thus: 'I never yet saw Poem that had so much shape of Art, health of Morality, and vigour and beauty of Ex- pression as this of yours.' But these were not Temple's views. See his *Ancient and Modern Learning*, p. 55: '. . . If all this must be allowed, I will then yield *Gondi- bert* to have excelled *Homer*, as it pretended.'

[2] Cf. *Hudibras*, i. i. 437–40.
[3] See 'The Session of the Poets' in *Poems on Affairs of State*, vol. i (ed. 1699, p. 210):

Then in came *Denham*, that
   limping old Bard,
Whose fame on the *Sophy* and
   Cooper's Hill stands; . . .
But *Apollo* advis'd him to write
   something more,
To clear a suspicion which
   possess'd the Court,
That *Cooper's Hill*, so much
   bragg'd on before,
Was writ by a Vicar, who had
   forty pound for 't.
And cf. Butler's 'Panegyric upon

wallowing upon the Ground. Then *Homer* slew *W--sl--y*[1] with a kick of his Horse's heel; He took *Perrault* by mighty Force out of his Saddle, then hurl'd him at *Fontenelle*,[2] with the same Blow dashing out both their Brains.

ON the left Wing of the Horse, *Virgil* appeared in shining Armour, compleatly fitted to his Body; He was mounted on a dapple grey Steed, the slowness of whose Pace, was an Effect of the highest Mettle and Vigour. He case his Eye on the adverse Wing, with a desire to find an Object worthy of his valour, when behold, upon a sorrel Gelding[3] of a monstrous Size, appear'd a Foe, issuing from among the thickest of the Enemy's Squadrons; But his Speed was less than his Noise; for his Horse, old and lean, spent the Dregs of his Strength in a high Trot, which tho' it made slow advances, yet caused a loud Clashing of his Armor, terrible to hear. The two Cavaliers had now approached within the Throw of a Lance, when the Stranger desired a Parley, and lifting up the Vizard of his Helmet, a Face hardly appeared from within, which after a pause, was known for that of the renowned *Dryden*. The brave *Antient* suddenly started, as one possess'd with Surprize and Disappointment together: For, the Helmet was nine times

---

Denham's Recovery', l. 16:
  'Than the bought *Cooper's Hill*, or borrow'd *Sophy*.'
  [1] Sam Westley, with contempt [*MS. Pate*]. Samuel Wesley (1662–1735), rector of Epworth, Lincolnshire, was the father of John and Charles Wesley. He collaborated with John Dunton, his brother-in-law, in the *Athenian Mercury*. He wrote much verse that is now forgotten, his most ambitious attempt being *The Life*

of *Christ* (1693), an heroic poem in ten books. Cf. Garth, *The Dispensary*, canto v, ll. 71–72.
    Had *W[esley]* never aim'd in Verse to please,
    We had not rank'd him with our *Ogilbys*.
See Swift's *Correspondence*, vol. iv, pp. 130–1, 147, 152.
  [2] The two chief supporters of the Moderns in France.
  [3] Cf. *Hudibras*, part i, canto i, ll. 419 ff.

too large for the Head, which appeared Situate far in the hinder Part, even like the Lady in a Lobster,[1] or like a Mouse under a Canopy of State, or like a shrivled Beau from within the Penthouse of a modern Perewig: And the voice was suited to the Visage, sounding weak and remote. *Dryden* in a long Harangue[2] soothed up the good *Antient*, called him *Father*, and by a large deduction of Genealogies, made it plainly appear, that they were nearly related. Then he humbly proposed an Exchange of Armor, as a lasting Mark of Hospitality between them. *Virgil* consented (for the Goddess *Diffidence* came unseen, and cast a Mist before his Eyes) tho' his was of Gold,[3] and cost a hundred Beeves, the others but of rusty Iron. How- *Vid. Homer.* ever, this glittering Armor became the *Modern* yet worse than his Own. Then, they agreed to exchange Horses; but when it came to the Trial, *Dryden* was afraid, and utterly unable to mount. * * *

Alter hiatus * * * * * * *
in MS. * * * * * *
* * * * * Lucan appeared upon a fiery Horse, of admirable Shape, but head-strong, bearing the Rider where he list, over the Field; he made a mighty Slaughter among the Enemy's Horse; which Destruction to stop, *Bl--ckm--re*,[4] a famous *Modern* (but one of the *Mercenaries*) strenuously opposed

---

[1] A name given by fisherfolk to a part of the stomach of the lobster. Cf. Herrick, *The Fairie Temple: or Oberon's Chappell*, ll. 129–31:

The Saint, to which the most he prayes
And offers *Incense* Nights and dayes,
The *Lady* of the *Lobster* is.

[2] A reference to the 'Dedication of the Aeneis', where Dryden says 'I must acknowledge that *Virgil* in Latin, and *Spencer* in English, have been my Masters' (ed. 1697, p. 237).

[3] Cf. *Iliad*, vi. 234–6.

[4] Sir Richard Blackmore (*c.* 1650–1729), who wrote long epics in the intervals of his medical duties (hence the mention of Æsculapius). Cf. p. 182, note 2.

himself; and darted a Javelin, with a strong Hand, which falling short of its Mark, struck deep in the Earth. Then *Lucan* threw a Lance; but *Æsculapius* came unseen, and turn'd off the Point. *Brave* Modern, *said* Lucan, *I perceive some God protects you, for never did my Arm so deceive me before; But, what Mortal can contend with a God? Therefore, let us Fight no longer, but present Gifts to each other.* Lucan then bestowed the *Modern* a *Pair of Spurs,* and *Bl--ckm--re* gave Lucan a Bridle.[1]

Pauca desunt.   *   *   *   *

*   *   *   *   *   *   *   *   *

Creech;[2] But, the Goddess *Dulness* took a Cloud, formed into the Shape of *Horace*, armed and mounted, and placed it in a flying Posture before Him. Glad was the Cavalier, to begin a Combat with a flying Foe, and pursued the Image, threatning loud; till at last it led him to the peaceful Bower of his Father *Ogleby*,[3] by whom he was disarmed, and assigned to his Repose.

THEN *Pindar* slew ———, and ———, and *Oldham*,[4] and ——— and *Afra* the *Amazon* light of foot;[5] Never advancing in a direct Line,[6] but wheeling with incredible Agility and Force, he made a terrible Slaughter among

[1] His skill as a physician attoned for his dullness as a poet [Hawkesworth].

[2] Thomas Creech (1659–1700), translator of Lucretius (1682), Horace (1684, dedicated to Dryden), and other classical authors. His Horace was not so successful as his Lucretius, which won high praise. See pp. 60, 100.

[3] John Ogleby, or Ogilby (1600–76), notorious for his translations of Virgil and Homer, which were chiefly remarkable for their excellent printing and paper and illustrations. Cf. *MacFlecknoe*, l. 102; *The Dunciad*, i, l. 141; and the quotation from Garth, p. 246, note 1.

[4] John Oldham (1653–83), satirist, here mentioned for his Pindarics.

[5] Mrs. Aphra Behn (1640–89), novelist and dramatist, but named here, like Oldham, for her Pindarics.

[6] An allusion to the complicated structure of Pindar's *Odes*.

the Enemy's[1] *Light-Horse.* Him, when *Cowley* observed, his generous Heart burnt within him, and he
advanced against the fierce *Antient,* imitating his Address, and Pace, and Career, as well as the Vigour of his
Horse, and his own Skill would allow. When the two
Cavaliers had approach'd within the Length of three
Javelins; first *Cowley* threw a Lance, which miss'd *Pindar,* and passing into the Enemy's Ranks, fell ineffectual to the Ground. Then *Pindar* darted a Javelin, so
large and weighty, that scarce a dozen *Cavaliers,* as
Cavaliers are in our degenerate Days,[2] could raise it
from the Ground: yet he threw it with Ease, and it
went by an unerring Hand, singing through the Air;
Nor could the *Modern* have avoided present Death, if
he had not luckily opposed the Shield that had been
given Him by *Venus.*[3] And now both Hero's drew
their Swords, but the *Modern* was so aghast and disordered, that he knew not where he was; his Shield
dropt from his Hands; thrice he fled, and thrice he
could not escape; at last he turned, and lifting up his
Hands, in the Posture of a Suppliant, *God-like* Pindar,
said he, *spare my Life, and possess my Horse with these
Arms; besides the Ransom which my Friends will give,
when they hear I am alive, and your Prisoner. Dog,* said
Pindar, *Let your Ransom stay with your Friends; But your
Carcass shall be left for the* Fowls of the Air, *and the*
Beasts of the Field.[4] With that, he raised his Sword, and
with a mighty Stroak, cleft the wretched *Modern* in
twain, the Sword pursuing the Blow; and one half lay
panting on the Ground, to be trod in pieces by the
Horses Feet, the other half was born by the frighted

---

[1] 'Enemy's' ed. 1; 'Enemies'
edd. 2–5.

[2] Cf. *Iliad,* v. 302–4; also *The
Dunciad,* ii, l. 40:

Twelve starv'ling bards of these

degen'rate days.

[3] A reference to Cowley's love-
verses, collected under the title *The
Mistress.*

[4] Cf. *Iliad,* xxii. 335.

Steed thro' the Field. This **Venus* took, and wash'd it seven times in *Ambrosia*, then struck it thrice with a Sprig of *Amarant*; upon which, the Leather grew round and soft, the[1] Leaves turned into Feathers, and being gilded before, continued gilded still; so it became a *Dove* and She harness'd it to her Chariot.   *   *

Hiatus valdè *   *   *   *   *   *   *
deflendus in MS. *   *   *   *   *   *   *
*   *   *   *   *   *   *   *   *

DAY being far spent, and the numerous Forces of the *Moderns* half inclining to a Retreat, there issued forth from a Squadron of their *heavy*

The Episode of *armed Foot*, a Captain, whose Name was
B--ntl--y and *B--ntl--y*; in Person, the most deformed
W--tt--n.[2] of all the *Moderns*; Tall, but without Shape or Comeliness; Large, but without Strength or Proportion. His Armour was patch'd up of a thousand incoherent Pieces;[3] and the Sound of it, as he march'd,

---

* *I do not approve the Author's Judgment in this, for I think* Cowley's *Pindaricks are much preferable to his* Mistress.[4]

---

[1] 'and the' edd. 2—5.

[2] As the account of the Battle of the Books is an allegorical representation of Sir *William Temple*'s essay, in which the antients are opposed to the moderns, the account of *Bentley* and *Wotton* is called an episode, and their intrusion represented as an under action [Hawkesworth].

[3] Bentley's critics sneered at his numerous quotations (which they said he got from Lexicons) and at his studies of the fragments of the Greek poets. See the *Tale of a Tub*, p. 145, note 1. In the Preface to Anthony Alsop's edition of Æsop's Fables, Bentley

is spoken of as *quendam Bentleium, virum in volvendis Lexicis satis diligentem.* Cf. also *The Dunciad*, iv, ll. 228–30:

> I poach in Suidas for unlicens'd Greek.
> In ancient Sense if any needs will deal,
> Be sure I give them Fragments, not a Meal.

[4] It may, however, be considered, that *Cowley*'s pindarics were but copies, of which *Pindar* was the original; before *Pindar* therefore his pindarics might fall; and his Mistress be preserved as properly his own [Hawkesworth].

was loud and dry, like that made by the Fall of a Sheet
of Lead, which an *Etesian* Wind[1] blows suddenly down
from the Roof of some Steeple. His Helmet was of old
rusty Iron, but the Vizard was Brass, which tainted by
his Breath, corrupted into Copperas, not wanted Gall[2]
from the same Fountain; so, that whenever provoked
by Anger or Labour, an atramentous Quality, of most
malignant Nature, was seen to distil from his Lips. In
his *right Hand he grasp'd a Flail, and (that he might
never be unprovided of an *offensive* Weapon) a Vessel
full of *Ordure* in his Left: Thus, compleatly arm'd, he
advanc'd with a slow and heavy Pace, where the *Modern*
Chiefs were holding a Consult upon the Sum of Things;
who, as he came onwards, laugh'd to behold his crooked
Leg, and hump Shoulder, which his Boot and Armour
vainly endeavouring to hide were forced to comply with,
and expose.[3] The Generals made use of him for his
Talent of Railing; which kept within Government,
proved frequently of great Service to their Cause, but
at other times did more Mischief than Good; For at
the least Touch of Offence, and often without any at
all, he would, like a wounded Elephant, convert it
against his Leaders. Such, at this Juncture, was the
Disposition of *B--ntl--y*, grieved to see the Enemy prevail, and dissatisfied with every Body's Conduct but his
own. He humbly gave the *Modern* Generals to understand, that he conceived, with great Submission, they
were all a Pack of *Rogues*, and *Fools*, and *Sons* of *Whores*,

---

* *The Person here spoken of, is famous for letting fly at every Body
without Distinction, and using mean and foul Scurrilities.*

[1] Bentley against Boyle [*MS.
Pate*]. The name, from ἔτος, a
year, was given to the north-west
wind which blows in the Mediter-
ranean every summer; hence a
gale of regular recurrence. The
word is twice used in Wotton's
Reflections (1697), pp. 104, 135.
[2] Cf. p. 221, l. 20.
[3] Cf. Homer's description of
Thersites, *Iliad*, ii. 212–64.

and *d——mn'd Cowards*, and *confounded Loggerheads*,
and *illiterate Whelps*, and *nonsensical Scoundrels*;[1] That
if Himself had been constituted General, those *presump-*
tuous Dogs, the *Antients*, would long
before this, have been beaten out of the
Field.[2] *You*, said he, *sit here idle, but,*
when I, or any other valiant Modern, *kill an Enemy, you*
are sure to seize the Spoil. But, I will not march one Foot
against the Foe, till you all swear to me, that, whomever I
take or kill, his Arms I shall quietly possess. B--ntl--y having
spoke thus, *Scaliger*[3] bestowing him a sower Look;
Miscreant Prater, said he, *Eloquent only in thine own Eyes,*
Thou railest without Wit, or Truth, or Discretion, The
Malignity of thy Temper perverteth Nature, Thy Learning
makes thee more Barbarous, *thy Study of* Humanity,[4]
more Inhuman; *Thy* Convers *amongst Poets more* grovel-
ing, miry, *and* dull. *All Arts of* civilizing *others, render*
thee rude *and* untractable; Courts *have taught thee* ill
Manners, *and* polite Conversation *has finished thee a*
Pedant. *Besides, a greater Coward burtheneth not the*
Army. But never despond, I pass my Word, whatever
Spoil thou takest, shall certainly be thy own; though, I hope,
that vile Carcass will first become a prey to Kites and
Worms.

Vid. Homer de Thersite.

---

[1] This speech is a satire on
Bentley's 'low and mean' style in
controversy. See, for example, the
reference to his 'Manners' in
Boyle's *Examination*, pp. 220 ff.

[2] The marginal note ought to
be higher up. Thersites does not
make this boast.

[3] Probably Joseph Justus Scaliger (1540–1609), rather than his
father Julius Caesar Scaliger, who
is referred to in the *Tale*, p. 203.
The younger scholar's methods in

controversy were condemned in
Boyle's *Examination* (p. 225);
and Bentley replied in the Preface
to his *Dissertation* (1699), pp. c–
cii. The *Battle* was probably
written before the *Dissertation*;
but Scaliger's attack here on
Bentley is all the more effective
in view of Bentley's defence of
Scaliger against Boyle.

[4] i.e. 'classical literature'. See
p. 224, note 2.

B--NΤL--Υ durst not reply; but half choaked with Spleen and Rage, withdrew, in full Resolution of performing some great Achievment. With him, for his Aid and Companion, he took his beloved *W--tt--n*;[1] resolving by Policy or Surprize, to attempt some neglected Quarter of the *Antients* Army. They began their March over Carcasses of their slaughtered Friends; then to the Right of their own Forces: then wheeled Northward, till they came to *Aldrovandus's* Tomb,[2] which they pass'd on the side of the declining Sun. And now they arrived with Fear towards the Enemy's Outguards; looking about, if haply, they might spy the Quarters of the Wounded, or some straggling Sleepers, unarm'd and remote from the rest. As when two *Mungrel-Curs*, whom *native Greediness*, and *domestick Want*, provoke, and join in Partnership, though fearful, nightly to invade the Folds of some rich Grazier; They, with Tails depress'd, and lolling Tongues, creep soft and slow; mean while, the conscious *Moon*, now in her *Zenith*, on their guilty Heads, darts perpendicular Rays; Nor dare they bark, though much provok'd at her refulgent Visage, whether seen in Puddle by Reflexion, or in Sphear direct; but one surveys the Region round, while t'other[3] scouts the Plain, if haply, to discover at distance from the Flock, some *Carcass* half devoured, the Refuse of gorged Wolves, or ominous Ravens. So march'd this lovely, loving Pair of Friends, nor with less Fear and Circumspection; when, at distance, they might perceive two shining Suits of Armor, hanging upon an Oak, and the Owners not far off in a

---

[1] Bentley's first *Dissertation* (1697) was added as an appendix to the second edition of Wotton's *Reflections*.

[2] Ulisse Aldrovandi (1522–1605) of Bologna, the compiler of many monumental folio volumes on natural history. The *tomb* is, presumably, the work on which he spent his life and eyesight.

[3] 'the t'other' edd. 2–4.

profound Sleep. The two Friends drew Lots, and the pursuing of this Adventure, fell to *B--ntl--y*; On he went, and in his Van *Confusion* and *Amaze*; while *Horror* and *Affright* brought up the Rear. As he came near; Behold two Hero's of the *Antients* Army, *Phalaris* and *Æsop*, lay fast asleep: *B--ntl--y* would fain have dispatch'd them both, and stealing close, aimed his Flail at *Phalaris*'s Breast. But, then, the Goddess *Affright* interposing, caught the *Modern* in her icy Arms, and dragg'd him from the Danger she foresaw; For both the dormant Hero's happened to turn at the same Instant, tho' soundly Sleeping, and busy in a Dream. *For *Phalaris* was just that Minute dreaming, how a most vile *Poetaster* had lampoon'd him, and how he had got him roaring in his *Bull*.[1] And *Æsop* dream'd, that as he and the *Antient Chiefs* were lying on the Ground, a *Wild Ass*[2] broke loose, ran about trampling and kicking, and dunging in their Faces. *B--ntl--y* leaving the two Hero's asleep, seized on both their Armors, and withdrew in quest of his Darling *W--tt--n*.

H E, in the mean time, had wandred long in search of some Enterprize, till at length, he arrived at a small

* *This is according to* Homer, *who tells the Dreams of those who were kill'd in their Sleep.*

[1] The brazen bull in which the victims of Phalaris were roasted. A representation of the grim ceremony forms the frontispiece to Boyle's edition of the Epistles of Phalaris.

Boyle concluded his *Examination* with a reference to Bentley and the Bull: 'Many of *Phalaris's* Enemies . . . repented of their Vain Confidence afterwards in his *Bull*. Dr *Bentley* is perhaps by this time, or will suddenly be satisfied, that He also has presum'd a little too much upon his Distance: but 'twill be too late to Repent, when he begins to Bellow.' To this Bentley replied with happy ease, *Dissertation* (1699), pp. xlii–xliii.

In a Cambridge caricature Bentley was represented as saying 'I had rather be *Roasted* than *Boyled*': see E. Budgell, *Memoirs of the Boyles*, p. 193.

[2] Bentley: see p. 233, note 4.

Rivulet, that issued from a Fountain hard by, call'd in the Language of mortal Men, *Helicon*. Here he stopt, and, parch'd with thirst, resolved to allay it in this limpid Stream. Thrice, with profane Hands, he essay'd to raise the Water to his Lips, and thrice it slipt all thro' his Fingers. Then he stoop'd prone on his Breast, but e'er his Mouth had kiss'd the liquid Crystal, *Apollo* came, and, in the Channel, held his *Shield* betwixt the *Modern* and the Fountain, so that he drew up nothing but *Mud*.[1] For, altho' no Fountain on Earth can compare with the Clearness of *Helicon*, yet there lies at Bottom, a thick sediment of *Slime* and *Mud*; For, so *Apollo* begg'd of *Jupiter*, as a Punishment to those who durst attempt to taste it with unhallowed Lips, and for a Lesson to all, not to *draw too deep*, or *far from the Spring*.

AT the Fountain Head, *W--tt--n* discerned two Hero's; The one he could not distinguish,[2] but the other was soon known for *Temple*, General of the *Allies* to the *Antients*. His Back was turned, and he was employ'd in Drinking large Draughts in his Helmet, from the Fountain, where he had withdrawn himself to rest from the Toils of the War. *W--tt--n*, observing him, with quaking Knees, and trembling Hands, spoke thus to Himself: *Oh, that I could kill this Destroyer of our Army, what Renown should I purchase among the Chiefs! But to issue out against Him, Man for Man, Shield against Shield, and Launce against Launce; what* Modern *of us dare? For, he fights like a God, and* Pallas *or* Apollo *are ever at his Elbow. But, Oh,* Mother![3] *if what Fame reports, be true, that I am the Son of so great a Goddess, grant me to Hit* Temple *with this Launce, that the Stroak may send Him to Hell, and that I may return in Safety and Triumph, laden with his Spoils.* The first Part of his Prayer, the Gods granted,

Vid. Homer.

---

[1] Cf. Horace, *Satires*, i. i. 60.
[2] Boyle.   [3] i.e. Criticism: see p. 242.

at the Intercession of His *Mother* and of *Momus*; but the rest, by a perverse Wind sent from *Fate*, was scattered in the Air.[1] Then *W--tt--n* grasp'd his Launce, and brandishing it thrice over his head, darted it with all his Might, the *Goddess*, his *Mother*, at the same time, adding Strength to his Arm. Away the Launce went hizzing, and reach'd even to the Belt of the averted *Antient*, upon which, lightly grazing, it fell to the Ground. *Temple* neither felt the Weapon touch him, nor heard it fall; And *W--tt--n*, might have escaped to his Army, with the Honor of having remitted his Launce against so great a Leader, unrevenged; But, *Apollo* enraged, that a Javelin, flung by the Assistance of so foul a *Goddess*, should pollute his Fountain, put on the shape of ———,[2] and softly came to young *Boyle*, who then accompanied *Temple:* He pointed, first to the Launce, then to the distant *Modern* that flung it, and commanded the young Hero to take immediate Revenge.[3] *Boyle*, clad in a suit of Armor which had been *given him by all the Gods*,[4] immediately advanced against

[1] Wotton's *Reflections* were published, and thus the first part of his prayer was answered; but not the rest, as the *Reflections* did Temple no harm.

But Temple, in fact, was annoyed by Wotton's attack. Though representing him here as completely indifferent to it, Swift had the duty of publishing Temple's defence of his part in the controversy—*Some Thoughts upon Reviewing the Essay of Antient and Modern Learning* (*Miscellanea. The Third Part*, 1701).

[2] Atterbury, who helped Boyle with the *Examination.*

[3] Boyle said that one of his reasons for writing his *Examination* was his respect for Sir William Temple, 'upon whom I so unhappily occasion'd this Storm of Criticism to fall' (Preface, pp. iii, iv). He speaks of himself as 'a young writer'.

[4] Boyle was assisted in this dispute by Dean *Aldrich*, Doctor *Atterbury*, afterwards Bp. of *Rochester*, and other persons at *Oxford*, celebrated for their genius and their learning, then called the Christ-church wits [Hawkesworth]. Cf. E. Budgell, *Memoirs of the Boyles* (1732), pp. 194–5. See also Atterbury's letter to

the trembling Foe, who now fled before him. As a
young Lion, in the *Libyan Plains*, or *Araby Desart*, sent
by his aged Sire to hunt for Prey, or Health, or Exercise;
He scours along, wishing to meet some Tiger from the
Mountains, or a furious Boar; If Chance, a *Wild Ass*,
with Brayings importune, affronts his Ear, the generous
Beast, though loathing to distain his Claws with Blood
so vile, yet much provok'd at the offensive Noise;
which *Echo*, foolish Nymph, like her *ill judging Sex*,
repeats much louder, and with more Delight than
Philomela's Song: He vindicates the Honor of the
Forest, and hunts the noisy, long-ear'd Animal. So
W--tt--n fled, so *Boyle* pursued. But *W--tt--n* heavy-
arm'd, and slow of foot, began to slack his Course;
when his Lover *B--ntl--y* appeared, returning laden with
the Spoils of the two sleeping *Antients*. *Boyle* observed
him well, and soon discovering the Helmet and Shield
of *Phalaris*, his Friend, both which he had lately with
his own Hands, new polish'd and gilded;[1] Rage sparkled
in His Eyes, and leaving his Pursuit after *W--tt--n*, he
furiously rush'd on against this new Approacher. Fain
would he be revenged on both; but both now fled
Vid. Homer. different Ways: *And as a Woman in a
little House, that gets a painful Livelihood
by Spinning; if chance her *Geese* be scattered o'er the
Common, she courses round the Plain from side to side,
compelling here and there, the Stragglers to the Flock;
They cackle loud, and flutter o'er the Champain.[2] So

* *This is also, after the manner of* Homer; *the Woman's getting a
painful Livelihood by Spinning, has nothing to do with the Similitude,
nor would be excusable without such an Authority.*

Boyle (*Correspondence*, ed. J.
Nichols, 1783, vol. ii, pp. 21–23)
where he says that 'in laying the
design of the book, in writing
above half of it, in reviewing a
good part of the rest, in transcribing the whole, and attending the
press, half a year of my life went
away'.

[1] A reference to Boyle's edition
of the Epistles of Phalaris (1695).

[2] 'Champian' edd. 1–4.

Boyle pursued, so fled this Pair of Friends: finding at length, their Flight was vain, they bravely joyn'd, and drew themselves in *Phalanx*. First, *B--ntl--y* threw a Spear with all his Force,[1] hoping to pierce the Enemy's Breast; But *Pallas* came unseen, and in the Air took off the Point, and clap'd on one of *Lead*, which after a dead Bang against the Enemy's Shield, fell blunted to the Ground. Then *Boyle* observing well his Time, took a Launce of wondrous Length and sharpness; and as this Pair of Friends compacted stood close Side to Side, he wheel'd him to the right, and with unusual Force, darted the Weapon.[2] *B--ntl--y* saw his Fate approach, and flanking down his Arms, close to his Ribs, hoping to save his Body; in went the Point, passing through Arm and Side, nor stopt, or spent its Force, till it had also pierc'd the valiant *W--tt--n*, who going to sustain his dying Friend, shared his Fate. As, when a skilful Cook has truss'd a Brace of *Woodcocks*, He, with Iron Skewer, pierces the tender Sides of both, their Legs and Wings close pinion'd to their Ribs; So was this pair of Friends transfix'd, till down they fell, joyn'd in their Lives, joyn'd in their Deaths; so closely joyn'd, that *Charon* would[3] mistake them both for one, and waft them over *Styx* for half his Fare. Farewel, beloved, loving Pair; Few Equals have you left behind: And happy and immortal shall you be, if all my Wit and Eloquence can make you.

AND, now * * * * * * *
* * * * * * * * * *
* * * * *
* * * * *Desunt cætera.*

[1] Bentley's first *Dissertation* (1697).
[2] Boyle's *Examination*, a reply mainly to Bentley's *Dissertation*, but also incidentally to Wotton's *Reflections*. [3] 'will' edd. 1–4.

FINIS.

A

DISCOURSE

Concerning the

Mechanical Operation

OF THE

SPIRIT.

IN A

LETTER

To a FRIEND.

A

FRAGMENT.

LONDON:
Printed in the Year, MDCCX.

THE
BOOKSELLER'S
Advertisement.[1]

THE *following Discourse came into my Hands perfect and entire. But there being several Things in it, which the present Age would not very well bear, I kept it by me some Years, resolving it should never see the Light. At length, by the Advice and Assistance of a judicious Friend, I retrench'd those Parts that might give most Offence, and have now ventured to publish the Remainder; Concerning the Author, I am wholly ignorant; neither can I conjecture, whether it be the same with That of the two foregoing Pieces, the Original having been sent me at a different Time, and in a different Hand. The Learned Reader will better determine; to whose Judgment I entirely submit it.*

[1] This was probably written by Swift himself; cf. p. 28, note 1.

A
DISCOURSE
Concerning the
Mechanical Operation[1]
OF THE
SPIRIT, &c.

For T. H. *Esquire,[2] at his Chambers in the Academy of the* Beaux Esprits *in* New Holland.[3]

SIR,

IT is now a good while since I have had in my Head something, not only very material, but absolutely necessary to my Health, that the World should be informed in. For, to tell you a Secret, I am able to

This Discourse is not altogether equal to the two Former, the best Parts of it being omitted; whether the Bookseller's Account be true, that he durst not print the rest, I know not, nor indeed is it easie to determine whether he may be rely'd on, in any thing he says of this, or the former Treatises, only

[1] Cf. *Hudibras,* iii. i. 1497–8:
The Tools of working out Salvation
By meer Mechanick Operation.

[2] Hawkesworth says that *T. H.* was supposed to be Swift's friend Colonel Hunter, who was for some time believed to be the author of Shaftesbury's *Letter concerning Enthusiasm;* see the *Tale of a Tub,* p. 6, note 2. But his Christian name was Robert.

[3] See the note on the '*literati* of *Tobinambou*', p. 263. 'New Holland' was the name at this time of Australia, the western shore of which had been navigated by the

contain it no longer. However, I have been perplexed
for some time, to resolve what would be the most proper
Form to send it abroad in. To which End, I have three
Days been coursing thro' *Westminster-Hall*, and St.
Paul's Church yard, and *Fleet-street*,[1] to peruse *Titles*;
and, I do not find any which holds so general a Vogue,
as that of *A Letter to a Friend:*[2] Nothing is more common
than to meet with long Epistles address'd to Persons
and Places, where, at first thinking, one would be apt to
imagine it not altogether so necessary or Convenient;
Such as, *a Neighbour at next Door, a mortal Enemy, a
perfect Stranger,* or *a Person of Quality in the Clouds*; and
these upon Subjects, in appearance, the least proper for
Conveyance by the Post; as, *long Schemes in Philosophy*;
dark and Wonderful Mysteries of State; *Laborious Dissertations in Criticism and Philosophy, Advice to Parlia-
ments,* and the like.

NOW, Sir, to proceed after the Method in present
Wear. (For, let me say what I will to the contrary, I am

*as to the Time they were writ in, which, however, appears more from the
Discourses themselves than his Relation.*[3]

Dutch by 1665. Temple speaks
in his *Ancient and Modern Learning* (ed. 1696, p. 49), of 'a Continent . . . about the length of
Java, which is marked by the
Name of *New Holland* in the
Maps, and to what Extent, none
knows, either to the *South*, the
East, or the *West*'. Dampier had
contributed further information
shortly before Swift wrote the
Discourse, but New Holland continued for many years yet to be
part of Terra Australis Incognita.
Cf. the reference to it in *A Voyage
to the Houyhnhnms*, chap. xi.

[1] The chief bookselling centres
in London at this time.

[2] The vogue of this form of
title will be seen on consulting
Arber's *Term Catalogues*.

[3] This note, like all the footnotes, as distinct from the notes
in the margin, was added in the
edition of 1710.

The *Discourse* is clearly later
than the *Battle*, and was probably
written about the same time as the
later sections of the *Tale*. In the
unauthorized edition of 1720 it is
printed before the *Battle*, with the
running title 'A Fragment of|The
Tale of a Tub'.

afraid you will publish this *Letter*, as soon as ever it comes to your Hands;) I desire you will be my Witness to the World, how careless and sudden a Scribble it has been; That it was but Yesterday, when You and I began accidentally to fall into Discourse on this Matter: That I was not very well, when we parted; That the Post is in such haste, I have had no manner of Time to digest it into Order, or correct the Style; And if any other Modern Excuses, for Haste and Negligence, shall occur to you in Reading, I beg you to insert them, faithfully promising they shall be thankfully acknowledged.

PRAY, Sir, in your next Letter to the *Iroquois Virtuosi*, do me the Favour to present my humble Service to that illustrious Body, and assure them, I shall send an Account of those *Phenomena*, as soon as we can determine them at *Gresham*.

I have not had a Line from the *Literati* of *Tobinambou*,[1] these three last Ordinaries.

AND now, Sir, having dispatch'd what I had to say of Forms, or of Business, let me intreat, you will suffer me to proceed upon my Subject; and to pardon me, if I make no farther Use of the Epistolary Stile, till I come to conclude.

[1] When Perrault read to the French Academy his poem on *Le Siècle de Louis le Grand*, Boileau was moved to write an epigram concluding with these lines:

Où peut-on avoir dit une telle infamie ?
Est-ce chez les Hurons, chez les Topinamboux ?
C'est à Paris. C'est donc dans l'Hôpital des Fous ?
    Non, c'est au Louvre en pleine Académie.

And in another epigram he said that the Academy—

Souffrant chez soi de si grands Fous,
Me semble un peu Topinamboue.

The first epigram was quoted in full in Temple's *Thoughts upon Reviewing the Essay of Antient and Modern Learning*, which Swift saw through the press in 1701. Swift had it in mind when he spoke of the *Iroquois Virtuosi*, and it also gave him the suggestion of 'the Academy of the Beaux Esprits in New-Holland'.

SECTION I.

'TIS recorded of *Mahomet*, that upon a Visit he was going to pay in *Paradise*, he had an Offer of several Vehicles to conduct him upwards; as fiery Chariots, wing'd Horses, and celestial Sedans; but he refused them all, and would be born to Heaven upon nothing but his *Ass*. Now, this Inclination of *Mahomet*, as singular as it seems, hath been since taken up by a great Number of devout *Christians*; and doubtless, with very good Reason. For, since That *Arabian* is known to have borrowed a Moiety of his Religious System from the *Christian* Faith; it is but just he should pay Reprisals to such as would Challenge them; wherein the good People of *England*, to do them all Right, have not been backward. For, tho' there is not any other Nation in the World, so plentifully provided with Carriages for that Journey, either as to Safety or Ease;[1] yet there are abundance of us, who will not be satisfied with any other Machine, beside this of *Mahomet*.

FOR my own part, I must confess to bear a very singular Respect to this Animal, by whom I take human Nature to be most admirably held forth in all its Qualities as well as Operations: And therefore, whatever in my small Reading, occurs, concerning this our Fellow-Creature, I do never fail to set it down, by way of Common-place; and when I have occasion to write upon Human Reason, Politicks, Eloquence, or Knowledge; I lay my *Memorandums* before me, and insert them with a wonderful Facility of Application. However, among all the Qualifications, ascribed to this distinguish'd Brute, by Antient or Modern Authors;

[1] England is famous for good Pads for common journys, and our Author seems here to recommend those of the Establisht Church, as the safest, or easyest for this journy [1720].

I cannot remember this Talent, of bearing his Rider to Heaven, has been recorded for a Part of his Character, except in the two Examples mentioned already;[1] Therefore, I conceive the Methods of this Art, to be a Point of useful Knowledge in very few Hands, and which the Learned World would gladly be better informed in. This is what I have undertaken to perform in the following Discourse. For, towards the Operation already mentioned, many peculiar Properties are required, both in the *Rider* and the *Ass*; which I shall endeavour to set in as clear a Light as I can.

BUT, because I am resolved, by all means, to avoid giving Offence to any Party whatever; I will leave off discoursing so closely to the *Letter* as I have hitherto done, and go on for the future by way of Allegory, tho' in such a manner, that the judicious Reader, may without much straining, make his Applications as often as he shall think fit. Therefore, if you please from hence forward, instead of the Term, *Ass*, we shall make use of *Gifted*, or *enlightened Teacher*; And the Word *Rider*, we will exchange for that of *Fanatick Auditory*, or any other Denomination of the like Import. Having settled this weighty Point; the great Subject of Enquiry before us, is to examine, by what Methods this *Teacher* arrives at his *Gifts* or *Spirit*, or *Light*; and by what Intercourse between him and his Assembly, it is cultivated and supported.

IN all my Writings, I have had constant Regard to this great End, not to suit and apply them to particular Occasions and Circumstances of Time, of Place, or of Person; but to calculate them for universal Nature, and Mankind in General. And of such Catholick use,

---

[1] See the story of *Balaams'* Ass. Num. XXII. 21, &c. See also 1 Kings XIII. 29. Zach. [IX.] 9. Math. XXI. 5 . . . 9. John XII. 14. 15 [1720].

I esteem this present Disquisition: For I do not remember any other Temper of Body, or Quality of Mind, wherein all Nations and Ages of the World have so unanimously agreed, as That of a *Fanatick* Strain, or Tincture of *Enthusiasm*; which improved by certain Persons or Societies of Men, and by them practised upon the rest, has been able to produce Revolutions of the greatest Figure in History; as will soon appear to those who know any thing of *Arabia*, *Persia*, *India*, or *China*, of *Morocco* and *Peru*: Farther, it has possessed as great a Power in the Kingdom of Knowledge, where it is hard to assign one Art or Science, which has not annexed to it some *Fanatick* Branch: Such are the *Philosopher's Stone*; *The Grand Elixir*; *The Planetary Worlds*;[1] *The Squaring of the Circle*;[2] *The Summum bonum*; Utopian *Commonwealths*; with some others of less or subordinate Note; which all serve for nothing else, but to employ or amuse this Grain of *Enthusiasm*, dealt into every Composition.

* Some Writers hold them for the same, others not.

B U T, if this Plant has found a Root in the Fields of *Empire*, and of *Knowledge*, it has fixt deeper, and spread yet farther upon *Holy Ground*.[3] Wherein, though it hath pass'd under the general Name of *Enthusiasm*, and perhaps arisen from the same Original, yet hath it produced certain Branches of a very different Nature, however often mistaken for each other. The Word in its universal Acceptation, may be defined, *A lifting up of the Soul or its Faculties above Matter*. This Description will

[1] Swift refers to the belief that the planets might be inhabited, and especially to John Wilkins's book *The Discovery of a World in the Moone*. See p. 237, note 7.

[2] Hobbes (among many others) worked at this problem, and be- lieved that he had solved it. See the account of his controversy with Wallis in Isaac D'Israeli's *Quarrels of Authors* (1814), iii, pp. 89–119.

[3] Exodus iii. 5.

hold good in general; but I am only to understand it, as applied to *Religion*; wherein there are three general Ways of ejaculating the Soul, or transporting it beyond the Sphere of Matter. The first, is the immediate Act of God, and is called, *Prophecy* or *Inspiration*. The second, is the immediate Act of the Devil, and is termed *Possession*. The third, is the Product of natural Causes, the effect of strong Imagination, Spleen, violent Anger, Fear, Grief, Pain, and the like. These three have been abundantly treated on by Authors, and therefore shall not employ my Enquiry. But, the fourth Method of *Religious Enthusiasm*, or launching out[1] the Soul, as it is purely an Effect of Artifice and *Mechanick Operation*, has been sparingly handled, or not at all, by any Writer; because tho' it is an Art of great Antiquity, yet having been confined to few Persons, it long wanted those[2] Advancements and Refinements, which it afterwards met with, since it has grown so Epidemick, and fallen into so many cultivating Hands.

I T is therefore upon this *Mechanical Operation of the Spirit*, that I mean to treat, as it is at present performed by our *British Workmen*. I shall deliver to the Reader the Result of many judicious Observations upon the Matter; tracing, as near as I can, the whole Course and Method of this *Trade*, producing parallel Instances, and relating certain Discoveries that have luckily fallen in my way.

I have said, that there is one Branch of *Religious Enthusiasm*, which is purely an Effect of Nature; whereas, the Part I mean to handle, is wholly an Effect of Art, which, however, is inclined to work upon certain Natures and Constitutions, more than others. Besides, there is many an Operation, which in its Original, was purely an Artifice, but through a long Succession of

---

[1] 'out of' edd. 4, 5.   [2] 'these' edd. 2–5.

Ages, hath grown to be natural. *Hippocrates* tells us,[1]
that among our Ancestors, the *Scythians*, ***Macrocephali.*** there was   Nation call'd, **Long-heads*, which at first began by a Custom among Midwives and Nurses, of molding, and squeezing, and bracing up the Heads of Infants; by which means, Nature shut out at one Passage, was forc'd to seek another, and finding room above, shot upwards, in the Form of a Sugar-Loaf; and being diverted that way, for some Generations, at last found it out of her self, needing no Assistance from the Nurse's Hand. This was the Original of the *Scythian Long-heads*, and thus did Custom, from being a second Nature proceed to be a first. To all which, there is something very analogous among Us of this Nation, who are the undoubted Posterity of that refined People. For, in the Age of our Fathers, there arose a Generation of Men in this Island call'd *Round-heads*,[2] whose Race is now spread over three Kingdoms, yet in its Beginning, was meerly an Operation of Art, produced by a pair of Cizars,[3] a Squeeze of the Face, and a black Cap.[4] These

---

[1] *De Aere, Aquis et Locis*, 35, 36; but Hippocrates does not mention the Scythians in connexion with the Macrocephali. The passage is quoted in Sir Thomas Browne's *Vulgar Errors*, bk. vi, chap. 10.

[2] The fanatics in the time of *Charles* I, ignorantly applying the text, 'Ye know that it is a shame for men to have long hair', cut their's very short. It is said, that the queen once seeing *Pym*, a celebrated patriot, thus cropped, enquired who that *round-headed* man was, and that from this incident the distinction became general, and the party were called

round-heads [Hawkesworth]. The name may not have had so definite an origin.

[3] A late instance of a spelling of 'scissors' that was common in the seventeenth century.

[4] Cf. *Hudibras*, I. iii. 1161, where Zachary Grey writes: 'George Fox, the Quaker, observes (*Journal*, p. 254), "That the Priests in those times had on their Heads two Caps, a Black one and a White one." And Mr. Petyt, speaking of their Preachers (*Visions of the Reformation*, p. 84) says, "The white Border upon his Black Cap, made him look like a Black-Jack tipt with Silver "'

Heads, thus formed into a perfect Sphere in all Assemblies, were most exposed to the view of the Female Sort, which did influence their Conceptions so effectually, that Nature, at last, took the Hint, and did it of her self; so that a *Round-head* has been ever since as familiar a Sight among Us, as a *Long-head* among the *Scythians*.

UPON these Examples, and others easy to produce, I desire the curious Reader to distinguish, First between an Effect grown from *Art* into *Nature*, and one that is natural from its Beginning; Secondly, between an Effect wholly natural, and one which has only a natural Foundation, but where the Superstructure is entirely Artificial. For, the first and the last of these, I understand to come within the Districts of my Subject. And having obtained these allowances, they will serve to remove any objections that may be raised hereafter against what I shall advance.

THE Practitioners of this famous Art, proceed in general upon the following Fundamental; That, *the Corruption of the Senses is the Generation of the Spirit*:[1] Because the *Senses* in Men are so many Avenues to the Fort of *Reason*, which in this Operation is wholly block'd up. All Endeavours must be therefore used, either to divert, bind up, stupify, fluster, and amuse the

---

Grey also quotes John Phillips's *Satyr against Hypocrites* (1655), p. 6:

> Two caps he had, and turns up that within,
> You'd think he wore a black pot tipt with tin.

The preacher in Plate 2 has a cap of this kind. Cf. p. 58, l. 13.

[1] The antithesis of 'corruption' and 'generation' is common in medieval philosophy, and is derived from Aristotle. Cf. Sir Thomas Browne, *Vulgar Errors*, III. ix: 'that axiom in Philosophy, that the generation of one thing, is the corruption of another'. Applications of it are frequent in seventeenth-century literature, e.g. Middleton and Dekker, *The Roaring Girle*, iii, 'the corruption of a Citizen is the generation of a serieant', and Dryden, *Defence of an Essay of Dramatic Poesy*, 'the corruption of a poet is the generation of a statesman'.

Senses, or else to justle them out of their Stations; and while they are either absent, or otherwise employ'd or engaged in a Civil War against each other, the *Spirit* enters and performs its Part.

NOW, the usual Methods of managing the Senses upon such Conjunctures, are what I shall be very particular in delivering, as far as it is lawful for me to do; but having had the Honour to be Initiated into the Mysteries of every Society, I desire to be excused from divulging any Rites, wherein the *Profane* must have no Part.

BUT here, before I can proceed farther, a very dangerous Objection must, if possible, be removed: For, it is positively denied by certain Cricks, that the *Spirit* can by any means be introduced into an Assembly of Modern Saints, the Disparity being so great in many material Circumstances, between the Primitive Way of Inspiration, and that which is practised in the present Age. This they pretend to prove from the second Chapter of the *Acts*, where comparing both, it appears; First, that *the Apostles were gathered together with one accord in one place*; by which is meant, an universal Agreement in Opinion, and Form of Worship; a Harmony (say they) so far from being found between any two Conventicles among Us, that it is in vain to expect it between any two Heads in the same. Secondly, the *Spirit* instructed the Apostles in the Gift of speaking several Languages; a Knowledge so remote from our Dealers in this Art, that they neither understand Propriety of Words, or Phrases in their own. Lastly, (say these Objectors) The Modern Artists do utterly exclude all Approaches of the *Spirit*, and bar up its antient Way of entring, by covering themselves so close, and so industriously a top. For, they will needs have it as a Point clearly gained, that the *Cloven Tongues* never sat upon the Apostles Heads, while their Hats were on.

NOW, the Force of these Objections, seems to consist in the different Acceptation of the Word, *Spirit:* which if it be understood for a supernatural Assistance, approaching from without, the Objectors have Reason, and their Assertions may be allowed; But the *Spirit* we treat of here, proceeding entirely from within, the Argument of these Adversaries is wholly eluded. And upon the same Account, our Modern Artificers, find it an Expedient of absolute Necessity, to cover their Heads as close as they can, in order to prevent Perspiration, than which nothing is observed to be a greater Spender of Mechanick Light, as we may, perhaps, farther shew in convenient Place.

TO proceed therefore upon the *Phænomenon* of *Spiritual Mechanism*, It is here to be noted, that in forming and working up the *Spirit*, the Assembly has a considerable Share, as well as the Preacher; The Method of this *Arcanum*, is as follows. They violently strain their Eye balls inward, half closing the Lids; Then, as they sit, they are in a perpetual Motion of *See-saw*, making long Hums at proper Periods, and continuing the Sound at equal Height, chusing their Time in those Intermissions, while the Preacher is at Ebb. Neither is this Practice, in any part of it, so singular or improbable, as not to be traced in distant Regions, from Reading and Observation. For, first, the *Jauguis, * *Bernier,* or enlightened Saints of *India*,[1] see all *Mem. de Mogol.*

[1] See *Suite des Memoires du Sr Bernier, sur l'Empire du grand Mogol* (Paris, 1671), pp. 57, 60–61: 'Entre tous ceux que je viens de dire il s'en trouve qu'on croit pour de vrais Saints illuminez & parfaits Jauguis ou parfaitement unis à Dieu . . . ils disent . . . qu'apres avoir jeusné plusieurs jours au pain & à l'eau, il faut premierement se tenir seul dans un lieu retiré, les yeux fichez en haut quelque temps sans branler aucunement, puis les ramener doucement en bas, & les fixer tous deux à regarder en mesme temps le bout de son nez également & autant d'un costé que de l'autre (ce qui est assez difficile) & se tenir là ainsi bandez & attentifs

their Visions, by help of an acquired straining and pressure of the Eyes. Secondly, the Art of *See-saw* on a Beam,[1] and swinging by Session upon a Cord, in order to raise artificial Extasies, hath been derived to Us, from our *Scythian Ances-tors, where it is practised at this Day, among the Women.[2] Lastly, the whole Proceeding, as I have here related it, is performed by the Natives of *Ireland*, with a considerable Improvement; And it is granted, that this noble Nation, hath of all others, admitted fewer Corruptions, and degenerated least from the Purity of the Old *Tartars*. Now it is usual for a Knot of *Irish*, Men and Women, to abstract themselves from Matter, bind up all their Senses, grow visionary and spiritual, by Influence of a short Pipe of Tobacco, handed round the Company; each preserving the Smoak in his Mouth, till it comes again to his Turn to take in fresh:[3] At the same Time, there is a Consort of a con-tinued gentle Hum, repeated and renewed by Instinct,

*Guagnini
Hist. Sarmat.*

---

sur le bout du nez jusqu'à ce que cette lumiere vienne . . .' (English translation, by 'H.O.' (1672), iii, pp. 136–8).

[1] 'an beam' edd. 4, 5.

[2] See Alexander Guagninus, *Sarmatiæ Europeæ descriptio* (1578), Moschoviae descriptio, fol. 24, under *Mulierum conditio*: 'Certis tamen & festivis æstate diebus, hanc prærogativam exhila-randi animi gratia habent: Omnes communiter cum filiabus in cam-pis viridiferis deambulant, ibique super quadam trabe, duabus fines trabis occupantibus, alternatim sursum ac deorsum moventur, aut frequentius funem in medii circuli modum duobus stipitibus appen-

dunt, desuperque insidentes hinc & inde impulsæ feruntur.'

[3] An exact parallel to the first part of Swift's description occurs in *The Journal of John Stevens*, 1689–91, ed. R. H. Murray (1912), p. 139: 'They [the Irish near Limerick] all smoke, women as well as men, and a pipe an inch long serves the whole family several years and though never so black or foul is never suffered to be burnt. Seven or eight will gather to the smoking of a pipe and each taking two or three whiffs gives it to his neighbour, commonly holding his mouth full of smoke till the pipe comes about to him again.'

as Occasion requires, and they move their Bodies
up and down, to a Degree, that sometimes their Heads
and Points lie parallel to the Horison. Mean while,
you may observe their Eyes turn'd up in the Posture of
one, who endeavours to keep himself awake; by which,
and many other Symptoms among them, it manifestly
appears, that the Reasoning Faculties are all suspended
and superseded, that Imagination hath usurped the
Seat, scattering a thousand Deliriums over the Brain.
Returning from this Digression, I shall describe the
Methods, by which the *Spirit* approaches. The Eyes
being disposed according to Art, at first, you can see
nothing, but after a short pause, a small glimmering
Light begins to appear, and dance before you. Then,
by frequently moving your Body up and down, you
perceive the Vapors to ascend very fast, till you are
perfectly dosed and flustred like one who drinks too
much in a Morning. Mean while, the Preacher is also
at work; He begins a loud Hum, which pierces you
quite thro'; This is immediately returned by the Audience, and you find your self prompted to imitate them,
by a meer spontaneous Impulse, without knowing
what you do. The *Interstitia*[1] are duly filled up by the
Preacher, to prevent too long a Pause, under which
the *Spirit* would soon faint and grow languid.

THIS is all I am allowed to discover about the
Progress of the *Spirit*, with relation to that part, which
is born by the *Assembly*; But in the Methods of the
Preacher, to which I now proceed, I shall be more large
and particular.

---

[1] Cf. John Phillips, *A Satyr against Hypocrites* (1655), p. 23:

The lest he should like a de-
ceiver come

'Twixt the two Sundays *inter-
stitium*.

Phillips's *Satyr* serves to illustrate several points in the *Discourse*.

SECTION II.

YOU will read it very gravely remarked in the Books of those illustrious and right eloquent Pen-men, the Modern Travellers; that the fundamental Difference in Point of Religion, between the wild *Indians* and Us, lies in this; that We worship *God*, and they worship the *Devil*. But, there are certain Criticks, who will by no means admit of this Distinction; rather believing, that all Nations whatsoever, adore the *true God*, because, they seem to intend their Devotions to some invisible Power, of greatest *Goodness* and *Ability* to help them, which perhaps will take in the brightest Attributes ascribed to the Divinity. Others, again, inform us, that those Idolaters adore two *Principles*; the *Principle* of *Good*, and That of *Evil:* Which indeed, I am apt to look upon as the most Universal Notion, that Mankind, by the meer Light of Nature, ever entertained of Things Invisible. How this Idea hath been managed by the *Indians* and Us, and with what Advantage to the Understandings of either, may well deserve to be examined. To me, the difference appears little more than this, That They are put oftener upon their Knees by their *Fears*, and We by our *Desires*; That the former set them a *Praying*, and Us a *Cursing*. What I applaud them for, is their Discretion, in limiting their Devotions and their Deities to their several Districts, nor ever suffering the Liturgy of the *white* God, to cross or interfere with that of the *Black*. Not so with Us, who pretending by the Lines and Measures of our Reason, to extend the Dominion of one invisible Power, and contract that of the other, have discovered a gross Ignorance in the Natures of Good and Evil, and most horribly confounded the Frontiers of both. After Men have lifted up the Throne of their Divinity to the

Cælum Empyræum, adorned him[1] with all such Qualities
and Accomplishments, as themselves seem most to value
and possess; After they have sunk their *Principle* of
Evil to the lowest Center, bound him with Chains,
loaded him with Curses, furnish'd him with viler
Dispositions than any *Rake-hell* of the Town, accoutred
him with Tail, and Horns, and huge Claws, and Sawcer
Eyes; I laugh aloud, to see these Reasoners, at the same
time, engaged in wise Dispute, about certain Walks
and Purlieus, whether they are in the Verge of God or
the Devil, seriously debating, whether such and such
Influences come into Mens Minds, from above or below,
or[2] whether certain Passions and Affections are guided
by the Evil Spirit or the Good.

> *Dum fas atque nefas exiguo fine libidinum*
> *Discernunt avidi———.*[3]

Thus do Men establish a Fellowship of *Christ* with
Belial, and such is the Analogy they make[4] between
cloven Tongues, and *cloven Feet*. Of the like Nature is the
Disquisition before us: It hath continued these hundred
Years an even Debate, whether the Deportment and
the Cant of our *English* Enthusiastick Preachers, were
Possession, or *Inspiration*, and a World of Argument has
been drained on either side, perhaps, to little Purpose.
For, I think, it is in *Life* as in *Tragedy*, where, it is held,
a Conviction of great Defect, both in Order and Invention, to interpose the Assistance of preternatural Power
without an absolute and last Necessity.[5] However, it is
a Sketch of Human Vanity, for every Individual, to
imagine the whole Universe is interess'd in his meanest

---

[1] 'him' omitted edd. 4, 5.
[2] 'or' omitted edd. 4, 5.
[3] Horace, *Odes*, i. xviii. 10, 11.
[4] 'they make' inserted ed. 5.

[5] Nec Deus intersit, nisi dignus
    vindice nodus
Inciderit. Hor. de Arte Poeticâ
    [*MS. Pate*].

Concern. If he hath got cleanly over a Kennel, some Angel, unseen, descended on purpose to help him by the Hand; if he hath knockt his Head against a Post, it was the Devil, for his Sins, let loose from Hell, on purpose to buffet him. Who, that sees a little paultry Mortal, droning, and dreaming, and drivelling to a Multitude, can think it agreeable to common good Sense, that either Heaven or Hell should be put to the Trouble of Influence or Inspection upon what he is about? Therefore, I am resolved immediately, to weed this Error out of Mankind, by making it clear, that this Mystery, of venting[1] spiritual Gifts is nothing but a *Trade*, acquired by as much Instruction, and mastered by equal Practice and Application as others are. This will best appear, by describing and deducing the whole Process of the Operation, as variously as it hath fallen under my Knowledge or Experience.

* * * * * * * * *

Here the whole Scheme * * * * *
of spiritual Mechanism * * * * *
was deduced and ex- * * * * *
plained, with an Appear- * * * * *
ance of great reading and * * * * *
observation; but it was * * * * *
thought neither safe nor * * * * *
Convenient to Print it. * * * * *
* * * * * * * * *

HERE it may not be amiss, to add a few Words upon the laudable Practice of wearing *quilted Caps*;[2] which is not a Matter of meer Custom, Humor, or Fashion, as some would pretend, but an Institution of great Sagacity and Use; these, when moistned with

---

[1] 'vending' edd. 4, 5.

[2] Cf. Aubrey's account of William Prynne (*Brief Lives*, ed. A. Clark, 1898, ii, p. 174): 'His manner of studie was thus: he wore a long quilt cap, which came 2 or 3, at least, inches, over his eies, which served him as an umbrella to defend his eies from the light.' Cf. also *The Spectator*, No. 494.

Sweat, stop all Perspiration, and by reverberating the Heat, prevent the Spirit from evaporating any way, but at the Mouth; even as a skilful Housewife, that covers her Still with a wet Clout, for the same Reason, and finds the same Effect. For, it is the Opinion of Choice *Virtuosi*, that the Brain is only a Crowd of little Animals, but with Teeth and Claws extremely sharp, and therefore, cling together in the Contexture we behold, like the Picture of *Hobbes*'s *Leviathan*,[1] or like Bees in perpendicular swarm upon a Tree, or like a Carrion corrupted into Vermin, still preserving the Shape and Figure of the Mother Animal. That all invention is formed by the Morsure of two or more of these Animals, upon certain capillary Nerves, which proceed from thence, whereof three Branches spread into the Tongue, and two into the right Hand. They hold also, that these Animals are of a Constitution extremely cold; that their Food is the Air we attract, their Excrement Phlegm; and that what we vulgarly call Rheums, and Colds, and Distillations, is nothing else but an Epidemical Looseness, to which that little Commonwealth is very subject, from the Climate it lyes under. Farther, that nothing less than a violent Heat, can disentangle these Creatures from their hamated[2] Station of Life, or give them Vigor and Humor, to imprint the Marks of their little Teeth. That if the Morsure be Hexagonal, it produces Poetry; the Circular gives Eloquence; If the Bite hath been Conical, the Person, whose Nerve is so affected, shall be disposed to write upon the Politicks; and so of the rest.

I shall now Discourse briefly, by what kind of Practices the Voice is best governed, towards the Composition and Improvement of the *Spirit*; for, without

---

[1] '*Hobs*'s' edd. 3, 4. Cf. p. 40. Swift refers to the figure at the top of the engraved title-page of the *Leviathan* (1651).

[2] Furnished with hooks (Lat. *hamus*, hook).

a competent Skill in tuning and toning each Word, and Syllable, and Letter, to their due Cadence, the whole Operation is incompleat, misses entirely of its effect on the Hearers, and puts the Workman himself to continual Pains for new Supplies, without Success. For, it is to be understood, that in the Language of the Spirit, *Cant* and *Droning* supply the Place of *Sense* and *Reason*, in the Language of Men: Because, in Spiritual Harangues, the Disposition of the Words according to the Art of Grammar, hath not the least Use, but the Skill and Influence wholly lye in the Choice and Cadence of the Syllables; Even as a discreet *Composer*, who in setting a Song, changes the Words and Order so often, that he is forced to make it *Nonsense*, before he can make it *Musick*.[1] For this Reason, it hath been held by some, that the Art of Canting is ever in greatest Perfection, when managed by *Ignorance:* Which is thought to be enigmatically meant by *Plutarch*, when he tells us, that the best Musical Instruments were made from the Bones of an *Ass*.[2] And the profounder Criticks upon that Passage, are of Opinion, the Word in its genuine Signification, means no other than a *Jaw-bone:* tho' some rather think it to have been the *Os sacrum*;[3] but in so nice a Case, I shall not take upon me to decide: The Curious are at Liberty, to *pick* from it whatever they please.

THE first Ingredient, towards the Art of Canting, is a competent Share of *Inward Light:* that is to say, a large Memory, plentifully fraught with Theological Polysyllables, and mysterious Texts from holy Writ, applied and digested by those Methods, and Mechani-

---

[1] Swift's references to contemporary music may be compared with Addison's in *The Spectator*, e.g. No. 18, where it is said to be an established rule 'That nothing is capable of being well set to Musick, that is not Nonsense'.

[2] *Septem Sapientium Convivium*, 5 (*Opera*, Didot, vol. iii, p. 179).

[3] Cf. *Hudibras*, iii. ii. 1624.

cal Operations already related: The Bearers of this *Light*, resembling *Lanthorns*, compact of Leaves from old *Geneva* Bibles; Which Invention, Sir *H-mphry Edw-n*,[1] during his Mayoralty, of happy Memory, highly approved and advanced; affirming, the Scripture to be now fulfilled, where it says, *Thy Word is a Lanthorn to my Feet, and a Light to my Paths.*[2]

NOW, the Art of *Canting* consists in skilfully adapting the Voice, to whatever Words the Spirit delivers, that each may strike the Ears of the Audience, with its most significant Cadence. The Force, or Energy of this Eloquence, is not to be found, as among antient Orators, in the Disposition of Words to a Sentence, or the turning of long Periods; but agreeable to the Modern Refinements in Musick, is taken up wholly in dwelling, and dilating upon Syllables and Letters. Thus it is frequent for a single *Vowel* to draw Sighs from a Multitude; and for a whole Assembly of Saints to sob to the Musick of one solitary *Liquid*. But these are Trifles; when even Sounds inarticulate are observed to produce as forcible Effects. A Master Work-man shall *blow his Nose so powerfully*, as to pierce the Hearts of his People, who are disposed to receive the *Excrements* of his Brain with the same Reverence, as the *Issue* of it. Hawking, Spitting, and Belching, the Defects of other Mens Rhetorick, are the Flowers, and Figures, and Ornaments of his. For, the *Spirit* being the same in all, it is of no Import through what Vehicle it is convey'd.

IT is a Point of too much Difficulty, to draw the Principles of this famous Art within the Compass of certain adequate Rules. However, perhaps, I may one day, oblige the World with my Critical Essay upon the Art of *Canting, Philosophically, Physically, and Musically considered.*[3]

---

[1] See p. 205, note 1.
[2] Psal. CXIX. v. 105 [1720].
[3] See the Catalogue, before the Title [1720.] See p. 2.

BUT, among all Improvements of the *Spirit*, wherein the Voice hath born a Part, there is none to be compared with That of *conveying the Sound thro' the Nose*, which under the Denomination of *Snuffling, hath passed with so great Applause in the World. The Originals of this Institution are very dark; but having been initiated into the Mystery of it, and Leave being given me to publish it to the World, I shall deliver as direct a Relation as I can.

THIS Art, like many other famous Inventions, owed its Birth, or at least, Improvement and Perfection, to an Effect of Chance, but was established upon solid Reasons, and hath flourished in this Island ever since, with great Lustre. All agree, that it first appeared upon the Decay and Discouragement of *Bag-pipes*, which having long suffered under the Mortal Hatred of the *Brethren*, tottered for a Time, and at last fell with *Monarchy*. The Story is thus related.

AS yet, *Snuffling* was not; when the following Adventure happened to a *Banbury Saint*.[1] Upon a certain Day, while he was far engaged among the Tabernacles of the *Wicked*, he felt the Outward Man put into odd Commotions, and strangely prick'd forward by the Inward: An Effect very usual among the Modern Inspired. For, some think, that the *Spirit* is apt to feed on the *Flesh*, like hungry Wines upon raw Beef. Others rather believe, there is a perpetual Game at *Leap-Frog* between both; and, sometimes, the *Flesh* is uppermost, and sometimes the *Spirit*; adding, that the former,

---

* *The* Snuffling *of Men, who have lost their Noses by lewd Courses, is said to have given Rise to that Tone, which our Dissenters did too much Affect.* W. Wotton.

---

[1] Banbury was famous for its Puritanism. There is a section on 'the reputed zeal of Banbury', with an interesting series of quotations, in Alfred Beesley's *History of Banbury* (1841), pp. 454–62.

while it is in the State of a *Rider*, wears huge *Rippon* Spurs,[1] and when it comes to the Turn of being *Bearer*, is wonderfully headstrong, and hard-mouth'd. However it came about, the *Saint* felt his *Vessel* full *extended* in every Part (a very natural Effect of strong *Inspiration*;) and the Place and Time falling out so unluckily, that he could not have the Convenience of Evacuating upwards, by Repetition, Prayer, or Lecture;[2] he was forced to open an inferior Vent. In short, he wrestled with the Flesh so long, that he at length subdued it, coming off with honourable Wounds, all *before*. The Surgeon had now cured the Parts, primarily affected; but the Disease driven from its Post, flew up into his Head; And, as a skilful General, valiantly attack'd in his Trenches, and beaten from the Field, by flying Marches withdraws to the Capital City, breaking down the Bridges to prevent Pursuit; So the Disease repell'd from its first Station, fled before the *Rod* of *Hermes*, to the upper Region, there fortifying it self; but, finding the Foe making Attacks at the *Nose*, broke down the *Bridge*, and retir'd to the *Head*-Quarters. Now, the Naturalists observe, that there is in human Noses, an *Idiosyncrasy*, by Virtue of which, the more the Passage is obstructed, the more our Speech delights to go through, as the Musick of a Flagelate is made by the *Stops*. By this Method, the Twang of the Nose, becomes perfectly to resemble the *Snuffle* of a Bag-pipe,[3] and is found to be equally attractive of *British* Ears; whereof the Saint had sudden Experience, by practising his new Faculty with wonderful Success in the Operation of the

---

[1] Ripon was renowned for the manufacture of spurs. Cf. Ben Jonson, *The Staple of Newes*, i. iii: 'if my Spurres be not right *Rippon*'; and see Ray, *Proverbs*, (1670), p. 256.

[2] i.e. 'discourse'.

[3] Cf. *Hudibras*, i. i. 515–16:
This Light inspires, and plays upon
The nose of Saint, like Bag-pipe drone.

Spirit: For, in a short Time, no Doctrine pass'd for Sound and Orthodox, unless it were delivered thro' the Nose. Strait, every Pastor copy'd after this Orignal; and those, who could not otherwise arrive to a Perfection, spirited by a noble Zeal, made use of the same Experiment to acquire it. So that, I think, it may be truly affirmed, the *Saints* owe their Empire to the *Snuffling* of one *Animal*, as *Darius* did his, to the *Neighing* of another; * *Herodot.* and both Stratagems were performed by the same Art; for we read, how the **Persian* *Beast* acquired his Faculty, by *covering a Mare* the Day before.[1]

I should now have done, if I were not convinced, that whatever I have yet advanced upon this Subject, is liable to great Exception. For, allowing all I have said to be true, it may still be justly objected, that there is in the Commonwealth of *artificial Enthusiasm*, some real Foundation for Art to work upon in the Temper and Complexion of Individuals, which other Mortals seem to want. Observe, but the Gesture, the Motion, and the Countenance, of some choice Professors, tho' in their most familiar Actions, you will find them of a different Race from the rest of human Creatures. Remark your commonest Pretender to a Light *within*, how dark, and dirty, and gloomy he is *without*; As Lanthorns, which the more Light they bear in their Bodies, cast out so much the more Soot, and Smoak, and fuliginous Matter to adhere to the Sides. Listen, but to their ordinary Talk, and look on the Mouth that delivers it; you will imagine you are hearing some antient Oracle, and your Understanding will be *equally* informed. Upon these, and the like Reasons, certain Objectors pretend to put it beyond all Doubt, that there must be a sort of preter-

[1] Herodotus, iii. 85–86: cf.   Kings were proclaim's by a
Hudibras, i. ii. 137–8:   Horse that neigh'd.
    As once in *Persia*, tis said,

natural *Spirit*, possessing the Heads of the Modern Saints; And some will have it to be the *Heat* of Zeal, working upon the *Dregs* of Ignorance, as other *Spirits* are produced from *Lees*, by the Force of Fire. Some again think, that when our earthly Tabernacles are disordered and desolate, shaken and out of Repair; the *Spirit* delights to dwell within them, as Houses are said to be haunted, when they are forsaken and gone to Decay.

TO set this Matter in as fair a Light as possible; I shall here, very briefly, deduce the History of *Fanaticism*, from the most early Ages to the present. And if we are able to fix upon any one material or fundamental Point, wherein the chief Professors have universally agreed, I think we may reasonably lay hold on That, and assign it for the great Seed or Principle of the *Spirit*.

THE most early Traces we meet with, of *Fanaticks*, in antient Story, are among the *Ægyptians*, who instituted those Rites, known in *Greece* by the Names of *Orgya*, *Panegyres*, and *Dionysia*, whether introduced there by *Orpheus* or[1] *Melampus*, we shall not dispute at present, nor in all likelihood, at any time for the future. These feasts were celebrated to the Honor of *Osyris*, whom the *Grecians* called *Dionysius*, and is the same with *Bacchus:* Which has betray'd some *Diod. Sic. L. 1. Plut. de Isside & Osyride.*[2] superficial Readers to imagine, that the whole Business was nothing more than a Set or roaring, scouring Companions, over-charg'd with Wine; but this is a scandalous Mistake foisted on the World, by a sort of Modern Authors, who have too *literal* an Understanding; and, because Antiquity is to be traced *backwards*, do therefore, like *Jews*, begin their Books at the wrong

---

[1] 'or' edd. 1–4; 'and' ed. 5.   [2] Diodorus Siculus, i. 97, 286.

End, as if Learning were a sort of *Conjuring*. These are the Men, who pretend to understand a Book, by scouting thro' the *Index*,[1] as if a Traveller should go about to describe a *Palace*, when he had seen nothing but the *Privy*; or like certain Fortune-tellers in *Northern America*, who have a Way of reading a Man's Destiny, by peeping in his *Breech*. For, at the Time of instituting these Mysteries, *there was not one Vine in all *Egypt*,[2] the Natives drinking nothing but *Ale*; which Liquor seems to have been far more antient than Wine, and has the Honor of owing its Invention and Progress, not only to the †*Egyptian Osyris*,[3] but to the *Grecian Bacchus*, who in their famous Expedition, carried the Receipt of it along with them, and gave it to the Nations they visited or subdued. Besides, *Bacchus* himself, was very seldom, or never Drunk: For, it is recorded of him, that he was the first ‡Inventor of the *Mitre*,[4] which he wore continually on his Head (as the whole Company of *Bacchanals* did) to prevent Vapors and the Head-ach, after hard Drinking. And for this Reason (say some) the *Scarlet Whore*, when she makes the Kings of the Earth drunk with her Cup of Abomination, is always sober her self, tho' she never balks the Glass in her Turn, being, it seems, kept upon her Legs by the Virtue of her *Triple Mitre*. Now, these Feasts were instituted in imitation of the famous Expedition *Osyris* made thro' the World, and of the Company that attended him, whereof the *Bacchanalian* Ceremonies were so many Types and Symbols. From which Account, it is manifest, that the Fanatick Rites of these *Bacchanals*, cannot be imputed to

Herod. L. 2.

† *Diod. Sic.* L. 1. & 3.

‡ *Id.* L. 4.

See the Particulars in Diod. Sic. L. 1. & 3.

[1] Cf. p. 145, notes 1 and 2. 62.
[2] Herodotus, ii. 77.
[3] Diodorus Siculus, i. 15; iii.
[4] Ibid. iv. 4.

Intoxications by Wine, but must needs have had a deeper Foundation. What this was, we may gather large Hints from certain Circumstances in the Course of their Mysteries. For, in the first Place, there was in their Processions, an entire *Mixture and Confusion of Sexes*; they affected to ramble about Hills and Desarts: Their Garlands were of *Ivy* and *Vine*, Emblems of Cleaving and Clinging; or of *Fir*, the Parent of *Turpentine*. It is added, that they imitated *Satyrs*, were attended by *Goats*, and rode upon *Asses*, all Companions of great Skill and Practice in Affairs of Gallantry. They bore for their Ensigns, certain curious Figures, perch'd upon long Poles, made into the Shape and Size of the *Virga genitalis*, with its *Appurtenances*, which were so many Shadows and Emblems of the whole Mystery, as well as Trophies set up by the Female Conquerors. Lastly, in a certain Town of *Attica*, the whole Solemnity *stript of all its Types, was performed in *puris naturalibus*, the Votaries, not flying in Coveys, but sorted into Couples.[1] The same may be farther conjectured from the Death of *Orpheus*, one of the Institutors of these Mysteries, who was torn in Pieces by Women, because he refused to †*communicate his Orgyes* to them; which others explained, by telling us, he had *castrated* himself upon Grief, for the Loss of his Wife.[2]

* *Dionysia Brauronia.*

† *Vid. Photium in excerptis è Conone.*

OMITTING many others of less Note, the next *Fanaticks* we meet with, of any Eminence, were the numerous Sects of *Hereticks* appearing in the five first Centuries of the *Christian Æra*, from *Simon Magus* and his Followers, to those of *Eutyches*. I have collected their Systems from infinite Reading, and comparing them

---

[1] The quinquennial festival called Brauronia, celebrated by men and women, at Brauron, in honour of Dionysus.

[2] Photius, ed. Bekker (1824), p. 140a.

with those of their Successors in the several Ages since, I find there are certain Bounds set even to the Irregularities of Human Thought, and those a great deal narrower than is commonly apprehended. For, as they all frequently interfere,[1] even in their wildest Ravings; So there is one fundamental Point, wherein they are sure to meet, as Lines in a Center, and that is the *Community of Women:* Great were their Sollicitudes in this Matter, and they never fail'd of certain Articles in their Schemes of Worship, on purpose to establish it.

THE last *Fanaticks* of Note, were those which started up in *Germany,* a little after the *Reformation* of *Luther*; Springing, as *Mushrooms* do at the *End of a Harvest*; Such were *John* of *Leyden*,[2] *David George*,[3] *Adam Neuster*,[4] and many others; whose Visions and Revelations, always terminated in *leading about half a dozen Sisters, apiece,* and making That Practice a fundamental Part of their System. For, Human Life is a continual Navigation, and, if we expect our *Vessels* to pass with Safety, thro' the Waves and Tempests of this fluctuating World, it is necessary to make a good Provision of the *Flesh,* as Sea-men lay in store of *Beef* for a long Voyage.

NOW from this brief Survey of some Principal Sects, among the *Fanaticks,* in all Ages (having omitted the *Mahometans* and others, who might also help to confirm the Argument I am about) to which I might add several among our selves, such as the *Family of Love*,[5] *Sweet*

---

[1] Cf. p. 146, l. 9.

[2] See p. 170, note 3.

[3] David George, or Joris (1501–56), a Dutch Anabaptist, founder of the 'Familists', or the 'Family of Love'.

[4] Adam Neuster (d. 1576), a German Socinian theologian, who became a Mussulman and died at Constantinople in the Mohammedan faith.

[5] Members of the *Family of Love* settled in England in the sixteenth century, and won over many disciples from among the Puritans. The new sect attracted

Singers of Israel,[1] and the like: And from reflecting upon that fundamental Point in their Doctrines, about *Women,* wherein they have so unanimously agreed; I am apt to imagine, that the Seed or Principle, which has ever put Men upon *Visions* in Things *Invisible,* is of a Corporeal Nature: For the profounder Chymists inform us, that the Strongest *Spirits* may be extracted from *Human Flesh.* Besides, the Spinal Marrow, being nothing else but a Continuation of the Brain, must needs create a very free Communication between the Superior Faculties and those below: And thus the *Thorn in the Flesh* serves for a *Spur* to the *Spirit.* I think, it is agreed among Physicians, that nothing affects the Head so much, as a tentiginous Humor, repelled and elated to the upper Region, found by daily practice, to run frequently up into Madness. A very eminent Member of the Faculty, assured me, that when the *Quakers* first appeared, he seldom was without some Female Patients among them, for the *furor*——[2] Persons of a visionary Devotion, either Men or Women, are in their Complexion, of all others, the most amorous: For, *Zeal* is frequently kindled from the same Spark with other Fires, and from inflaming Brotherly Love, will proceed

attention during the reigns of Queen Elizabeth and James I: it seems to have come to an end about the middle of the seventeenth century. See J. H. Blunt, *Dictionary of Sects,* s.v. *Familists.*

[1] See *An Account of the Life of Bunyan,* 1692, p. 22: 'About this time, a very large Liberty being given as to Conscience, there started up a Sect of loose prophane Wretches, afterward called Ranters and sweet Singers, pretending themselves [free] from,

or being incapable of Sinning; though indeed they were the Debauchest and [most] Profligate Wretches living, in their Baudy Meetings and Revels.' They were distinct from the Scottish fanatics, called 'Sweet Singers' from their habit of 'wailing a portion' of the Psalms, who were committed to prison in Edinburgh in 1681.

[2] '*furor*   ' (blank) edd. 1, 4; '*furor Uterinus*' ed. 2; '*furor* * * *' ed. 3.

to raise That of a Gallant. If we inspect into the usual Process of modern Courtship, we shall find it to consist in a devout Turn of the Eyes, called *Ogling*; an artificial Form of Canting and Whining by rote, every Interval, for want of other Matter, made up with a Shrug, or a Hum, a Sigh or a Groan; The Style compact of insignificant Words, Incoherences and Repetition. These, I take, to be the most accomplish'd Rules of Address to a Mistress; and where are these performed with more Dexterity, than by the *Saints?* Nay, to bring this Argument yet closer, I have been informed by certain Sanguine Brethren of the first Class, that in the Height and *Orgasmus* of their Spiritual exercise it has been frequent with them * * * * *; immediately after which, they found the *Spirit* to relax and flag of a sudden with the Nerves, and they were forced to hasten to a Conclusion. This may be farther Strengthened, by observing, with Wonder, how unaccountably all Females are attracted by Visionary or Enthusiastick Preachers, tho' never so contemptible in their *outward Men*;[1] which is usually supposed to be done upon Considerations, purely Spiritual, without any carnal Regards at all. But I have Reason to think, the *Sex* hath certain Characteristicks, by which they form a truer Judgment of Human Abilities and Performings, than we our selves can possibly do of each other. Let That be as it will, thus much is certain, that however Spiritual Intrigues begin, they generally conclude like all others; they may branch upwards towards[2] Heaven, but the Root is in the Earth. Too intense a Contemplation is not the Business of Flesh and Blood; it must by the necessary Course of Things, in a little Time, let go its Hold, and fall into *Matter*. Lovers, for the sake of Celestial Converse, are

---

[1] '*Mien*' edd. 1711, 1720, Hawkesworth.   [2] 'toward' ed. 1 (cf. p. 198, l. 18).

but another sort of *Platonicks*, who pretend to see Stars and Heaven in Ladies Eyes, and to look or think no lower; but the same *Pit* is provided for both; and they seem a perfect Moral to the Story of that Philosopher, who, while his Thoughts and Eyes were fixed upon the *Constellations*, found himself seduced by his *lower Parts* into a *Ditch*.[1]

I had somewhat more to say upon this Part of the Subject; but the Post is just going, which forces me in great Haste to conclude,

SIR,

Yours, &c.

*Pray, burn this
   Letter as soon
   as it comes to
   your Hands.*

[1] Thales. Cf. Diogenes Laertius, 1. i. 8. 34: and Plato, *Theaetetus*, 174 A.

F I N I S.

THE six Appendixes added to this edition of *A Tale of a Tub* consist of

- A. New matter in the *Miscellaneous Works* of Swift published in 1720

- B. The portion of Wotton's *Observations*, 1705, that deals directly with the *Tale*

- C. A full reprint of the *Complete Key* published by Edmund Curll in 1710

- D. Two letters that passed between Swift and Benjamin Tooke in 1710

- E. Notes on 'Treatises wrote by the same Author'

- F. Notes on Swift's 'Dark Authors'.

MISCELLANEOUS
WORKS,

Comical & Diverting:

BY

T. R. D. J. S. D. O. P. I. I.

IN TWO PARTS.

I. The TALE *of a* TUB; with the *Fragment*, & the BATTEL *of the* BOOKS; with confiderable *Additions*, & explanatory *Notes*, never before printed.

II. MISCELLANIES in PROSE & VERSE, by the fuppofed Author of the firft part.

LONDON,
Printed by Order of the Society
de propaganda, *&c.*

M. DCC. XX.

THE BOOKSELLERS

ADVERTISEMENT

On this new Edition.

TO give the curious Reader a just Idea of what he may expect in this Volume, I cannot do better than transcribe a part of a Letter sent me with the Copy, from an ingenious Gentleman of my acquaintance, whose advice I have followed exactly.

.... You have here also according to your desire my *Tale of a Tub*, with all the Notes you have formerly seen, & several others I have added since. You may make what use you please of it, provided you return it me safe when you have done, & that you let no body see it, or know from whom you had it. You'l perhaps find some of these Notes of no great use, because you understand all without 'em; but some Readers will be apt to wish there were more, to explain some other passages they may not perfectly understand.

I think it's almost needless to tell the Readers, they ought not to impute to the Author the sense given to his words in these Notes; especialy in those taken from his Adversarys, such as M. *Wotton*, one of the Heroes of the piece. Any one that reads the praises given him by our Author, will easily see his reasons for giving the worst turn imaginable to every thing he has written. I once hoped to have found a great many more curious Notes of this kind, in the Remarks made on this Book by D. *Bentley* the Author's principal Hero. I am told this is a Masterpiece of modern Criticism, & that this Prince of Pedants has, with a vast deal of laborious learning, shewn that he can interpret almost nine passages of *Antient Authors* in a sense different from that which our Author has given them; but particularly that he has most terribly maul'd this Author with those Arms he had so bountifully bestowed on him in the 240 page of this

Treatise, & especially with that of his left hand, of which according to his custom he has been very liberal. I'm informed from some of his Friends, that he expects the Thanks of both Houses of Parliament for this performance, as he had lately those of both our learned & wise Universitys for another of the same kind; but that he does not find the present conjuncture favourable for publishing it. When these Remarks appear you may expect an ample Commentary on this Work; in the mean time you may be satisfied with these few Notes I send you.

As for the Manuscript I told you I had seen, which contains a great deal more than what is printed, I would very willingly have taken a copy of what is ommitted, & have sent it you; but I was not allowed that liberty, having only had leave to read it. I can assure you I found those parts not at all inferior to the others that are printed; but I believe some prudential considerations have hindered their publication. I have writ down the heads of the most material, as near as I can now remember, on the leaves put in at the end of my book, where you'l find a general Table* or Index of the whole work, which may serve for a Recapitulation to those that have read it through. I have extended such parts as have not been printed, somthing more largely than the others, & as near as I can remember in the Authors own words. And who knows of what great use this may be in future Ages, to some learned *Freinshemius*, who may undertake to gratify the World with a Supplement of what has been lost of this curious Treatise.

I would advise you (if it can be conveniently done in the same volume) to print all the comical Pieces of the *Miscellanies in Prose & Verse*, generally attributed to the same Author: as for the serious Pieces in that Collection, tho' some of them be very good in their kind, yet being of a very different nature, I think you may leave them out; there being but few that buy the volume for their sake, & the generality of Readers will be very glad to find the others in the same volume with the *Tale of a Tub*. The Pieces I mean are, *The Meditation upon a Broomstick*; *Various Thoughts*; *The Tritical Essays*; *The Argument against abolishing Christianity*, The *Predictions* &c. with all the Pieces in Verse, to which I would have you add the *Imitation* of part of the seventh

* *See p.* 247, *&c.* [p. 298 of this volume].

Epist. *Lib. I.* of *Horace,* addressed to the Earl of *Oxford,* which is an excellent Piece. You have not seen perhaps how the last lines of this Epistle of *Horace* (which our Author left untouch'd) have been imitated by one that's no great friend to the Doctor.

> *Qui semel aspexit quantum dimissa petitis*
> *Præstent, mature redeat. . . .*
> *Metiri se quemque suo modulo, ac pede, verum est.*

> This Reverend Dean may teach us all
> What merit goes to fill a Stall;
> To weigh our strength, & be so wise
> As not to swell beyond our size:
> Nor aim at Posts of power & profit
> Due to desert, with little of it.

Although I advise the printing all those pieces together in one volume, because I think it will take very well (especially when done so neat & correct as you are used to doe) yet I would not have any body take this for a proof of their being all of the same Author. So long as Dr. *Swift* does not own the *Tale of a Tub,* I think no man has a right to charge him with it, whatever common Fame may report. I know several persons of good sense, that imagine Sr. *William Temple* to have the Author of it, & find several passages in his other Writings, pretty much in the same strain. Even Dr. *Wotton,* who is certainly no friend to Dr. *Swift,* seems to be of this opinion, when he says (Def. p. 67) that *in his own Conscience he acquits him from composing it; & believes that the Author is dead, & that it was probably written in 1697.* As for what the Author of the pretended *Key to the Tale of a Tub* says about *Jonathan, & Thomas Swift* having joyn'd in this work, I lay no manner of stress on it. . . . . . .

The passage of that Author here mention'd runs thus.
The Preface of the Bookseller before *the Battle of the Books* shews the cause and design of the whole Work, which was perform'd by* a couple of young Clergymen in the Year 1697. who

* *Generally (and not without sufficient reason) said to be Dr.* Jonathan *and* Thomas Swift; *but since they don't think fit publickly to own it, wherever I mention their names, 'tis not upon any other affirmation than as they are the* reputed Authors.

having been Domestick Chaplains to Sir *William Temple*, thought themselves oblig'd to take up his Quarrel in relation to the Controversy then in dispute between him and Mr. *Wotton* concerning *Ancient* and *Modern* Learning.

The *one of 'em began a *Defence* of Sir *William*, under the Title of *A Tale of a Tub*, under which he intended to couch the general History of Christianity; shewing the rise of all the remarkable Errors of the *Roman Church*; in the same order they enter'd, and how the Reformation endeavour'd to root 'em out again, with the different Temper of *Luther* from *Calvin* (and those more violent Spirits) in the way of his Reforming: His aim is to ridicule the stubborn errors of the Romish Church, and the humours of the Fanatick Party, and to shew that their Superstition has somewhat very fantastical in it, which is common to both of 'em, notwithstanding the abhorrence they seem to have for one another.

The Author intended to have it very regular, and withal so particular, that he thought not to pass by the Rise of any one single Error or its Reformation: He design'd at last to shew the purity of the Christian Church in the primitive times, and consequently how weakly Mr. *Wotton* pass'd his judgment, and how partially, in preferring the *modern* Divinity before the *Ancient*, with the confutation of whose Book he intended to conclude. But when he had not yet gone half way, his †Companion borrowing the *Manuscript* to peruse, carried it with him to *Ireland*, and having kept it seven Years, at last publish'd it imperfect; for indeed it was not able to carry it on after the intended method; because *Divinity* (tho it chanc'd to be his Profession) had been the least of his study: However he added to it the *Battle of the Books*, wherein he effectually pursues the main design of lashing Mr. *Wotton*, and having added a jocose Epistle Dedicatory to my Lord *Sommers*, and another to Prince *Posterity*, with a pleasant Preface, and interlarded it with one *Digression* concerning *Criticks*, and another in the *modern* kind, a third in praise of *Digressions*, and a fourth in praise of *Madness* (with which he was not unacquainted) concludes the Book with a *Fragment* which the first Author made, and intended should have come in about the middle of the *Tale*, as a Preliminary to *Jack*'s Character.

* *Thomas Swift.*   † Dr. *Jonathan Swift.*

Having thus shewn the reasons of the little order observ'd in the Book, and the imperfectness of the *Tale*, 'tis so submitted to the Reader's censure.

Thomas Swift is Grandson to Sir *William D'avenant*: *Jonathan Swift* is Cousin German to *Thomas Swift*, both Retainers to Sir *William Temple*.[1]

---

[1] 'The Booksellers Advertisement' in the *Miscellaneous Works* of 1720 occupies pp. iii–ix. The 'Table', including 'The History of Martin', is there printed after the *Battel of the Books* (which follows the *Mechanical Operation*), and occupies pp. 247–68.

A Table, or Index, or Key, to the Tale *of a* Tub, &c.

---

[1] The numbers within square brackets give the pages in this edition.

Table   299

Table 301

Abstract of what follows after Sect. IX[1] in the
Manuscript.

The History of Martin.

HOw *Jack* & *Martin* being parted, set up each for himself.
How they travel'd over hills & dales, met many disasters,
suffered much for the good cause, & strugled with difficultys &
wants, not having where to lay their head; by all which they
afterwards proved themselves to be right Father's Sons, & *Peter*
to be spurious. Finding no shelter near *Peter's* habitation, *Martin*
travel'd northwards, & finding the *Thuringians* & neighbouring
people disposed to change, he set up his Stage first among them;
where making it his business to cry down *Peter's* pouders, plaisters, salves, & drugs, which he had sold a long time at a dear rate,
allowing *Martin* none of the profit, tho he had been often employed in recommending & putting them off; the good people willing to save their pence began to hearken to *Martin's* speeches. How
several great Lords took the hint & on the same account declared
for *Martin*; particularly one, who not having enough of one
Wife, wanted to marry a second, & knowing *Peter* used not to
grant such licenses but at a swinging price, he struck up a bargain
with *Martin* whom he found more tractable, & who assured him
he had the same power to allow such things. How most of the
other Northern Lords, for their own privat ends, withdrew
themselves & their Dependants from *Peters* authority & closed
in with *Martin*. How *Peter*, enraged at the loss of such large
Territorys, & consequently of so much revenue, thunder'd
against *Martin*, & sent out the strongest & most terrible of his
Bulls to devour him; but this having no effect, & *Martin* defending himself boldly and dexterously, *Peter* at last put forth Pro-
clamations declaring *Martin* & all his Adherents, Rebels and
Traytors, ordaining & requiring all his loving Subjects to take up
Arms and to kill burn & destroy all & every one of them, promising
large rewards &c. upon which ensued bloody wars & Desolations.
How *Harry Huff* Lord of Albion, one of the greatest Bullys

[1] A mistake for 'X'.

of those days, sent a Cartel to *Martin* to fight him on a stage, at Cudgels, Quarterstaff, Back-Sword &c. Hence the origine of that genteel custom of *Prize-fighting*, so well known & practised to this day among those polite Islanders, tho' unknown every where else. How *Martin* being a bold blustering fellow, accepted the Challenge; how they met & fought, to the great diversion of the Spectators; & after giving one another broken heads & many bloody wounds & bruises, how they both drew off victorious; in which their Exemple has been frequently imitated by great Clerks & others since that time. How *Martin's* friends aplauded his victory; & how Lord *Harrys* friends complimented him on the same score; & particularly Lord *Peter*, who sent him a fine Feather for his Cap, to be worn by him & his Successors, as a perpetual mark of his bold defense of Lord *Peter's* Cause. How *Harry* flushed with his pretended victory over *Martin*, began to huff *Peter* also, & at last down right quarrelled with him about a Wench. How some of Lord *Harry's* Tennants, ever fond of changes, began to talk kindly of *Martin*, for which he mauld 'em soundly; as he did also those that adhered to *Peter*; how he turn'd some out of house & hold, others he hanged or burnt &c.

How *Harry Huff* after a deal of blustering, wenching, & bullying, died, & was succeeded by a good natured Boy, who giving way to the general bent of his Tennants, allowed *Martin's* notions to spread every where & take deep root in Albion. How after his death the Farm fell into the hands of a Lady, who was violently in love with Lord *Peter*. How she purged the whole Country with fire & Sword, resolved not to leave the name or remembrance of *Martin*. How *Peter* triumphed, & set up shops again for selling his own pouders plaisters and salves, which were now called the only true ones, *Martins* being all declared counterfeit. How great numbers of *Martin's* friends left the Country, & traveling up & down in foreign parts, grew acquainted with many of *Jack's* followers, & took a liking to many of their notions & ways, which they afterwards brought back into Albion, now under another Landlady more moderate & more cunning than the former. How she endeavoured to keep friendship both with *Peter* & *Martin* & trimm'd for some time between the two, not without countenancing & assisting at the same time many of *Jack's* followers, but finding no possibility of reconciling all the three

Brothers, because each would be Master & allow no other salves pouders or plaisters to be used but his own, she discarded all three, & set up a shop for those of her own Farm, well furnished with pouders plaisters salves & all other drugs necessary, all right & true, composed according to receipts made up by Physicians & Apothecarys of her own creating, which they extracted out of *Peter*'s & *Martin*'s & *Jack*'s Receipt-books; & of this medly or hodgpodge made up a Dispensatory of their own; strictly forbiding any other to be used, & particularly *Peter*'s from which the greatest part of this new Dispensatory was stollen. How the Lady further to confirm this change, wisely imitating her Father, degraded *Peter* from the rank he pretended as eldest Brother, & set up her self in his place as head of the Family, & ever after wore her Fathers old Cap with the fine feather he had got from *Peter* for standing his friend; which has likewise been worn, with no small ostentation to this day, by all her Successors, tho declared Ennemys to *Peter*. How Lady Bess & her Physicians being told of many defects & imperfections in their new medley Dispensatory, resolve on a further alteration, & to purge it from a great deal of *Peter*'s trash that still remained in it; but were prevented by her death. How she was succeeded by a North Country Farmer, who pretended great skill in managing of Farms, tho' he cou'd never govern his own poor little old Farm, nor yet this large new one after he got it. How this new Landlord, to shew his Valour & dexterity, fought against Enchanters, Weeds, Giants, & Windmills, & claimed great Honnour for his Victorys, tho' he oftimes beshit himself when there was no danger. How his Successor, no wiser than he, occasion'd great disorders by the new methods he took to manage his Farms. How he attempted to establish in his northern Farm the same Dispensatory used in the southern, but miscarried, because *Jack*'s pouders, pills, salves, & plaisters, were there in great vogue.

How the Author finds himself embarassed for having introduced into his History a new Sect, different from the three he had undertaken to treat of; & how his inviolable respect to the sacred number *three* obliges him to reduce these four, as he intends to doe all other things, to that number; & for that end to drop the former *Martin*, & to substitute in his place Lady *Besses* Institution, which is to pass under the name of *Martin* in the sequel of this true History. This weighty point being clear'd, the Author goes on & describes mighty quarrels and squables between *Jack* & *Martin*, how sometimes the one had the better & sometimes the other, to the great desolation of both Farms, till at last both sides concur to hang up the Landlord, who pretended to die a Martyr for *Martin*, tho he had been true to neither side, & was suspected by many to have a great affection for *Peter*.

A Digression on the nature usefulness & necessity of Wars & Quarels.

THis being a matter of great consequence the Author intends to treat it methodically & at large in a Treatise apart, & here to give only some hints of what his large Treatise contains. The State of War natural to all Creatures. War is an attempt to take by violence from others a part of what they have & we want. Every man full sensible of his own merit, & finding it not duly regarded by others, has a natural right to take from them all that he thinks due to himself: & every creature finding its own wants more than those of others has the same right to take every thing its nature requires. Brutes much more modest in their pretensions this way than men; & mean men more than great ones. The higher one raises his pretensions this way, the more bustle he makes about them, & the more success he has, the greater Hero. Thus greater Souls in proportion to their superior merit claim a greater right to take every thing from meaner folks. This the true foundation of Grandeur & Heroism, & of the distinction of degrees among men. War therfor necessary to establish subordination, & to found Cities, States, Kingdoms, &c. as also to purge Bodys politick of gross humours. Wise Princes find it necessary to have wars abroad to keep peace at home. War, Famine, & Pestilence the usual cures for corruptions in Bodys politick. A comparaison of these three. The Author is to write a Panegyrick on each of them. The greatest part of Mankind loves War more than peace: They are but few & mean spirited that live in peace with all men. The modest & meek of all kinds always a prey to those of more noble or stronger apetites. The inclination to war universal: those that cannot or dare not make war in person, employ others to doe it for them. This maintains Bullys, Bravos, Cutthroats, Lawyers, Soldiers, &c. Most Professions would be useless if all were peaceable. Hence Brutes want neither Smiths nor Lawyers, Magistrats nor Joyners, Soldiers nor Surgeons. Brutes having but narrow appetites are incapable of carrying on or perpetuating war against their own species, or of being led out in troops & multitudes to destroy one another. These prerogatives proper to Man alone. The excellency of human nature demonstrated by the vast train of apetites, passions, wants, &c. that attend it. This matter to be more fully treated in the Author's Panegyrick on Mankind.

The History of Martin.

How *Jack* having got rid of the old Landlord & set up another to his mind, quarrel'd with *Martin* & turn'd him out of doors. How he pillaged all his shops, & abolished the whole Dispensatory. How the new Landlord laid about him, maul'd *Peter*, worry'd *Martin*, & made the whole neighborhood tremble. How *Jack*'s friends fell out among themselves, split into a thousand partys, turn'd all things topsy turvy, till every body grew weary of them, & at last the blustering Landlord dying *Jack* was kick'd out of doors, a new Landlord brought in, & *Martin* reestablished. How this new Landlord let *Martin* doe what he pleased, & *Martin* agreed to every thing his pious Landlord desired, provided *Jack* might be kept low. Of several efforts *Jack* made to raise up his head, but all in vain: till at last the Landlord died & was succeeded by one who was a great friend to *Peter*, who to humble *Martin* gave *Jack* some liberty. How *Martin* grew enraged at this, called in a Foreigner & turn'd out the Landlord; in which *Jack* concurred with *Martin*, because this Landlord was entirely devoted to *Peter*, into whose arms he threw himself, & left his Country. How the new Landlord secured *Martin* in the full possession of his former rights, who would not allow him to destroy *Jack* who had always been his friend. How *Jack* got

Table 307

up his head in the North and put himself in possession of a whole Canton, to the great discontent of *Martin*, who finding also that some of *Jack*'s friends were allowed to live & get their bread in the south parts of the country, grew highly discontent of the new Landlord he had called in to his assistance. How this Landlord kept *Martin* in order, upon which he fell into a raging fever, & swore he would hang himself or joyn in with *Peter*, unless *Jack*'s children were all turn'd out to starve. Of several attempts made to cure *Martin* & make peace between him & *Jack*, that they might unite against *Peter*, but all made ineffectual by the great adress of a number of *Peter*'s friends, that herded among *Martin*'s, & appeared the most zealous for his interest. How *Martin* getting abroad in this mad fit, look'd so like *Peter* in his air & dress, and talk'd so like him, that many of the Neighbours could not distinguish the one from the other; especially when *Martin* went up & down strutting in *Peter*'s Armour, which he had borrowed to fight *Jack*. What remedys were used to cure *Martin*'s distemper, &c.

NB. Some things that follow after this are not in the MS. but seem to have been written since to fill up the place of what was not thought convenient then to print.

The Conclusion.

Of the proper Seasons for of [sic] *publishing books,* [207.] *Of profound Writers,* [207.] *Of the ghost of Wit,* [208.] *Sleep & the Muses nearly related,* [208.] *Apology for the Authors fits of dulness,* [209.] *Method & Reason the Lacqueys of Invention,* [209.] *Our Authors great collection of* flowers *of litle use till now,* [210.]

A Discourse concerning the Mechanical operation of the Spirit.

The Author at a loss what Title to give this piece, finds after much pains that of a Letter to a friend *to be most in vogue,* [262.] *Of modern excuses for haste & negligence &c,* [263.]

I. Sect. Mahomet's *fancy of being carried to Heaven by an Ass, followed by many Christians,* [264.] *A great affinity between this Creature & Man,* [264.] *That talent of bringing his Rider to Heaven the subject of this discourse: but for Ass & Rider the Author uses the synonimous terms of Enlightened Teacher, and Fanatick Hearer,* [265.] *A tincture of Enthousiasm runs through all men & all Sciences,* [266.] *but prevails most in Religion,* [266.] *Enthousiasm defined & distinguished,* [266, 267.] *That which is Mechanical & Artificial is treated of by our Author,* [267.] *Tho' Art oftimes changes into Nature: examples in the Scythian Longheads & English Roundheads,* [268.] *Sense & Reason must be laid aside to let this Spirit operate,* [269.] *The Objections about the Manner of the Spirit from above descending on the Apostles, make not against this Spirit that arises within,* [270, 271.] *The methods by which the Assembly helps to work up this Spirit jointly with the Preacher* [271–273.]

II. Sect. *How some worship a good Being, others an evil* [274.] *Most people confound the bounds of good & evil,* [274, 275.] *Vain mortals think the Divinity interested in their meanest actions,* [275, 276.] *The scheme of spiritual mechanism left out,* [276.] *Of the usefulness of quilted nightcaps, to keep in the heat, to give motion & vigour to the little animals that compose the brain,* [276, 277.] *Sound of far greater use than sense in the operations of the Spirit, as in Musick,* [278.] *Inward light consists of theological po[l]ysyllables*

Table 309

A PROJECT,
For the universal benefit of Mankind.

The Author having laboured so long & done so much to serve & instruct the Publick, without any advantage to himself, has at last thought of a project which will tend to the great benefit of all Mankind, & produce a handsom Revenue to the Author. He intends to print by Subscription in 96. large volumes in *folio*, an exact Description of *Terra Australis incognita*, collected with great care & pains from 999. learned & pious Authors of undoubted veracity. The whole Work, illustrated with Maps & Cuts agreable to the subject, & done by the best Masters, will cost but a Guiney each volume to Subscribers, one guinea to be paid in advance, & afterwards a guinea on receiving each volume, except the last. This Work will be of great use for all men, & necessary for all familys, because it contains exact accounts of all the Provinces, Colonys & Mansions of that spacious Country, where by a general Doom all transgressors of the law are to be transported: & every one having this work may chuse out the fittest & best place for himself, there being enough for all so as every one shall be fully satisfied.

The Author supposes that one Copy of this Work will be bought at the publick Charge, or out of the Parish rates, for every Parish Church in the three Kingdoms, & in all the Dominions thereunto belonging. And that every family that can command ten pounds *per annum*, even tho' retrenched from less necessary expences, will also subscribe for one. He does not think of giving out above 9 volumes yearly; & considering the number requisite, he intends to print at least 100000. for the first Edition. He's to print Proposals against next Term, with a Specimen, & a curious Map of the Capital City, with its 12 Gates, from a known Author who took an exact survey of it in a dream. Considering the great care & pains of the Author, & the usefulness of the Work, he hopes every one will be ready, for their own good as well as his, to contribute chearfully to it, & not grudge him the profit he may have by it, especially if it comes to a 3. or 4. Edition, as he expects it will very soon.

He doubts not but it will be translated into foreign languages by most Nations of Europe as well as of Asia & Africa, being of as great use to all those Nations as to his own; for this reason he designs to procure Patents & Privileges for securing the whole benefit to himself, from all those different Princes & States, & hopes to see many millions of this great Work printed in those different Countrys & languages before his death.

After this business is pretty well establisht, he had promised to put a Friend on another Project almost as good as this; by establishing Insurance-Offices every where for securing people from shipwreck & several other accidents in their Voyage to this Country; & these Offices shall furnish, at a certain rate, Pilots well versed in the Route, & that know all the Rocks, shelves, quicksands &c. that such Pilgrims & Travelers may be exposed to. Of these he knows a great number ready instructed in most Countreys: but the whole Scheme of this matter he's to draw up at large & communicate to his Friend.

Here ends the Manuscript, there being nothing of the following piece in it.

Table 311

The Battel of the Books.

The Preface tells how this piece was written in 1697. *on accasion of a famous dispute about Ancient & Modern Learning, between Sr.* William Temple *& the Earl of* Orrery, *on the one side, &* W. Wotton *& Dr.* Bentley *on the other,* [213, 214.]

War & Invasions generaly proceed from want & poverty upon plenty & Riches, [217.] *The* Moderns *quarrel with the* Ancients *about the possession of the highest top of Parnassus, & desire them to surrender it, or to let it be levelled,* [219, 220.] *The Answer of the* Antients, *not accepted, a War ensues* [221.] *in which rivulets of Ink are spilt, & both parties hang out their Trophys, books of Controversy,* [221, 222.] *These books haunted with disorderly Spirits, tho often bound to the peace in Librarys,* [223.] *The Author's advice in this case neglected, occasions a terrible fight in St. James's Library,* [224.] *Dr.* Bentley *the Library keeper a great Enemy to the Antients,* [224, 225.] *The Moderns finding themselves* 50000. *strong give the Antients ill language,* [227, 228.] Temple *a favourite of the Antients,* [228.] *An incident of a quarrel between a Bee & a Spider, with their Arguments on both sides,* [228–232.] Æsop *applys them to the present dispute,* [233–235.] *The Order of Battel of the Moderns, & names of their Leaders,* [235–238.] *The Leaders of the Antients,* [238.] Jupiter *calls a Council of the Gods & consults the book of Fate,* [239.] *& then sends his Orders below,* [239.] Momus *brings the news to* Criticism, *whose habitation & company is described,* [240, 241.] *She arrives, & sheds her influence on her Son* Wotton, [242.] *The Battel described:* Paracelsus *engages* Galen: Aristotle *aims at* Bacon *& kills* Des Cartes, [244.] Homer *overthrows* Gondibert; *kills* Denham *& Westly,* Perrault, *& Fontenelle,* [245, 246.] *Encounter of* Virgil & Dryden, [247.] *of* Lucan *& Blackmore, & of* Creech *& Horace,* [247, 248.] *of* Pindar *& Cowley,* [249.] *The Episode of* Bentley *& Wotton,* [250.] Bentleys *Armour, his Speech to the Modern Generals,* [251, 252.] Scaliger's *Answer,* [252.] Bentley *& Wotton march together,* [253.] Bentley *attacks* Phalaris *& Æsop* [254.] Wotton *attacks* Temple *in vain,* [255, 256.] Boyle *pursues* Wotton, *& meeting* Bentley *in his way he pursues & kills them both,* [257, 258.]

Desunt cœtera.

FINIS.

A

DEFENSE

OF THE

REFLECTIONS

UPON

Ancient and *Modern Learning,*

In Anſwer to the

OBJECTIONS

OF

Sir *W. Temple,* and Others.

With OBSERVATIONS upon
The Tale of a Tub.

L O N D O N:

Printed for *Tim. Goodwin,* at the *Queen*'s
Head, againſt St. *Dunstan*'s Church
in *Fleetſtreet.* MDCCV.

[Wotton's own copy of the *Tale*, a first edition, is in the possession of Major Chetwood-Aiken, of Woodbrook, Queen's County, the present representative of Swift's friend and correspondent, Knightley Chetwood. It contains several notes and jottings, some of which are undoubtedly in Wotton's hand, and mark the first stage in the preparation of the *Observations*. They are almost wholly confined to the sections containing the allegory, i.e. Sections II, IV, VI, VIII, XI. The more interesting are here set down, with page references to the present edition:

P. 80, l. 19 (on 'Vein and Race') 'This is like Sr W. Temple'

P. 86, l. 14 'C——' explained as 'Conway', and 'J. W.' as 'John Walters'.

P. 100, ll. 15–17 (perhaps not in Wotton's hand) 'Salamand^r L^d. Cutts'.

P. 111, l. 5 (on 'Decline') 'This word is frequent with Sr W. T.'

P. 115, l. 19 (on '*Boutade*') 'Any Body but Sr W. Temple would have said *Sally*'.

P. 151, ll. 8–12 (opposite 'Farther . . . *Mysteries*') 'All this is like Mr Hobbes's banter upon in-blowing'.

P. 175, ll. 26, 27, 'Seymour', 'Musgrave', 'Bolls', 'How'.

P. 191, l. 11 (on 'Authentick') 'i.e. a Scripture phrase: possibly Sr W. T. might not know what *the uncovering of the Feet* meant'.

Wotton thought that Temple was the author of the *Tale*. The notes show suspicion becoming mistaken certainty.

It is a pleasure to thank Mr. Walter G. Strickland, late Director of the National Gallery of Ireland, for drawing attention to this volume and sending it to Oxford for inspection, and Major Chetwood-Aiken for granting permission to make use of the notes.—March 1919.]

A

DEFENSE

OF THE

REFLECTIONS

UPON

Ancient and *Modern Learning*.[1]

To Anthony Hammond, *Esq*;

*   *   *   *   *   *   *   *

I have now given a full Answer, as I think, Sir, to all the Argumentative part of Sir *W.* Temple's *Thoughts* upon the *Reflexions*. If we do not allow that he misunderstood the Question as I had plainly stated it (t), we must believe that he wilfully mistook it; and the rather, because when he was to examine the several Particulars in which I apprehended that the Preference was to be given to the Moderns, he drops the Question. It is done decently indeed, and there is a *Hiatus in Manuscripto*, as the *Publisher of the Tale of a Tub* expresses it (u), that so we may suppose the Comparison was intended to be made, and only by accident left imperfect. For after Sir *William Temple* had said, "Since the Modern Advocates yield, though very unwillingly, the "Pre-eminence of the Ancients in Poetry, Oratory, Painting, "Statuary and Architecture; I shall proceed to examine the "Account they give of those Sciences, wherein they affirm the "Moderns to excel the Ancients; whereof they make the chief

(t) *Vide supra Reflex.* pag. 7.

(u) P. 42.

[1] The *Defense* was printed both separately and at the conclusion (with continuous pagination) of the third edition of Wotton's *Reflections*, 1705. It there occupies pp. 471–541. The portion here reprinted begins on p. 517. The page references in the margin are to the first edition.

"to be the Invention of Instruments; Chymistry; Anatomy;
"Natural History of Minerals, Plants, and Animals; Astronomy
"and Optics; Music; Physick; Natural Philosophy; Philology
"and Theology; of all which I shall take a short survey." There is
a Gap, and Dr. *Swift* fills it up thus, *Here it is supposed; the
Knowledge of the Ancients and Moderns last mentioned, was to
have been compared: But whether the Author designed to have gone
through such a Work himself, or intended these Papers only for
Hints to some body else that desired them, is not known. After
which, the rest was to follow written in his own Hand as before.*

(w) *De-*
fense of Es-
say, p. 230,
231.

(w) This Method of answering of Books, and of publishing such
Answers, is very dissatisfactory. Just where the Pinch of the
Question lay, there the Copy fails, and where there was more
Room for flourishing, there Sir *W. Temple* was as copious as one
would wish. To use his own Words, *This is very wonderful, if it
be not a Jest*; and I take it for granted, Dr. *Swift* had express
Orders to print these *Fragments* of an Answer.

This way of printing Bits of Books that in their Nature are
intended for Continued Discourses, and are not loose Apoph-
thegms, Occasional Thoughts, or incoherent Sentences, is what
I have seen few Instances of; none more remarkable than this,
and one more which may be supposed to imitate this, *The Tale
of a Tub*, of which a Brother of Dr. *Swift's* is publicly reported
to have been the Editor at least, if not the Author. In which
though Dr. *Bentley* and my self are coursely treated, yet I believe
I may safely answer for us both, that we should not have taken
any manner of notice of it, if upon this Occasion I had not been
obliged to say something in answer to what has been seriously
said against us.

For, believe me, Sir, what concerns us, is much the inno-
centest part of the Book, tending chiefly to make Men laugh for
half an Hour, after which it leaves no farther Effects behind it.
When Men are jested upon for what is in it self praiseworthy, the
World will do them Justice: And on the other hand, if they
deserve it, they ought to sit down quietly under it. Our Cause
therefore we shall leave to the Public very willingly, there being
no occasion to be concerned at any Man's Railery about it. But
the rest of the Book which does not relate to us, is of so irreligious a nature, is so crude a Banter upon all that is esteemed as

Sacred among all Sects and Religions among Men, that, having so fair an Opportunity, I thought it might be useful to many People who pretend they see no harm in it, to lay open the Mischief of the Ludicrous Allegory, and to shew what that drives at which has been so greedily brought up and read. In one Word, God and Religion, Truth and Moral Honesty, Learning and Industry are made a May-Game, and the most serious Things in the World are described as so many several Scenes in a *Tale of a Tub*.

That this is the true Design of that Book, will appear by these Particulars. The *Tale* in substance is this; "A Man had three "Sons, all at a Birth, by one Wife; to whom when he died, because "he had purchased no Estate, nor was born to any, he only pro- "vided to each of them a New Coat, which were to last them fresh "and sound as long as they lived, and would lengthen and widen "of themselves, so as to be always fit." (*x*) By the Sequel of the *Tale* it appears, that by these three Sons, *Peter*, *Martin*, and *Jack*; *Popery*, the *Church of England*, and our *Protestant Dissenters* are designed. What can now be more infamous than such a *Tale*? The Father is *Jesus Christ*, who at his Death left his WILL or TESTAMENT to his Disciples, with a Promise of Happiness to them, and the Churches which they and their Successors should found for ever. So the Tale-teller's Father to his three Sons, "You will find in my WILL full Instructions in "every Particular concerning the wearing and managing of your "Coats; wherein you must be very exact, to avoid the Penalties "I have appointed for every Transgression or Neglect, upon which "your *Future Fortunes* will *entirely* depend." (*y*) By his Coats which he gave his Sons, the Garments of the *Israelites* are exposed, which by the Miraculous Power of God waxed not old, nor were worn out for Forty Years together in the Wilderness. (*z*) The number of these Sons born thus at one Birth, looks asquint at the TRINITY, and one of the Books in our Author's Catalogue in the Off-page over-against the Title, is a Panegyric upon the Number THREE, which Word is the only one that is put in Capitals in that whole Page (*a*).

(*x*) P. 54.

(*y*) Ibid. P. 54, 55.

(*z*) Deut. VIII. 4.

(*a*) In the Citations
out of the *Tale of a Tub*, the first Impression is constantly quoted.

In the pursuit of his Allegory, we are entertain'd with the

Lewdness of the Three Sparks. Their Mistresses are the *Dutchess d' Argent*, Madamoizelle *de Grands Titres*, and the Countess d' *Orgueil* (b) i.e. *Covetousness, Ambition* and *Pride*, which were the Three great Vices that the Ancient Fathers inveighed against as the first Corrupters of Christianity. Their Coats having such an extraordinary Virtue of never wearing out, give him large Scope for his Mirth, which he employs in burlesquing *Religion, Moral Honesty* and *Conscience*, which are the strongest Ties by which Men can be tied to one another. *Is not Religion a Cloak, Honesty a Pair of Shoes worn out in the Dirt, Self-love a Surtout, Vanity a Shirt, and Conscience a Pair of Breeches?* (c) Which last Allusion gives him an opportunity that he never misses of talking obscenely.

His Whim of Clothes is one of his chiefest Favourites. "Man, "says he, is an Animal compounded of two *Dresses*, the *Natural* "and the *Coelestial-Suit*, which were the Body and the Soul.' (d) "And That the Soul was by daily Creation and Circumfusion "they proved by Scripture, because *In them we live, and move,* "*and have our Being.*" *In them* (i.e. *in the Clothes of the Body:*) Words applicable only to the Great God of Heaven and Earth, of whom they were first spoken by *St. Paul* (e). Thus he introduces his Tale; then that he might shelter himself the better from any Censure here in *England*, he falls most unmercifully upon *Peter* and *Jack*, i.e. upon *Popery* and *Fanaticism*, and gives *Martin*, who represents the *Church of England*, extream good Quarter. I confess, Sir, I abhor making Sport with any way of worshipping God, and he that diverts himself too much at the Expense of the *Roman Catholics* and the *Protestant Dissenters*, may lose his own Religion e're he is aware of it, at least the Power of it in his Heart. But to go on.

The first Part of the *Tale* is the *History of Peter*. Thereby *Popery* is exposed. Everybody knows the *Papists* have made great Additions to Christianity. That indeed is the great Exception which the Church of *England* makes against them. Accordingly *Peter* begins his Pranks with *adding a Shoulderknot to his Coat*, "whereas his Father's Will was very precise, and it was "the main Precept in it with the greatest Penalties annexed, not "to add to, or diminish from their Coats one Thread, without a "positive Command in the WILL." (f) His Description of the

Marginal notes: (b) P.[55]. (c) P. 60. (d) P. 61. (e) Acts XVII. 28. (f) P. 63.

Cloth of which the Coat was made, has a farther Meaning than the Words may seem to import. "The Coats their Father had "left them were of very good Cloth, and besides so neatly sown, "you would swear they were all of a Piece, but at the same time "very plain, with little or no Ornament." (*f*) This is the Distin- (*f*) Ibid. guishing Character of the Christian Religion. *Christiana Religio absoluta & simplex*, was *Ammianus Marcellinus*'s Description of it, who was himself a Heathen. (*g*) When the *Papists* cannot find (*g*) Lib. any thing which they want in Scripture, they go to *Oral Tradi-* XXI. *in tion*: Thus *Peter* is introduced dissatisfied with the tedious Way *fine.* of looking for all the Letters of any Word which he had occasion for in the *Will*, when neither the constituent Syllables, nor much less the whole Word were there *in Terminis*, and he expresses himself thus; "Brothers, if you remember, we heard a "Fellow say when we were Boys, that he heard my Father's Man "say, that he heard my Father say, that he would advise his Sons "to get *Gold-Lace* on their Coats, as soon as ever they could "procure Money to buy it." (*h*) Which way of coming at any thing (*h*) P. 67. that was not expressly in his Father's W I L L, stood him afterwards in great stead.

The next Subject of our *Tale-Teller*'s Wit is the *Glosses* and *Interpretations of Scripture*, very many absurd ones of which kind are allow'd in the most Authentic Books of the Church of *Rome*: The Sparks wanted Silver Fringe to put upon their Coats. Why, says *Peter*, (seemingly perhaps to laugh at Dr. *Bentley* and his Criticisms); "I have found in a certain Author, which shall be "nameless, that the same Word which in the Will is called *Fringe*, "does also signifie a *Broomstick*, and doubtless ought to have the "same Interpretation in this Paragraph." (*i*) This affording great (*i*) P. 70. Diversion to one of the Brothers; "You speak, says *Peter*, very "irreverently of a *Mystery*, which doubtless was very useful and "significant, but ought not to be overcuriously pry'd into, or nicely "reason'd upon." (*k*) The Author, one would think, copies from (*k*) Ibid. Mr. *Toland*, who always raises a Laugh at the Word *Mystery*, the Word and Thing whereof he is known to believe to be no more than a *Tale of a Tub*.

Images in the Church of *Rome* give our *Tale-teller* but too fair a Handle. "The Brothers remembered but too well how their "Father abhorred the Fashion of Embroidering their Clothes "with *Indian* Figures of Men, Women and Children; that he "made several Paragraphs on purpose, importing his utter Detesta- "tion of it, and bestowing his Everlasting Curse to his Sons,

(*l*) P. 71.

"whenever they should wear it." (*l*) The Allegory here is direct. The *Papists* formerly forbad the People the use of Scripture in a Vulgar Tongue; *Peter* therefore *locks up his Father's Will in a strong Box brought out of* Greece *or* Italy: Those Countries are named, because the *New Testament* is written in *Greek*; and the *Vulgar Latin*, which is the Authentic Edition of the Bible in the

(*m*) P. 72.

Church of *Rome*, is in the Language of Old *Italy*. (*m*) The Popes in their *Decretals* and *Bulls* have given their Sanction to very many gainful Doctrines which are now receiv'd in the Church of *Rome*, that are not mentioned in Scripture, and are unknown to the Primitive Church. *Peter* accordingly pro- nounces *ex Cathedra*, that *Points tagged with Silver were abso-*

(*n*) Ibid.

lutely Jure Paterno, and so they wore them in great numbers. (*n*) The Bishops of *Rome* enjoy'd their Privileges in *Rome* at first by the Favour of Emperors, whom at last they shut out of their own Capital City, and then forged a Donation from *Constantine the Great*, the better to justifie what they did. In imitation of this, *Peter*, "having run something behindhand with the World, "obtained leave of a certain Lord to receive him into his House, "and to teach his Children. A while after the Lord died, and he "by long Practise upon his Father's Will, found the way of con- "triving a Deed of Conveyance of that House to himself and his "Heirs: Upon which he took possession, turned the Young

(*o*) P. 93.

"Squires out, and receiv'd his Brothers in their stead." (*o*) *Pennance* and *Absolution* are plaid upon under the Notion of a Sovereign Remedy for the Worms, especially in the Spleen, which by observing of *Peter's* Prescriptions, would void insensibly by

(*p*) P. 94.

Perspiration ascending through the Brain. (*p*) By his *Whispering Office* for the Relief of Eves-droppers, Physicians, Bawds and Privy-Councellors, he ridicules *Auricular Confession*, and the

(*q*) P. 95.

Priest who takes it is described by the Ass's Head. (*q*) Holy- Water he calls an Universal Pickle, *to preserve Houses, Gardens, Towns, Men, Women, Children and Cattle, wherein he could pre-*

(*r*) P. 96, 97.

serve them as sound as Insects in Amber; (*r*) and because Holy- Water differs only in Consecration from Common Water, therefore our Tale-teller tells us that his Pickle by the Powder of

Pimperlimpimp receives new Virtues, though it differs not in Sight nor Smell from the Common Pickle which preserves Beef, and Butter, nor Herrings. (*s*) The *Papal Bulls* are ridiculed by (*s*) P. 97. Name, so there we are at no loss for our *Tale-teller*'s Meaning. (*t*) (*t*) P. 97– *Absolution in Articulo Mortis*, and the *Taxa Camerae Apostolicae* 100. are jested upon in Emperor *Peter*'s Letter. (*u*) The *Pope's Uni-* (*u*) P. 101. *versal Monarchy*, and his *Triple Crown*, and *Key's* and *Fishers Ring* have their turns of being laughed at; (*w*) nor does his Arro- (*w*) P. 103. gant way of requiring Men to kiss his Slipper, escape Reflexion (*x*). (*x*) Ibid. The *Celibacy of the Romish Clergy* is struck at in *Peter*'s turning his own and Brothers Wives out of Doors. (*y*) But nothing makes (*y*) P. 104. him so merry as *Transubstantiation* (*z*): *Peter* turns his Bread (*z*) P. 104– into Mutton, and according to the Popish Doctrine of Con- 108. comitance, his Wine too, which in his way he calls *pauming his damned Crust upon the Brothers for Mutton* (*a*). The ridiculous (*a*) P. 130. multiplying of the *Virgin Mary*'s *Milk* among the Papists, he banters under the Allegory of a *Cow* which gave as much Milk at a Meal, as would fill Three thousand Churches: (*b*) and the (*b*) P. 108. *Wood of the Cross* on which our Saviour suffered, is prophanely likened to an "Old Signpost that belonged to his Father, with "Nails and Timber enough upon it to build Sixteen large Men of "War": (*c*) And when one talked to *Peter* of *Chinese* Waggons (*c*) P. 109. which were made so light as to sail over Mountains, he swears and curses four times in Eleven Lines, that the *Chapell* of *Loretto* had travelled Two Thousand *German* Leagues, though built with Lime and Stone, over Sea and Land (*d*). (*d*) Ibid.

But I expect, Sir, that you should tell me, that the *Tale-teller* falls here only upon the Ridiculous Inventions of Popery; that the Church of *Rome* intended by these things to gull silly Supersti- tious People; and to rook them of their Money; that the World had been but too long in Slavery; that our Ancestors gloriously redeemed us from that Yoak; that the Church of *Rome* therefore ought to be exposed, and that he deserves well of Mankind that does expose it.

All this, Sir, I own to be true: but then I would not so shoot at an Enemy, as to hurt my self at the same time. The Foundation of the Doctrines of the Church of *England* is right, and came from God: Upon this the Popes, and Councils called and confirmed by them, have built, as St. *Paul* speaks, *Hay and Stubble*, perishable and slight Materials, which when they are once consum'd, that the Foundation may appear, then we shall see what is faulty, and what is not. But our *Tale-teller* strikes at the very Root. *'Tis all* with him *a Farce, and all a Ladle*, as a very facetious Poet says upon another occasion. The *Father*, and the *WILL*, and *his Son Martin*, are part of the *Tale*, as well as *Peter* and *Jack*, and are all usher'd in with the Common Old Wives Introduction,

(e) P. 54. *Once upon a Time (e)*. And the *main Body of the Will* we are told consisted in *certain admirable Rules about the wearing of* their

(f) P. 124. Coats *(f)*. So that let *Peter* be mad one way, and *Jack* another, and let *Martin* be sober, and spend his Time with Patience and Phlegm in picking the Embroidery off his Coat never so carefully, "firmly resolving to alter whatever was already amiss, and reduce "all their future Measures to the strictest Obedience prescribed

(g) Ibid. "therein" *(g)*; Yet still this is all part of a *Tale of a Tub*, it does but enhance the *Teller's* Guilt, and shews at the bottom his contemptible Opinion of every Thing which is called Christianity.

For pray, Sir, take notice that it is not saying he personates none but Papists or Fanatics, that will excuse him; for in other Places, where he speaks in his own Person, and imitates none but himself, he discovers an equal mixture of Lewdness and Irreligion. Would any Christian compare a *Mountebank's-Stage*, a *Pulpit*, and a *Ladder* together? A *Mountebank* is a profess'd Cheat, who turns it off when he is press'd, with the Common Jest, *Men must live*; and with this Man the Preacher of the Word of God is compared, and the Pulpit in which he preaches,

(h) P. 34. is called *an Edifice* (or Castle) *in the Air:* (h) This is not said by *Peter*, or *Jack*, but by the Author himself, who after he has gravely told us, that he has had Poxes ill cured by trusting to Bawds and Surgeons, reflects with "unspeakable Comfort, upon "his having past a long Life with a *Conscience void of Offence to-*

(i) P. 51. *"wards God and towards Man"* (i).

In his own Person, the Author speaks in one of his Digressions of "Books being not bound to Everlasting Chains of Dark-"ness in a Library; but that when the Fulness of Time should "come, they should happily undergo the Tryal of Purgatory, in

(k) P. 144. "order to ascend the Sky." (k) In another Digression our Author describes one of his Madmen in *Bedlam*, who was distemper'd by the Loose Behaviour of his Wife, to be like *Moses: Ecce Cornuta erat ejus Facies*; (*l*) which is the rendring of the *Vulgar Latin* of (*l*) P. 179. that which in the *English* Bible is called *the shining of his Face* when he came down from the Mount. (*m*) Our Author himself (*m*) Exod. asserts, that the "Fumes issuing from a Jakes, will furnish as XXXIV. "comely and useful a Vapor, as Incense from an Altar." (*n*). And 29, 30, 35. (*n*) P. 160. 'tis our Author in his own Capacity, who among many other Ludicrous Similes upon those that get their Learning out of *Indices*, which are commonly at the End of a Book, says, "Thus "Human Life is best understood by the *Wise-man*'s Rule of "*regarding the End*." (*o*) 'Tis in the *Fragment*, which has nothing (*o*) P. 139. to do with the *Tale*, that Sir *Humphrey Edwin* is made to apply the Words of the *Psalmist, Thy Word is a Lanthorn to my Feet, and a Light to my Paths*, to a Whimsical Dark Lanthorn of our Authors own contrivance; wherein he poorly alludes to *Hudibras*'s *Dark-Lanthorn of the Spirit, which none see by but those that bear it.* (*p*) His whole VIIIᵗʰ Section concerning the (*p*) P. 307. *Aeolists*, in which he banters Inspiration, is such a Mixture of Impiety and Immodesty, that I should have as little regard to you, Sir, as this Author has had to the Public, if I should barely repeat after him what is there. And it is somewhat surprizing that the Citation out of *Irenaeus*, in the Title-Page, which seems to be all *Gibberish*, should be a Form of Initiation used anciently by the *Marcosian* Heretics (*q*). So great a delight has this Un- (*q*) The happy Writer, to play with what some part or other of Mankind Words of have always esteemed as Sacred! this *Form of Redemption*, as

these Heretics called it, are *Basima eaca basa ea naa irraurista, diarbada caeotaba fobor camelanthi.* So it is in the Old Editions of *Irenaeus*, from one of which it is here transcribed. *Irenaeus* thus interprets them, *Hoc quod est super omnem virtutem Patris invoco, quod vocatur Lumen & Spiritus & Vita, quoniam in corpore regnasti.* i.e. *I call upon this, which is above all the Power of the Father, which is called Light, and Spirit, and Life, because thou hast reigned in the Body.* The *Greek* Words which were faulty at first, made the *Latin* ones yet more so; it is probable that *Irenaeus* might not understand them right at first: They are *Syriac*, and in the very Learned Mr. *Grabe*'s Edition of *Irenaeus*, they are very ingeniously restored out of *Jacobus Rhenferdius*'s *Dissertation, upon the Redemption of the Marcosians and Heracleonites.*

And therefore when he falls upon *Jack*, he deals as freely with him, and wounds Christianity through his Sides as much as he had done before through *Peter*'s. The *Protestant Dissenters use Scripture-Phrases* in their Serious Discourses and Composures more than the Church of *England-men*. Accordingly *Jack* is introduced, making "his Common Talk and Conversation to

"run wholly in the Phrase of his W I L L, and circumscribing the
"utmost of his Eloquence within that compass, not daring to let
(*r*) P. 197. "slip a Syllable without Authority from thence." (*r*) And because
he could not of a sudden recollect *an Authentic Phrase*, for the
(*s*) P. 198. Necessities of Nature, he would use no other: (*s*) Can any thing
be prophaner than this? Things compared, always shew the
Esteem or Scorn of the Comparer. To ridicule Praedestination,
Jack walks blindfold through the Streets; the Body of our Dissenters having till of late been *Calvinists* in the Questions concerning the *Five Points*. "It was ordained, said he, some few days
"*before* the Creation (*i.e.* immediately by God himself) that my
"Nose and this very Post should have a Rencounter; and there-
"fore Providence thought fit to send us both into the World in
"the same Age, and to make us Country-men and Fellow
(*t*) P. 199. "Citizens." (*t*) This is a direct Prophanation of the Majesty of
God. "*Jack* would run Dog-mad at the Noise of Music, especially
(*u*) P. 203. "a Pair of Bagpipes." (*u*) This is to expose our Dissenters Aversion to Instrumental Music in Churches. The Agreement of our
Dissenters and the Papists, in that which Bishop *Stillingfleet*
called the *Fanaticism of the Church of Rome*, is ludicrously
described for several Pages together, by *Jack's* likeness to *Peter*,
and their being often mistaken for each other, and their frequent
(*w*) P. 206, meeting when they least intended it: (*w*) In this, singly taken,
207, 208. there might possibly be little harm, if one did not see from what
Principle the whole proceeded.

This 'tis which makes the difference between the sharp and
virulent Books written in this Age against any Sect of Christians, and those which were written about the beginning of the
Reformation between the several contending Parties then in
Europe. For tho' the Rage and Spight with which Men treated
one another was as keen and as picquant then as it is now, yet the
Inclination of Mankind was not then irreligious, and so their
Writings had little other effect but to encrease Mens Hatred
against any one particular Sect, whilst Christianity, as such, was
not hereby at all undermined. But now the Common Enemy
appears barefaced, and strikes in with some one or other Sect of
Christians, to wound the whole by that means. And this is the
Case of this Book, which is one of the Prophanest Banters upon
the Religion of *Jesus Christ*, as such, that ever yet appeared. In

the *Tale*, in the *Digressions*, in the *Fragment*, the same Spirit
runs through, but rather most in the *Fragment*, in which all
extraordinary Inspirations are the Subjects of his Scorn and
Mockery, whilst the Protestant Dissenters are, to outward appearance, the most directly levelled at. The Bookseller indeed in
his Advertisement prefixed to the *Fragment*, pretends to be *wholly
ignorant of the Author, and he says, he cannot conjecture whether
it be the same with that of the two foregoing Pieces, the Original
having been sent him at a different Time, and in a different Hand.*
It may be so; but the Stile, and Turn, and Spirit of this *Fragment*, and of the *Tale* being the same, no body, I believe, has
doubted of their being written by the same Author: If the
Authors are different, so much the worse, because it shews there
are more Men in the World acted by the same Spirit. But be the
Author one or more, the Mask is more plainly taken off in the
Fragment. The Writer uses the Allegory of an *Ass's bearing his
Rider up to Heaven*: (*x*) And presently after he owns his Ass to (*x*) P. 287.
be allegorical, and says, "That if we please, instead of the Term
"*Ass*, we may make use of *Gifted* or *Enlightned Preacher*, and the
"Word *Rider* we may exchange for that of *Fanatic Auditory*, or
"any other Denomination of the like Import:" (*y*) And now *hav-* (*y*) P. 288.
ing setled this Weighty Point, (as he contemptuously calls it) he
enquires *by what Methods this Teacher arrives at his Gifts, or
Spirit, or Light* (*z*). Enthusiasm with him is an Universal Decep- (*z*) Ibid.
tion which has run through all Sciences in all Kingdoms, and
every thing has some *Fanatic Branch annexed to it*; (*a*) among (*a*) P. 289.
which he reckons the *Summum Bonum*, or *an Enquiry after Happiness*. The *Descent of the H. Ghost* after our Blessed Saviour's
Ascension in the Shape of Cloven Tongues, at the First *Pente-
cost*, in the Second of the *Acts*, is one of the Subjects of his Mirth:
And because in our Dissenting Congregations, the Auditory used
formerly with great Indecency to keep on their Hats in Sermon
Time, therefore, says he, "They will needs have it as a Point
"clearly gained, that the Cloven Tongues never sat upon the
"Apostles Heads, while their Hats were on:" (*b*) using that Ridi- (*b*) P. 295,
culous Argument to prove that the Dissenting Ministers are not 296.
divinely inspired. And he does not mince the Matter when he
says, "That he is resolved immediately to weed this Error out of
"Mankind, by making it clear, that this Mystery of venting

"Spiritual Gifts is nothing but a Trade acquired by as much
"Instruction, and master'd by equal Practice and Application as
(c) P. 303. "others are." (c) Can any thing be more blasphemous than his
(d) P. 310. *Game at Leap-Frog between the Flesh and Spirit?* (d) This affects
(e) Rom. the Doctrine of St. *Paul,* (e) and not the Private Interpretations
VII.
of this or that Particular Sect; and this too is described in the
Language of the Stews, which with now and then a Scripture-
Expression, compose this Writer's Stile. Thus when the *Snuffling*
of Men who have lost their Noses by Lewd Courses, is said to
have given rise to that Tone which our Dissenters did too much
affect formerly, He subjoins, "That when our Earthly Taber-
"nacles are disordered and desolate, shaken and out of Repair, the
"*Spirit* delights to dwell within them, as Houses are said to be
(f) P. 313. "haunted, when they are forsaken and gone to decay." (f) And in
his Account of Fanaticism, he tells us, *That the Thorn in the Flesh,*
(g) P. 319. *serves* for a Spur to the Spirit. (g) Is not this to ridicule St.
Paul's own Description of his own Temptation; in which the
Apostle manifestly alludes to a Passage in the Prophet *Ezekiel*
(h) 2 Cor. (h)?
XII. 7.
and Ezek.   What would Men say in any Country in the World but this,
XXVIII. to see their Religion so vilely treated from the Press? I remember
24.   to have seen a *French* Translation of the Learned Dr. *Prideaux*
(the present Worthy Dean of *Norwich's*) *Life of Mahomet,*
printed in *France,* I think at *Paris,* in the *Advertisement* before
which, the Translator tells the Public, That he did not translate
the *Letter to the Deists,* thereto annexed in *English,* because, says
he, our Government suffers no such People, and there is no need
of Antidotes where there is no Poison. Be this true or false in
France, it matters not to our present Purpose; but it shews that
no Man dares publickly play with Religion in that Country.
How much do the *Mahometans* reverence the *Alcoran?* Dares
any Man among them openly despite their Prophet, or ridicule
the Words of his Law? How strictly do the *Banians,* and the
other Sects of the *Gentile East-Indians* worship their Pagods,
and respect their Temples? This Sir, you well know, is not
Superstition nor Bigottry. It is of the Essence of Religion, that
the utmost Regard should be paid to the *Name* and *Words of
God,* both which upon the slightest, and the most ridiculous Occasions, are play'd upon by Common Oaths, and Idle Allusions to

Scripture Expressions in this whole Book. I do not carry my Charge too far.

For admitting that this Writer intended to make himself and his Readers Sport, by exercising his Wit and Mirth upon a Couple of Pedants, as he esteems Dr. *Bentley* and my self; yet since the *Tale* may thus be explain'd, and since to your knowledge and mine, Sir, it has been thus interpreted by Unconcerned Readers, the Mischief which it does is equally great to Mankind. Besides, even that Excuse will not serve in the *Fragment*, which is levelled at no particular Man that I can find whatsoever. Dr. *King*, late of *Christ-Church*, was so sensible of this, that when by reason of the Personalities (as the *French* call them) in the Book, it was laid at his Door, he took care immediately to print such *Remarks* upon it, as effectually cleared him from the Imputation of having writ it: He therein did like a Christian; and he that is one, would be very uneasie under the Character of being none. And this is what Mr. *Swift* is yet under greater Obligations to do, because of his Profession. The World besides will think it odd, that a Man should in a Dedication play upon that Great Man, to whom he is more obliged than to any other Man now living; for it was at Sir *William Temple*'s Request, that my Lord *Sommers*, then Lord-Keeper of the Great-Seal of *England*, gave Mr. *Swift* a very good Benefice in one of the most Delicious Parts of one of the Pleasantest Counties of *England*. It is publicly reported that he wrote this Book: It is a Story, which you know, Sir, I neither made, nor spread; for it has been long as public as it can well be. The Injury done to *Religion*, that any of its Ministers should lie under the Imputation of writing such a *Burlesque* upon it, will be irreparable, if the Person so charged does not do *it* and *himself* Justice. I say *Himself*, for *in my own Conscience* I acquit him from composing it. The Author, I believe, is dead, and it is probable that it was writ in the Year 1697, when it is said to have been written.

Before I leave this Author, be he who he will, I shall observe, Sir, that his *Wit* is *not his own*, in many places. The *Actors* in his *Farce*, *Peter*, *Martin*, and *Jack*, are by Name borrowed from a Letter written by the late Witty D. of *Buckingham*, concerning Mr. *Clifford*'s *Human Reason*: (*i*) And *Peter*'s Banter upon (*i*) P. 67. *Transubstantiation*, is taken from the same D. of *Buckingham*'s (*k*) P. 37. *Conference with an Irish Priest*, (*k*) only here *Bread* is *changed into Mutton* and *Wine*, that the Banter might be the more crude; there a *Cork* is *turned into a Horse*. But the *Wondrings* on the one side, and the *Asseverations* on the other, are otherwise exactly alike. And I have been assured that the *Battel in St.* James's *Library* is *Mutandis Mutandis* taken out of a *French* Book, entituled, *Combat des Livres*, if I misremember not.

And now, Sir, I heartily ask your Pardon for troubling you with so long a Letter. You know the true Reasons and Inducements of my Writing the *Reflexions* at first; I cannot think it needed any Apology then, and so I do not write this Letter as an Apology now. I wrote then of the Writings of one Gentleman at the Command of another, who is an exact Judge of Decency and Good Manners. I would say a great deal more, but that I write *to*, as well as *of* your self. But I should have been inexcusable, if, when you saw and gave your self the Trouble of reading the *Reflections* before they went to the Press, I should not have composed them so, as that you should not have needed to disown them afterwards. Your Friendship, in truth, has been for many Years so generous towards me, and so disinterested, that I have often found you could as willingly have made Excuses for my Failings, as have commended my good Management. But as the Office of an Excuser is what for ones Friend's sake, as well as ones own, a Man is not too frequently to put his Friend upon, so the principal Design of my Writing this long Narrative, was to satisfie you, Sir, who are so very much concerned, that all the Objections hitherto made against the *Reflexions*, will easily admit of a direct and full Answer. I have nothing more to say, but that it is necessary for your sake, that I should inform the Public, that the Faults in this Letter are all my own, and that I will not desire you to stand by me upon the account of any Mistakes of which I may have been guilty. I am,

SIR,

May 21.   *Your most Obliged and*
1705.   *Faithful Servant,*

W. Wotton.

FINIS.

A

COMPLETE KEY

TO THE

TALE of a *TUB*;

With fome Account of the

AUTHORS,

The Ocafion and Defign of Writing it,
and Mr. WOTTON's *Remarks* examin'd.

L O N D O N:

Printed for EDMUND CURLL at the *Dial and
Bible* againſt St. *Dunſtan's* Church in
Fleetſtreet. 1710. Price *6d.*

Where may be had *A Meditation upon a Broomſtick,*
and fomewhat befide, *utile dulci*; by one of the
Authors of the *Tale of a Tub.* Price *6d.*

I

TO THE
READER.

*A*S *these* Notes *were communicated to me purely for my own Use,* *so had I never the least Intention of making 'em publick: But finding what various Opinions are entertain'd of the* Authors, *and Misrepresentations of the* Work *to which they belong, insomuch that Mr.* Wotton *has added to his* Reflections upon Learning *some severe* Remarks, *in which he represents the* Book *as a design'd Satyr upon the* Church of England, *and even to ridicule the Doctrine of the* Trinity; *upon which score these Papers now appear, plainly to demonstrate, that the true Intent and Aim of the* Authors *was not to ridicule all Religion, but to assert and defend the Purity of our Church's Doctrine, which Mr.* Wotton *and his Party would insinuate they have aspers'd, and to display the Innovations of* Rome *and Fanatical Hypocrisy in their proper Colours.*[1]

[1] In his private copy of the *Complete Key*, now in the British Museum (C 28 b. 11), Curll recorded his authorship of this note 'To the Reader' by appending to it his signature 'E Curll'. At the top of p. 1 (p. 331 of this reprint) he wrote 'Given me by Ralph Noden, Esq; of the Middle Temple. E Curll'.

The page references are to the first edition.

SOME
ANNOTATIONS
AND
EXPLANATORY NOTES
UPON THE
TALE of a *TUB*.

The Occasion of Writing it.

A Preface of the *Bookseller* to the *Reader* before *the *Battle of the Books* shews the Cause and Design of the whole Work, which was perform'd by †a couple of young Clergymen in the Year 1697. who having been Domestick Chaplains to Sir *William Temple*, thought themselves oblig'd to take up his Quarrel in Relation to the Controversy then in Dispute between him and Mr. *Wotton* concerning *Ancient* and *Modern* Learning.

The ‡one of 'em began a *Defence* of Sir *William* under the Title of *A Tale of a Tub*, under which he intended to couch the General History of Christianity; shewing the Rise of all the Remarkable Errors of the *Roman Church* in the same order they enter'd, and how the Reformation endeavoured to root 'em out again, with the different Temper of *Luther* from *Calvin* (and those more violent Spirits) in the way of his Reforming: His aim is to Ridicule the stubborn Errors of the *Romish Church*, and the Humours of the *Fanatick Party*, and to shew that their

* Generally (and not without sufficient Reason) said to be Dr. *Jonathan* and *Thomas Swift*; but since they don't think fit publickly to own it, wherever I mention their Names, 'tis not upon any other Affirmation than as they are the *Reputed Authors.*

† *Pag.* 225 [i.e. p. 213 of this edition].   ‡ *Thomas Swift.*

Superstition has somewhat very fantastical in it, which is common to both of 'em, notwithstanding the Abhorrence they seem to have for one another.

The Author intended to have it very regular, and withal so particular, that he thought not to pass by the Rise of any one single Error or its Reformation: He design'd at last to shew the Purity of the Christian Church in the primitive Times, and consequently how weakly Mr. *Wotton* pass'd his Judgment, and how partially in preferring the *Modern* Divinity before the *Ancient*, with the Confutation of whose Book he intended to conclude. But when he had not yet gone half way, his *Companion borrowing the *Manuscript* to peruse, carried it with him to *Ireland*, and having kept it seven Years, at last publish'd it imperfect; for indeed he was not able to carry it on after the intended Method: because *Divinity* (tho it chanc'd to be his Profession) had been the least of his Study; However he added to it the *Battle of the Books*, wherein he effectually pursues the main Design of lashing Mr. *Wotton*, and having added a jocose Epistle Dedicatory to my Lord *Sommers*, and another to Prince *Posterity*, with a pleasant Preface, and interlarded with one *Digression* concerning *Criticks*, and another in the *Modern* kind, a *Third* in Praise of *Digressions*, and a Fourth in Praise of *Madness* (with which he was not unacquainted) concludes the Book with a *Fragment* which the first Author made, and intended should have come in about the middle of the *Tale*, as a Preliminary to *Jack*'s Character.

Having thus shewn the Reasons of the little Order observ'd in the Book, and the Imperfectness of the *Tale*, 'tis so submitted to the Reader's Censure.

Thomas Swift is Grandson to Sir *William D'avenant*, *Jonathan Swift* is Cousin German to *Thomas Swift* both Retainers to Sir *William Temple*.

The two Gentlemen as before hinted being the reputed Authors of the *Work*, the several Parts of the Book are thus attributed to 'em, *viz.*

The Dedication to my Lord *Sommers*, the Preface, Epistle to

* Dr. *Jonathan Swift*.

Prince *Posterity*, the four Digressions, *viz.* 1. Concerning *Criticks*.
2. In the Modern kind. 3. In Praise of *Digressions*. 4. In Praise
of *Madness* and *the Battle of the Books* are assign'd to Dr. *Jonathan Swift*; and the *Tale of a Tub*, and the *Fragment* containing
a Mechanical Account of the *Operation of the Spirit*, to *Thomas
Swift*.

CLAVIS.

In blank *Page* 32. Insert these Words.
Democritus dum Ridet Philosophatur.

Page 33. SECT. I. *The Introduction.*
Pag. 47. last *Line.* The Word *Exantlation* (signifies) an over-
coming with much Labour and Difficulty.

Page 54. SECT. II.
The three Sons mention'd in the 2^d. Section are the three
Religions, *Viz.* the Church of *Rome*, *England*, and *Presbytery.*

Pag. Idem. Line 15.
After the old Man's Description of the Virtues of the Coats,
bequeath'd to his Sons, and Instructions given for the wearing
of 'em add this Note.
Religion, if well us'd, will continue still the same, (alluding to the
first Virtue of the Coats, that they would last fresh and sound to their
Lives end) and admits of decent Ceremonies, according to Times and
Places; (second Virtue, Lengthening and widening of themselves.)
Keep up to the Purity of it, and if there creeps in any Corruption
correct it; *i.e.* wear them clean, and brush them often.

Pag. Idem, Line 23. The *Will* mention'd is the *Bible.*

Pag. 55. *Line* 7. By the old Man's Advice to his Sons, *of living
together in one House like Brethren and Friends*, Unity is enjoined.

Pag. Idem, Line 14. The first seven Years the *Sons* carefully
observ'd their Father's *Will.*
i.e. The first Centuries kept pure, and abolish'd Heathenism.

Pag. Idem, Line 25. The three Ladies they fell in Love with,
allude to the Vices of *Covetousness*, *Ambition*, and *Pride.*

The *Idol* mention'd in the 57th. Page is a Description of a
Taylor, the *Goose* the Iron he uses, *Hell* a Hole so call'd, where

he throws his Shreds; *the Creature whose hourly Food is human Gore*, is a *Louse*; the *Yard* and *Needle* two necessary Instruments belonging to the *Idol*.

Pag. 59. The Allusion of "*Religion* to a *Cloak*, *Honesty* to a "Pair of *Shoes* worn out in the Dirt, *Self-Love* a *Surtout*, *Vanity* "a *Shirt*, and *Conscience* a *Pair of Breeches*, which tho' a Cover for "*Lewdness*, as well as *Nastiness*, is easily slipt down for the Service "of both", "is a severe Satyr upon the *Fanaticks*, who have ever "made *Religion* a *Cloak* for all the Villanies committed by them, "despising and treading *real Honesty* under Foot, extolling the "divine Vertues of *Self-Love* and Vanity, and always making their Consciences subservient to their Interest.

Pag. 60. This and the next Page is a merry Banter upon those Gentlemen, *who reduce all Points of Gentility to this one of dressing nicely*, as is prov'd in the 62ᵈ. Page.

Pag. 63. The Allusion to *Shoulder-Knots* is to ridicule Innovations; and shews, That *the Plainness of Religion was corrupted by forming it so, as to comply with the Humours of the three Mistresses before mention'd; the Principles of Religion being too strict for the Modish* (as is prov'd *Pag*. 64.) *which are therefore stretch'd by degrees to give more Liberty.*

Pag. 65. Points out *The Distinctions of the School-Men, the first Corrupters of the holy Text, the frivolous nicety of which is here ridicul'd:* Aiming likewise at *The Roman Catholicks false printing of the* Fathers, *and corrupting and counterfeiting ancient Manuscripts, to countenance those Errors they have introduc'd.*

Pag. 66. *Jure Paterno* for *Jure Divino*, more corruption in *Religion*, for which, no warrant in Scripture; alluding to the introducing of *Gold Lace* after *Shoulder-Knots*.

Pag. 67. *Tradition* expos'd, a Point much rely'd on by the Roman Catholicks; also *Processions*, and such vain Pomp.

By Flame-colour'd Satin, in *Page* 68. is meant the *Fire of Purgatory*; and that Custom which hath arisen from it, of praying for *the Dead*, set forth as the *Lining*, because it is a very material Point, of which there is no warrant in Scripture. A mention of *Fire* by St. *Peter*, which is therefore laid hold on as an Argument, tho' nothing to the Purpose. Therefore *they* have added the *Apocrypha* to the *Scripture*, which expressly mentions and commends praying for the Dead, and making Offerings for them, as in *Maccab.* Chap. 12. Ver. 43, 44, 45.

Pag. 69. 'Tis the Prohibition of *Idolatry*, which so very positive is evaded by the *Romanists* frivolous Distinction of λατρεια and δουλεια, which is here ridicul'd by distorting the Word *Fringe.*

Pag. 70. The Word *Fringe* again is used to signify any thing quite different; as it is likewise in this *Page* made to signifie a *Broomstick*; under which Figure is couch'd, *Their* abusing the Distinctions of a literate and figurative Sense: *Their* commanding an *implicit Faith*, and the Authority of God's Commands lessen'd to increase the *Church's* Power.

Pag. 71. By the *Embroidery* of *Indian Figures*, *Image*-Worship is forbidden, but the Command evaded by Distinctions, in particular by denying *Theirs* to be that sort of *Worship* which was forbid the *Jews. The Son's locking up their Father's Will in a strong Box*, brought out of *Greece* and *Italy*, is meant of *Their Prohibition* of the Laity's reading the *Scriptures*, and using the Service of the Church in *Greek* and *Latin*, that it may not be understood by the common People.

The Mode of wearing an infinite number of *Poynts* most of 'em *tagg'd with Silver*, alludes to those several *Points* commanded merely by the Power of the Church, as doing Penance, &c. In the same Page, *ex Cathedra*, is the *Pope's* infallible Chair. *Paterno Divino* for *Jure Divino* as before; *The Power the Sons claim'd of adding Clauses to their Father's* Will, *shews the Power the Church of* Rome *claims in modelling Religion* according to the Times.

Pag. 73. The Lord here mention'd, is, *The* German *Emperor. The Deed of Conveyance* alludes to the *Pope's* setting up for a *temporal Sovereign* independent of the *Empire.*

Pag. 74. Sect. III.
A Digression concerning Criticks. By J. S.

Pag. 92. Sect. IV.

A Continuation of the *Tale.* This Section is begun with an

Allusion to the *Pope*'s setting up for the Supremacy, taking to himself the Title of *Papa & Dominus Dominorum*, and finding ways and means to raise a *Fund* for supporting his Grandure.

The middle of this *Page* mimicks the common Vanity of *Authors* in extolling their own Works.

In *Pag.* 94. Is ridicul'd, The imaginary Place between Heaven and Hell, which the *Pope* has sold to many Purchasers. *The Remedy for the Worms* is the Application of *Relicts* for Physical Cures.

Pag. 95. By the *whispering Office* is meant auricular Confession; and likewise alluding to *whispering Places*, such as the Hole in the Cathedral Church of *Gloucester*.

Pag. 96. *By Lord* Peter's *Office of Ensurance*, are meant such Indulgences as were to free the Sinner from *Purgatory*, sending him immediately to Heaven.

Lord *Peter* was *also held the original Author of Puppets and Raree-Shows*, &c.

This Paragraph relates to Images of Saints, that seem to perform the Actions of Life, such as the *Kentish* Idol at *Boxly Abby*, that moved by secret Wires, as Puppets do.

By Lord *Peter*'s Pickle is meant, *The holy Water* us'd by the *Papists* to consecretate Churches and Bells, to wash away Sin, to clear a House from Infection, to drive away evil Spirits, Witches, &c. from those who are haunted.

Pag. 97. The last Paragraph, Lord *Peter*'s sett of *Bulls*, wittily ridicules *Popish Bulls*, being not so effectual as the Absolution of the *Primitive Christians*, because corrupted by Partiality, and to be purchas'd with Money.

Pag. 98. "Lord *Peter*'s *Bulls* were extremely vitiated by the "rust of time in the *Metal* of their Feet, which was now sunk into "common *Lead*; (*this alludes to the* Leaden Seal.) However, the "terrible *roaring*, peculiar to their Lineage, was preserv'd; *i.e.* "The highest Excommunication of *Anathema Maranatha*, "which however some do not value.

Pag. 99. By *naughty Boys*, &c. are meant Refractory and Schismatical Persons, never leaving their Quality of thundering out Excommunication, till brib'd off with Gold.

Pag. 101. The Form of the Pope's General Pardon expos'd, concluding thus,

Your most humble,
Man's Man
EMPEROR PETER.

i.e. Servus Servorum Dei, being the words us'd at the Conclusion of a Pardon granted by the *Pope.*

Pag. 103. Exposes the Insolent Titles the *Pope* assumes to himself; the *Triple Mitre,* his mimicking St. *Peter,* and offering his Toe to kiss.

Pag. 104. His divorcing the married Priests and allowing them Concubines, Lord *Peter's* nailing up the Cellar Door, and not allowing his Brothers a Drop of Drink to their Victuals, *i.e.* Taking the Cup from the Laity, a Representation of the Absurdities of *Transubstantiation;* which Doctrine the *Pope* will not suffer to be so much as once Disputed.

Pag. 108. The *Rupture* mention'd, hints at the *Reformation,* which will be more largely treated on in the next Section.

Lord *Peter's* Faculty of Lying, alludes to the Positiveness and Impostures of the *Church of Rome,* "One time he swore, he had a "*Cow* at home, which gave as much Milk at a Meal, as would fill "Three Thousand Churches; and what was yet more extra- "ordinary, would never turn sower, *i.e.* meaning, *The Virgin* "Mary's *Milk which is pretended to be shewn in so many Places, by* "*the Papists.* "Another time, he was telling of an old *Sign-post* "that belong'd to his *Father,* with Nails and Timber enough in it "to build sixteen large Men of War, *i.e. The many Relicks which are shewn, as the Nails, and Part of the Wood of our Saviour's Cross.*

Pag. 109. Talking one Day of *Chinese* Waggons, which were made so light as to sail over Mountains: "Z—nds says *Peter,* "where's the Wonder of that? By G—, I saw a large House of "Lime and Stone travel over Sea and Land (granting that it stopt "sometimes to bait) above two Thousand *German* Leagues, *i.e. The Temple of* Loretto *carried thither by Angels, as pretended, which Legends whosoever will not believe must be Excommunicated.*

In short *Peter* grew so scandalous, that all the Neighbourhood began in plain words to say, "he was no better than a Knave, *i.e.*

expressing, *The Roman Church so full of Tricks, that at length it grows scandalous, upon which the Reformers desire the Liberty of Reformation according to Scripture,* (as hinted by Lord *Peter*'s two Brothers desiring a Copy of their Father's Will) *that is denied them, upon which they translate the Scriptures into their natural Language* (as hinted by Lord *Peter*'s two Brothers taking a true Copy of their Father's Will) *restored the Cup to the Laity,* (*as hinted by breaking open the Cellar Door to get a little good Drink to comfort and spirit their Hearts.*) *Marriage to the Priests,* (as hinted by the Precept they found in the *Will* against Whoring) *and rejecting Indulgences, advise Sinners to apply to God,* (as hinted by the Solicitor's petitioning Lord *Peter* for a Thief's Pardon) *upon which the Pope employs the Civil Powers against them,* (as hinted by Lord *Peter*'s Dragoons.)

Pag. 112. Sect. V.
A Digression in the Modern kind. By J. S.

Pag. 123. Sect. VI.

The *Tale* continued.

Pag. 124. The two Exiles (Lord *Peter*'s Brothers) so nearly united in Fortune and Interest, took a Lodging together *&c. i.e. The Reformers agree one with another at First. Pag.* 125. *Martin* and *Jack, i.e. Martin Luther* and *John Calvin.*

Pag. 126. Lord *Peter*'s Instructions to his Brothers "to wear "on their Coats whatever Trimmings came up in Fashion; never "pulling off any *&c.* alludes to *the Romish Ceremonies multiplying so fast that there was little left of Religion besides the Form.*

Pag. 127. *Poynts* tagg'd with Silver, *i.e. Such as brought in Gain.* The *Handful of Poynts which* Martin *pull'd off* the Coat at one twitch, allude to *those Ordinances of the Church which* Luther *abolish'd:* The ten Dozen Yards of *Fringe* tore off at the second Pull, *i.e. The abolishing of Image Worship.* The pulling the *Poynts* and *Fringe* off the Coats, alludes to *The Reformers leaving off the Ceremonies too hastily, which had like to have deform'd Religion.* The Coat very narrowly escap'd a swinging Rent by pulling off those *Poynts* tagg'd with Silver, *i.e. Those Ceremonies that brought in Gain were so firmly interwoven and so artificially inserted, that the Reformers found some Difficulty to abolish them: Therefore*

Luther (as hinted by the judicious Workman) *used Caution in Reforming even the useless Ceremonies* (and then fell about the embroider'd *Indian* Figures,) *i.e. Image Worship.*

Pag. 129. An Allusion to *Calvin*'s Proceedings, *viz.* Calvin *under whom the other Reformers are comprehended goes on more violently, acting with more Spite than Discretion in their Reforming; Throwing off at once all the Ceremonies of the ancient Church, not so much considering what they were in their own Nature, as rejecting 'em merely out of Indignation to the* Romanists, *in which* Martin *acts more considerately than the other,* as is shewn in the two following *Pages.*

Pag. 133. The Description given in this Page imports that, *The Whims of* Calvinistical *Zeal do in some things look very like the* Superstition *of the* Roman Catholicks.

Pag. 136. Sect. VII.
A *Digression* in Praise of *Digressions.* By *J. S.*

Pag. 146. Sect. VIII.
The *Tale* continued.

Pag. 148. *Inspiration* being grosly abus'd by the Ignorance of the illiterate *Fanatick,* is the *Author*'s Design in this Place to expose.

Pag. 151. "*Almighty North,* an ancient Deity, whom the "Inhabitants of *Megalopolis* in *Greece,* had in highest Reverence. This Passage alludes to the most *Northern* Parts of *Scotland,* from which *Region* the most rigid *Fanaticks* come; the Words *Gasp* and *Pant* in the last Line of this *Page,* are canting Words in common use among the *Fanaticks.*

Pag. 152. The Original of *Tub* Preaching describ'd. The *Funnel* mention'd, alludes to the way by which the *Priestess* of *Delphos* us'd her *Inspiration.*

Pag. 153. This *Page* paints some of the Sectaries in their odd Gestures at their Meetings.

Pag. 154. A farther Description of the manner by which the *Priestess* of *Delphos* us'd her *Inspiration,* the *Quakers* are alluded to in this Place.

Pag. 156. The *Camelion* mention'd in this Place, *i.e.* The Priest who denies *Inspiration*.

The Infidel who argues against such a Thing as a Deity from his shuffling and Turning every way that will make for his Argument is here (also) represented by *Moulinavent*.

Pag. 157. "The *Laplanders* mention'd for buying and selling "of Air, &c. An Allusion from the *Devil*'s being stil'd *The Prince of the Power of the Air*.

"The *Laplanders* again mention'd in the same *Page* for selling "their *Winds* either by Wholesale or Retail to their Customers; alludes to *those who are so weak as to give Credit to the Legends of the* Romish *Priests*.

In the middle of this *Page* the Question is put, *Whether Inspiration was originally from the* Fanaticks, *or borrow'd from the Heathens*. But tho' the Question is not absolutely determin'd, the Paragraph concludes thus, "This I may affirm, that *Jack*, "(*i.e. Calvin*) gave it at least a new Turn, and form'd it in the "same Dress and Model, as it lyes deduc'd by me.

Pag. 159. Sect. IX.

A Digression concerning the original Use and Improvement of *Madness* in a Commonwealth. By *J. S.*

Pag. 161. Two famous Instances of *Madness*.

I. "A certain great *Prince rais'd a mighty Army, fill'd his "Coffers with infinite Treasures, provided an invincible Fleet; "and all this, without giving the least part of his Design to his "greatest Ministers, or his greatest Favourites. Immediately the "whole World was alarm'd; the neighbouring Crowns in tremb- "ling Expectation, toward what Points the Storm would burst. "The small Politicians every where forming profound Conjec- "tures; some believ'd he had laid a Scheme for universal Mon- "archy; others, after much insight, determin'd the Matter to be a "Project for pulling down the *Pope*, and setting up the *reform'd* "Religion, which had once been his own. Some again, of a deeper "Sagacity, sent him into *Asia* to subdue the *Turk*, and recover "*Palestine*. In the midst of all these Projects and Preparations, a "certain *State-Surgeon* gathering the Nature of the Disease, by

* *Henry* IV. of *France* in Love, &c.

"these Symptoms, attempted the Cure, at one blow perform'd the
"Operation, broke the Bag, and out flew the *Vapour*. Nor did
"any thing want to render it a compleat Remedy, only, that the
"Prince unfortunately happen'd to die in the Performance.
————*Cunnus teterrimi Belli*
Causa.————

II. "The other Instance is what I have read somewhere, in a
"very ancient Author, of a *mighty King, who for the space of
"above thirty Years, amus'd himself to take and lose Towns, beat
"Armies, and be beaten; drive Princes out of their Dominions;
"fright Children from their Bread and Butter; burn, lay waste,
"plunder, dragoon, massacre Subject and Stranger, Friend and
"Foe, Male and Female. 'Tis recorded, that the Philosophers of
"each Country were in grave Dispute, upon Causes Natural,
"Moral, and Political, to find out where they should assign an
"original Solution of this *Phænomenon*. At last the *Vapour* or
"*Spirit*, which animated the Hero's Brain, being in perpetual
"Circulation, seiz'd upon that Region of human Body, so re-
"nowned for furnishing the *Zibeta Occidentalis*, and gathering
"there into a *Tumor*, left the rest to the World, for that time in
"Peace.

"Of such mighty Consequence it is, where these Exhalations
"fix; and of so little, from whence they proceed. The same Spirits,
"which in their superiour Progress would conquer a Kingdom,
"descending upon the *Anus*, conclude in a *Fistula*.

Pag. 177. The Persons here mention'd are suppos'd to be Sir
Edward Seymour, Sir *Christopher Musgrave*, Sir *John Bowles*,
and *John How, Esq*;

Pag. 184. Sect. X.
The *Tale* continued.

Pag. 185. A merry Description of *the Self-conceit of the
Scriblers of the Town, and the Humours of Booksellers.*

Pag. 186. A Ridicule upon *Authors*, in their Excuses *for writing, when 'tis commonly for want of Bread.*

Pag. 187. The writing of *second Parts* of Books merrily expos'd; a common way with the Hackney Authors, when a Piece

* *Lewis* XIV. of *France*.

takes, to write a second Part in Imitation. *O imitatores servum pecus.* A late Instance of which "Madam *Manley* has furnish'd us "with, in a *second* and *third* Part of her *Memoirs from the New* "Atalantis; but how successfully, I shall leave to the Opinion of the wide World; which if favourable and pleasing to her, I am apt to believe that a Lady of her obliging Complacency, and being qualifyed with the *Pen of a ready Writer*, will for the farther obliging of so august an Assembly, endeavour to let us see some other of her polite Productions, and masterly Stroaks in *Characterizing* so far as to vie with the voluminous *Greshamites*, even in the Choice of nice Subjects and new *Phænomena*, and at last end her most useful *Female* Labours (being particularly adapted to that part of the Globe) with an Essay towards compleating the *Character* of a *Character*.

Pag. 191. A Jeer upon those who ascribe a particular Power to odd Numbers, as 3, 9, *&c.* Toward the bottom of this *Page*, and part of the next, is a jocose Banter of Chymistry, by *Eugenius Philalethes*; about which the Author of this spent many Hours to little purpose.

☞ The Fragment concerning *Enthusiasm* was intended to be brought in hereabouts.

Pag. 196. —— Whose converting Imaginations dispose 'em "to reduce all things into *Types*; who can make *Shadows*, no "thanks to the Sun; and then mold 'em into Substances, no thanks "to Philosophy; whose peculiar Talent lies in fixing Tropes and "Allegories to the Letter, and refining what is *literal*, into Figure "and Mystery.
This Passage plainly describes the common Practice of the Fanaticks in perverting the Scripture.

"*Jack* (*i.e.* Calvin) had provided a fair Copy of his Father's "*Will*, engrossed in Form upon a large Skin of Parchment, and "resolving to act the part of a most dutiful Son, he became the "fondest Creature of it imaginable. For altho', as I have often told "the Reader, it consisted wholly in certain plain easie Directions "about the Management and wearing of their Coats, with "Legacies and Penalties, in Case of Obedience or Neglect. Yet

"he began to entertain a Fancy, that the Matter was *deeper* and
"*darker*, and therefore must needs have a great deal more of
"Mystery at the bottom. *Gentlemen*, said he, *I will prove this very*
"*Skin of Parchment to be Meat, Drink, and Cloth, to be the Philo-*
"*sopher's Stone, and the universal Medicine.*

This Passage shows *their* Affectation in bringing in the *Phrase*,
and Expressions of Scripture into the most trivial Concerns; and
pretending that nothing is lawful which is not expressly commanded, altho' it be of no Consequence, and in its own Nature
ever so indifferent, which is the import of this and the next *Page*.

Pag. 199, 200, and 201. *Predestination* set in its true Light, by a
Burlesque Description of it, in the Story of *Jack*'s Nose and the Post.

Pag. 232. "When *Jack* had some roguish Trick to play, he
"would down with his Knees, up with his Eyes, and fall to
"Prayers, tho' in the midst of the Kennel. Then it was, that those
"who understood his Pranks, would be sure to get far enough out
"of his way; and whenever Curiosity attracted Strangers to laugh,
"or to listen, he would of a sudden, with one Hand, out with his
"*Gear* and piss full in their Eyes, and with the other all to be-
"spatter them with Mud.

This Paragraph is a just Satyr, upon the *Fanaticks* Custom of
introducing the Scripture, when they are dealing with any
Person for the Commodities they are about to sell, ever and anon
larding their Discourse with a *Text* of Scripture, or those old
proverbial Scraps and *Sayings*, of *Let us do as we would be done
unto*, this is the *Golden Rule*, for *Honesty is the best Policy*, and will
carry a Man through the World. These indeed are the *Rules*
that every Man ought to walk by, but when mention'd by them
are not the least in their Thoughts, but only used as *mere Cant*,
to blind the Person from discovering the Cheat they intend to
put upon him, and when found out by any Person, he is not only
calumniated and abus'd by them, but an Opportunity watch'd
to do him some secret Prejudice, either in his Business or
Reputation.

The remaining part of this *Section*, and the *Fragment*, sets
their other Hypocrisies in a true Light; as their affected Tones,
and irreverent and noisy manner of preaching; (by which they

would insinuate a more than ordinary Earnestness;) the Inconveniences they run themselves into, and then pretend to suffer such Misfortunes for the Good of the Publick. In short, a complete Character of 'em is so truly drawn, and all their Evasions, Shiftings, and Villanies so clearly detected, that a Man of sincere Principles can pronounce no less a Sentence upon 'em than *Solomon* did against *Lying Lips,* That such Practices are *an Abomination to the Lord.*

A N
EXAMINATION
O F
Mr. *WOTTON*'s
OBSERVATIONS
Upon the TALE, *&c.*

MR. *Wotton* having been mention'd in the Advertisement to the Reader, it will not be improper in this Place, to produce a Copy of his Charge exhibited against the *Authors* of the *Tale, &c.* Upon Examination of which with these *Notes*, and the *Book* it self will be plainly seen, how far fetch'd, and groundless those Reasons are, by which he endeavours to maintain the *Aspersion* he has given out.

In the last Edition of his *Reflections upon Learning, Pag.* 520. He positively declares in one Word, "That 'tis a design'd Banter "upon all that is esteem'd sacred among Men; and that God and "Religion, Truth and moral Honesty, *Learning and Industry are made a *May-Game.*

To support which Charge he brings the following Reasons.

1. *The Coats given to* Peter, Martin, *and* Jack, *were to last 'em fresh and sound as long as they liv'd:* By this he says, *Pag.* 521. "The Garments of the *Israelites* are expos'd, which by the miracu- "lous Power of God waxed not old, nor were worn out for †40 "Years together in the Wilderness.

* Alluding to his own Book.

† The Coats were to last the three Sons as long as they liv'd, which might probably be to *David*'s Period of *Threescore* Years and *Ten*; whereas the Garments of the *Israelites* according to his own Computa- tion lasted but 40 Years; upon which 'tis presum'd the *Ground* for this Conjecture is not very strong.

2. "The *Number of these Sons born thus at one Birth, look
"asquint upon the *Trinity*, and one of the Books in the Catalogue
"fronting the Title, is a Panegyrick upon the Number *Three*,
"which Word is the only one that is put in Capitals in that whole
"*Page*.

The next Article against the *Tale* Teller is bearing so hard
upon the *Fanaticks*, and proving that they make no other use of
Religion but for Self-Interest; nay his Charity is equally exten-
sive to *Jews*, *Turks*, *Infidels*, *Heathens* and *Hereticks*, insomuch
that he thinks it an offence to expose in a *ludicrous manner* even
the Errors of the *Romanists*, but the greatest Difficulty he meets
with, is the Intricacy of the Author of the *Tale*; who, in the
Description of the †*Cloth of which the Coats were made*, he says,
has a farther *Meaning* than the Words may seem to import;
which if so, must be no small Mortification to a Man of Mr.
Wotton's Learning and Industry to think, that the *meaning* of
any Passage should be so far hid, as that he cannot be able to tell
what it really *means*.

He likewise thinks the *Author* guilty of a very heinous and
unpardonable Crime, in falling upon *Jack*, and dealing so freely
with the *sanctified Principles of* Geneva, as he has done through
his whole Tale, in comparing the Agreement between ‡Jack'*s
Nose and the Post* to *Predestination*, and by his Admiration and
love of ‖ a Musical *Bag-Pipe* to ridicule the Aversion which the
Protestant Dissenters have for the use of Church-*Music*.

Having thus shewn his Compassion for the erronious Doctrines of the Church of *Rome*, and asserted the Cause of the well-
meaning conscientious *Fanatick*, he concludes his Observations
with a *sparring* Blow upon the *Tale-Teller*; in behalf of whom,
the most that can be offer'd is the Opinion of a late eminent

---

* Three Children at a Birth, is such a *supernatural* Prodigy as perhaps Mr. *Wotton* has never heard or read of: I must own 'twas a little
unlucky that the Printer us'd his Capitals in the Word *Three* to make
the Essay upon that Number the more remarkable; but I am glad he
did not set it in a *Black* Letter which would have look'd much
Darker, and certainly have amounted to a plain Proof with a Man of
Mr. *Wotton*'s known *Erudition*.

† *Vid. Pag.* 63.   ‡ *Pag.* 198.   ‖ *Pag.* 203.

Author. But whether that will be allow'd as sufficient, in Mr. *Wotton*'s Esteem, I dare not take upon me to determine.

The Accusation is this, "Before I leave this Author, (says he) "be he who will, I shall observe that his *Wit is not his own*, in "many Places; and that his Banter of *Transubstantiation* is taken "from the Duke of *Buckingham's Conference with an* Irish *Priest*; "the Duke bantering that Doctrine by changing a *Cock* into a "*Horse*, which he has done by turning *Bread into *Mutton*, "*Wine*, &c. and that the *Battle of the Books* is taken *mutatis* "*mutandis* out of a *French* Book, entitul'd, *Combat des Livres*.

Now taking this Accusation for granted, the Earl of *Roscommon* has laid it down as an establish'd Maxim:

> *That by improving what was wrote before,*
> *Invention labours less, but Judgment more.*

Having gone through all I intended, in relation to Mr. *Wotton*'s Charge against the *Tale-Teller*, I cannot conclude without owning, that I think him and his Friend Dr. *Bentley*, are highly to be commended upon Account of their prudent Behaviour, as to that part of the Book which more immediately related to them, *viz.*

Mr. *Wotton* fairly owns to his Friend Mr. *Hammond*, to whom his Observations upon the *Tale are* address'd, "That as to what "concern'd them, they ought to sit down quietly under it, leaving "their Cause very willingly to the Publick, not being able to "undertake a Defence of it.

Thus from what has been said, and hoping it will appear that the *Authors* of the *Tale* had no other Design than to vindicate the Church of *England*, expose the Errors of the *Romanists*, and the Hypocrisie of the *Fanaticks*, I shall end all in Mr. *Wotton*'s own Words, "That by falling upon the ridiculous Inventions of "Popery, by which the Church of *Rome* intended to gull supersti-"tious People, and to rook 'em of their Money; that the World "had been but too long in Slavery; that our Ancestors gloriously "redeem'd us from that Yoak, that the Church of *Rome* therefore "ought to be expos'd (as well as the *Vizor* of the *Fanatick* pull'd "off) and that the Author of such a Work deserves well of "Mankind.

* *Pag.* 37. Of the *Tale.*

Mr. Wotton's *Remarks upon the Quotation out of* Irenæus *in the Title-Page, which it seems are the Words of a* Form of Redemption, *used some time* ago.

Thus transcrib'd from the *Title*,

BAsima eacabasa eanaa irraurista, diarba da caeotaba fobor camelanthi. Iren. Lib. I. C. 18.

A *various* Reading of it,
Basima eaca basa ea naa irraurista, diarbada caeotaba fobor camelanthi.

So it is in the old Editions of *Irenæus*, thus interpreted by him.

Hoc quod est super omnem virtutem Patris invoco, quod vocatur Lumen & Spiritus & Vita, quoniam in Corpore regnâsti, i.e.

I call upon this, which is above all the Power of the Father, which is called Light, and Spirit, and Life, because thou hast reigned in the Body.

"The *Greek* Words which were faulty as first, made the *Latin* "ones yet more so; it is probable that *Irenæus might not under- "stand 'em right at first. They are *Syriac*, and in the very learned "Mr. (now Dr.) *Grabe*'s Edition of *Irenæus*, they are very in- "geniously restor'd out of *Jacobus Rhenferdius* (*i.e.* James Rhen- "ford's) *Dissertation upon the Redemption of the* Marcosians *and* "Heracleonites.

* *Irenæus* corrected by Mr. *Wotton*: O! *the depth of Modern Learning.*

FINIS.

ERRATA.

P. 3. l. 26. for *acquainted,* read *unacquainted.* P. 19. l. 2. for *old* read *odd.*[1]

[1] The Errata are incorporated in this reprint. In Curll's private copy they are struck out and in- serted in ink in the text. The other manuscript marks or corrections in his copy are few and negligible.

LETTERS OF
SWIFT and *TOOKE*
RELATING TO
THE FIFTH EDITION OF
A TALE OF A TUB.[1]

Swift to Benjamin Tooke.

Dublin, June 29, 1710.

Sir,

I was in the country when I received your letter with the
Apology inclosed in it; and I had neither health nor humour to
finish that business. But the blame rests with you, that if you
thought it time, you did not print it when you had it. I have just
now your last, with the complete Key. I believe it is so perfect
a Grubstreet piece, it will be forgotten in a week. But it is
strange that there can be no satisfaction against a bookseller for
publishing names in so bold a manner. I wish some lawyer could
advise you how I might have satisfaction: for at this rate, there
is no book, however vile, which may not be fastened on me. I
cannot but think that little Parson-cousin of mine is at the bottom
of this; for, having lent him a copy of some part of, &c. and he
shewing it, after I was gone for Ireland, and the thing abroad,
he affected to talk suspiciously, as if he had some share in it. If he
should happen to be in town, and you light on him, I think you
ought to tell him gravely, 'That, if he be the author, he should
set his name to the &c.' and railly him a little upon it: and tell
him, 'if he can explain some things, you will, if he pleases, set his
name to the next edition.' I should be glad to see how far the
foolish impudence of a dunce could go. Well; I will send you the
thing, now I am in town, as soon as possible. But, I dare say, you
have neither printed the rest, nor finished the cuts; only are glad
to lay the fault on me. I shall, at the end, take a little contemp-

---

[1] These two letters were first printed by Deane Swift in 1765. The
manuscripts are lost.

tible notice of the thing you sent me; and I dare say it will do you more good than hurt. If you are in such haste, how came you to forget the Miscellanies? I would not have you think of Steele for a publisher;[1] he is too busy. I will, one of these days, send you some hints, which I would have in a preface, and you may get some friend to dress them up. I have thoughts of some other work one of these years: and I hope to see you ere it be long; since it is likely to be a new world, and since I have the merit of suffering by not complying with the old. Yours, &c.

BENJAMIN TOOKE TO SWIFT.

Sir,   London, July 10, 1710.

Inclosed I have sent the Key, and think it would be much more proper to add the notes at the bottom of the respective pages they refer to, than printing them at the end by themselves. As to the cuts, Sir Andrew Fountain has had them from the time they were designed, with an intent of altering them. But he is now gone into Norfolk, and will not return till Michaelmas; so that, I think, they must be laid aside; for, unless they are very well done, it is better they were quite let alone. As to the Apology, I was not so careless but that I took a copy of it before I sent it to you; so that I could have printed it easily, but that you sent me word not to go on till you had altered something in it. As to that cousin of yours which you speak of, I neither know him, nor ever heard of him till the Key mentioned him. It was very indifferent to me which I proceeded on first, the Tale, or the Miscellanies: but, when you went away, you told me there were three or four things should be sent over out of Ireland, which you had not here; which, I think is a very reasonable excuse for myself in all these affairs. What I beg of you at present is, that you would return the Apology and this Key, with directions as to the placing it: although I am entirely of opinion to put it at the bottom of each page; yet shall submit. If this be not done soon, I cannot promise but some rascal or other will do it for us both; since you see the liberty that is already taken. I think too much time has already been lost in the Miscellanies; therefore hasten that: and which-ever is in the most forwardness, I would begin on first. All here depend on an entire alteration. I am, &c.

[1] See footnote, p. 17.

NOTES ON
Treatises by the same Author

OF these eleven Treatises mentioned on p. 2, the first eight are named or referred to in the *Tale of a Tub* (pp. 38, 53, 54, 57, 67, 123, 137, 202) and the last in the *Mechanical Operation* (p. 279).

There remain *A Description of the Kingdom of Absurdities*, and *A Voyage into England, by a Person of Quality in Terra Australis incognita, translated from the Original*, to neither of which is there any direct allusion.

On the *Kingdom of Absurdities* John Nichols gave the following note in his edition of Swift's Works, 1808, vol. ii, p. 201:

As a part of this description, the following sketches are copied from Swift's own hand-writing: 'In the Kingdom of Absurdities. The bells of glass, with iron clappers. The houses of gun-powder; and as they are apt to get drunk, they leave candles lighting, so that they have fires very frequently. The children always die there before their parents. There is a sort of flying insect in their jakes, which has cruel teeth, and is fond of human testicles; so that when a man goes there upon his occasions, it is forty to one but he comes away without them. Nothing is so easy as to destroy those animals; and yet ask the reason, why they do it not? they say, It was their ancestors custom of old.

Nichols does not say who owned the manuscript, or where he saw it, and nothing more appears to be now known about it. But its authenticity may be accepted. Dr. John Lyon, in a note in his edition of Hawkesworth's *Life of Swift* (now preserved in the Forster Collection at South Kensington), says that 'He [Swift] wrote also an Account of the Kingdom of Absurditys at the same time, as appears from some sketches of it in his own hand'.

Of the *Voyage into England, by a Person of Quality in Terra Australis incognita* nothing further is known, but that Swift had such a work in his mind at this time is proved by a passage in his *Journal to Stella*, 28 April 1711:

The *Spectator* is written by Steele, with Addison's help: 'tis often very pretty. Yesterday it was made of a noble hint I gave him long ago for his *Tatlers*, about an Indian supposed to write his travels into England. I repent he ever had it. I intended to have written a book on that subject. I believe he has spent it all in one paper, and all the under-hints there are mine too.

The *Spectator* in question (No. 50, 27 April 1711), which is by Addison, purports to give in translation the substance of papers left behind by one of the four Indian kings who visited this country in 1710 and had provided Steele with matter for a *Tatler* (No. 171, 13 May 1710).

It is important to note that we have Swift's definite statement in 1711 that he 'intended to have written a book on that subject', and that the title of the book was made public as early as 1704. He did not carry out his Project, and it was left to Montesquieu in his *Lettres Persanes* (1721) and to Goldsmith in his *Citizen of the World* (1762) to win pre-eminence in the employment of a literary setting that Swift had long meditated. His satire ultimately took shape in another and a greater form. Instead of an account of England by a native of an undiscovered land he gave us *Gulliver's Travels*.

For allusions to *Terra Australis incognita* see p. 106, p. 125 note 3, and p. 261 note 3. Compare also 'A Project for the universal benefit of Mankind', which was to give 'an exact Description of *Terra Australis incognita*', printed in the *Miscellaneous Works* of 1720 (pp. 309, 310 of this volume).

NOTES ON
Dark Authors

THE extent to which Swift satirized Mysticism, Cabbalism, Alchemy, and Rosicrucianism may not be suspected. The more important passages are therefore collected here, with occasional explanations, some of which are too long to be given among the notes under the text.

Title-page
'Written for the Universal Improvement of Mankind'.

In this and in the many reference to the 'universal' benefits which his treatise will produce, Swift seems to have in mind the *Allgemeine und general Reformation der ganzen weiten Welt*, based on an 'advertisement' in Boccalini's *Ragguagli di Parnaso*, and printed together with the *Fama Fraternitatis* (1614), the first of the Rosicrucian manifestoes. See A. E. Waite, *The Real History of the Rosicrucians*, 1887, chaps. ii and iii.

'Basima eacabasa.' &c.

See note, p. 187. For Wotton's note see Appendix B, p. 323; also Appendix C, p. 348. For the restoration referred to by Wotton see the edition by Grabe, 1702, p. 90.

The following note appears in Nichols's edition of Swift's works (1808), vol. ii, p. 164: 'The words are taken from the first book of Irenæus against the Pagans; where he says that the followers of the Heretic Marcus hid their mysteries under these Greek letters, but that the words were Hebrew; of which he gives the following interpretation: "Hoc quod est super omnem virtutem Patris invoco, quod vocatur Lumen & Spiritus & Vita, quoniam in corpore regnâsti." Feuardentius, the commentator on Irenæus, says, that these are monstrous and barbarous words, and neither Hebrew, Greek, Chaldee, Syriac, or Arabic. In several antient jaspers, agates, and onyxes, we meet with these and such like extravagant words and figures, altogether as preposterous. See Chifflet's Abraxas &c.—This note is copied from one by Mr. Pate, whom Swift styles "the learned woollen draper;" and who had this and a few others, which will be found distinguished by his name, from the Dean's own mouth. N.'

Apology

'Four *being much more Cabalistick*', &c. (p. 8).

The virtues of the number Four are described in John Heydon's *The Rosie Crucian Infallible Axiomata* (1660), chap. iv, 'Of the signification of the Number 4', pp. 24–34.

In Cabbalistic literature this number is regarded as especially sacred because the Tetragrammaton, i.e. the quadriliteral name of God, contains four letters.

See note on *Cabbalist*, section V.

Preface

'The *Moderns* have artfully fixed this *Mercury*' (p. 43). See p. 43, note 6.

Introduction

'The next is Dr. *Faustus*, penn'd by *Artephius* . . . *Male* and *Female Dragon*' (p. 68).

Artephius was 'always regarded by the alchemists as one of the masters. By virtue of the elixir he is reputed to have lived a thousand and twenty-five years.' The *Clavis Majoris Sapientiae* was first printed at Paris in 1609. *The Liber Secretus* was translated into English and printed at London in 1624. See *Bibliotheca Chemica*, ed. John Ferguson, 1906, vol. i, p. 51.

Adeptus, the technical term for one who has succeeded in converting one of the baser metals into gold, and thus *has attained* the great secret.

Reincrudation, or 'Reduction'. 'This is the retrogradation of a substance which has reached a certain degree of perfection to a degree of a lower order. The reduction of metals into their first matter is their philosophic, not the vulgar, retrogradation into their proper seed, that is to say, into a Hermetic Mercury. It is also called reincrudation, and is performed by the dissolution of the fixed by its proper volatile, from which it has been made.' A. E. Waite, 'A Short Lexicon of Alchemy' in *The Hermetic and Alchemical Writings of Aureolus Philippus Theophrastus Bombast, called Paracelsus the Great*, 1894, vol. ii, p. 378.

Via humida. See, for example, 'The Humid Path, or Discourse on the Vegetable Menstruum of Saturn' in *The Alchemical Writings of Edward Kelly,* translated from the Hamburg edition of 1676 by A. E. Waite, 1893, pp. 55 ff.

The Male and Female Dragon, 'sulphur' and 'mercury', as understood by the alchemists: see the illustration in Abraham Eleazar's *Donum Dei,* reproduced in James Campbell Brown's *History of Chemistry,* p. 161. The alchemists derived many of their principles from analogies between living and dead matter; and some of their theories and technical terms are based upon sexual phenomena: see the article by H. S. Redgrove in the *Journal of the Alchemical Society,* vol. iii, pt. 18.

'Whittington and his Cat, is the work of that mysterious *Rabbi, Jehuda Hannasi,*' &c. (p. 68).

The *Rabbi* Judah Hannāsi is the most distinguished of the Tannāim ('Repeaters'), the Jewish scholars of the first two centuries A.D. who busied themselves in the codification of the previously unwritten Law. This Supplementary Law is the Mishna (repetition); and its completion was the achievement of Judah Hannāsi. The Gemara (Aramaic 'geᵐmar', 'to complete') is a rambling sort of commentary in Aramaic on the Hebrew Mishna. It came from the successors of the Tannāim, known as the Amorāim ('speakers'). The Mishna and the Gemara together form the Talmud ('Doctrine'). There is a Palestinian Talmud (*c.* fourth century) and a Babylonian (*c.* sixth century). They differ in the Gemara, but the Mishna is common to both.

Section IV

'I desire of those whom the *Learned* among Posterity will appoint for Commentators ... Operation must be divided' (p. 114).

This is a parody of alchemical writings. The authors commonly pretend that they have made their work unintelligible to all except true philosophers.

Section V

'This, *O Universe,* is the Adventurous Attempt of me thy Secretary' (p. 123).

This is Swift's modification of the phrase 'Secretary of Nature', itself suggested by the title γραμματεὺς τῆς φύσεως applied (in

Suidas) to Aristotle. John Heydon styles himself 'a Servant of God, and Secretary of Nature'; see the title-page of *The Rosie Crucian Infallible Axiomata*, 1660.

'You take fair correct Copies', &c. (pp. 126–7).
Compare Samuel Butler, 'An Hermetic Philosopher', *Characters*, ed. A. R. Waller (1908), p. 100: 'For they will undertake to teach any Kind of mysterious Learning in the World by way of Diet; and therefore have admirable Receipts, to make several Dishes for *Talisman*, *Magic*, and *Cabal*, in which Sciences a Man of an ingenious Stomach may eat himself into more Knowledge at a Meal, than he could possibly arrive at by seven Years Study.'

Also Rabelais, *Pantagruel*, v, ch. xlvi: 'Pourtant je ne vous dis: Lisez ce chapitre, entendez ceste glose; je vous dis: Tastez ce chapitre, avallez ceste belle glose. Jadis un antique prophete de la nation Judaïque mangea un livre, et fut clerc jusques aux dents; presentement vous en boirez un, et serez clerc jusques au foye. Tenez, ouvrez les mandibules.' See Ezekiel iii and compare Revelation x. 9.

For parallels see Tylor's *Early History of Mankind*, ed. 1878, p. 126.

'As eminent a *Cabbalist* as his Disciples would represent Him, his Account of the *Opus magnum* is extreamly poor,' &c. (pp. 127–8).

Cabbalist, one acquainted with the *Cabbala*, the secret tradition of mysticism, revealed in the remote past, and preserved orally by the initiated. See 'Cabala' in the 'Dictionariolum Paracelsicum' added to the third volume of the Works of Paracelsus, 1658.

Opus magnum, the technical term for the conversion of the baser metals into gold.

Sendivogius (died 1636 or 1646), alchemist. For a life and full bibliography see *Bibliotheca Chemica*, u.s. vol. ii, pp. 364 ff.

Behmen, i.e. Jacob Boehme (1575–1624), German mystic.

Anthroposophia Theomagica. The full title of Thomas Vaughan's book is 'Anthroposophia | Theomagica: | Or | A Discourse of the Nature of | Man and his state after death; | Grounded on his Creator's Proto- | Chimistry, and verifi'd by a practicall | Examina-

tion of Principles in | the Great World. | By Eugenius Phila-
lethes. | *Dan*: | Many shall run to and fro, and know- | ledge
shall be increased. | *Zoroaster in Oracul.* | Audi Ignis Vocem. |
London, | Printed by T. W. For H. Blunden at the | Castle in
Corn-hill. 1650.' In the same year Vaughan brought out his
Anima Magica Abscondita (see below), and Henry More, the
Platonist, wrote *Observations* on both works under the name
'Alazonomastix Philalethes'. A controversy ensued. Vaughan
replied in *The Man-Mouse Taken in a Trap* (1650), was answered
in *The Second Lash of Alazonomastix* (1651), and rejoined in
The Second Wash (1651). See the *Bibliotheca Chemica*, u.s. vol. ii,
pp. 195 ff., *The Magical Writings of Thomas Vaughan*, ed. A. E.
Waite, 1888, and *Works of Thomas Vaughan*, ed. A. E. Waite,
1919.

From the *Anthroposophia Theomagica* Swift has taken the
name *Sphæra Pyroplastica*. It occurs in Vaughan's recipe for the
universal medicine (ed. 1650, pp. 25–26): 'But in respect I have
proceeded thus far, I will give you a true Receipt of the Medicine.
R c. *Limi Cœlestis partes decem, Separetur Masculus a Fœminâ,
uterque porro à Terrâ suâ, physicè tamen & citra omnem violen-
tiam Separata proportione debitâ, harmonicâ, & vitali conjunge:
statimque Anima descendens a sphærâ pyroplasticâ, mortuum suum,
& relictum Corpus amplexu mirifico restaurabit. Conjuncta foveant-
tur Igne naturali in perfectum matrimonium spiritus, & Corporis.
Procedas Artificio Vulcanico-Magico, quousque exaltentur in Quin-
tam Rotam Metaphysicam. Hæc est Illa, de Quâ tot scribillarunt,
tam Pauci noverunt, Medicina.'*

The following note on *Sphæra Pyroplastica* has been supplied
by Mr. A. E. Waite: 'This term seems to be peculiar to Thomas
Vaughan, or at least I have failed to trace the use of it by other
writers. But it is possible to see how it may have originated in
his mind. Martinus Rulandus, in his *Lexicon Alchemiae*, 1612,
gives *Sphæra Solis*, and says that according to Paracelsus it
means Heaven or Quintessence. Elsewhere Rulandus explains
Quinta Essentia as that which is called usually "the Heaven and
Celestial Substance", and as (*a*) "the flowing down of the ether"
or (*b*) that "ray of the firmament which was flashed through the
soul of the world by the voice of the Creator". Many notions, and
part of the terminology of Paracelsus passed over to Jacob Boehme,

to whom Quintessence signified Eternal Nature. Boehme's Eternal Nature seems to be also his Third Principle and Paradisical Heaven, out of which the material heaven was created. It is a principle of life, but of the lower kind, in comparison with the life of the soul, which comes from the First Principle. If Vaughan's Medicine was an elixir for the physical body, his "pyroplastic sphere" was the Third Principle of Boehme. In the *Forty Questions* Boehme says that the soul of man is a "Fire-Globe", which is about as near as we shall get to *Sphæra Pyroplastica* in earlier writers.'

Vaughan's title-page suggested the Latin sentence which follows. *Audi ignis vocem* is the translation of κλῦθι πυρὸς φωνήν, the conclusion of the so-called *Oracles of Zoroaster*. See *The Chaldaick Oracles of Zoroaster*, ed. Thomas Stanley, 1661, p. 27, or Stanley's *History of Philosophy*, 1687, p. 1075. The phrase is also on the title-page of John Heydon's *Holy Guide*, 1662, Bk. iii.

Section VIII

'That Renowned *Cabbalist*, *Bumbastus*, of placing the Body of Man, in due position to the four *Cardinal* Points' (p. 152).

Swift is here indebted to Sir Thomas Browne, *Vulgar Errors*, Bk. ii, chap. iii: 'This Opinion confirmed would much advance the Microcosmical conceit, and commend the Geography of *Paracelsus*, who according to the Cardinal points of the World divideth the body of man; and therefore working upon humane ordure, and by long preparation rendring it odoriferous, he terms it *Zibeta Occidentalis*, Western *Civet*; making the face the East, but the posteriours the *America* or Western part of his Microcosm'.

Paracelsus believed man to be produced from the four elements, and held that there was a correspondence between these and the cardinal points. Compare Robert Fludd's *Philosophia Moysaica*, 1638, Fol. iii. b: 'tam rationibus Theologicis, quam ex sacris literis collectis sum persuasus, faciem humanam debere naturali postione solis ortui sive plagae orientali adaptari, & tunc ejus posteriora respicient occasum & consequenter manus ejus sinistra indicabit Polum septentrionalem, ut & dextra Meridionalem'.

'*Man* brings with him into the World a peculiar Portion or Grain of *Wind*, which may be called a *Quinta essentia*, extracted from the other four' (p. 152).

See Paracelsus, *Interpretatio Totius Astronomiae* (*opera*, 1658, ii, p. 664 a): 'Quatuor enim Elementa universus mundus sunt: Et ex illis homo constitutus est. In numero ergo Quintus est, hoc est, Quinta Essentia, extra Elementa quatuor, ex quibus ceu nucleus extractus est'. Compare also 'Quintessence' in A. E. Waite's 'Lexicon of Alchemy,' *u.s.*

Section IX

Zibeta Occidentalis (p. 165).
See quotation from Sir Thomas Browne, in notes on Section VIII above; and compare Paracelsus, *opera*, ii, p. 26 a.

Section X

'the *true illuminated*' (p. 186).
See note 1, p. 186.
'if a devout Brother of the *Rosy Cross* will pray fervently for sixty three Mornings . . . *Opus Magnum*' (p. 187).
The Rosicrucians called themselves 'Fratres Roseae Crucis.'
On the number sixty-three, the product of seven and nine and therefore of magical virtue, see Sir Thomas Browne, *Vulgar Errors*, Bk. ii, ch. xii, and compare p. 58, note 1.
'But then he must beware of *Bythus* and *Sigè*, and be sure not to forget the Qualities of *Acamoth*; *A cujus lacrymis humecta prodit Substantia, à risu lucida, à tristitiâ solida, & à timore mobilis*, wherein *Eugenius Philalethes* hath committed an unpardonable Mistake' (p. 187).
Bythus, Sigè, and *Acamoth* are taken from Irenæus's account of the doctrines of Valentinus the Gnostic. The Latin sentence comes from the same source, *Contra Haereses*, 1. iv. 2. *Acamoth* means 'Wisdom' (Hebrew 'hokhma').
The full title of Thomas Vaughan's book is as follows:—
Anima Magica | Abscondita: | Or | A Discourse of the universall | Spirit of Nature, | With his strange, abstruse, miraculous | Ascent, and descent. By Eugenius Philalethes. | *Stapul: in Dion*: | Est autem Universum speculum Unum, | ad Quod astans Amor, suum effor- | mat Idolum. | *Dû a Digon*: *Hêb Dhû, Hêb Dhim.* | London, | Printed by T. W. For H. B. 1650.
See note on Section V above. The renewed satire on Vaughan

has no connexion with what immediately precedes; it is 'nothing but amusement'.

Section XI

'*I will prove this very Skin of Parchment to be . . . the Philosopher's Stone, and the Universal Medicine*' (p. 190).

The chief objects of the Alchemists were to find the Philosopher's Stone, which would transmute base metals into gold, and the Universal Medicine, *elixir vitae*, which would indefinitely prolong life.

'by some called *Babel*, by others, *Chaos*' (p. 194).
See p. 194, note 2.

The Battle of the Books

'*Brutum hominis*' (p. 222).
See p. 222, note 5.

'After you had passed several Courts, you came to the Center . . . Occasions of Prey or Defence' (p. 229).

'*This large Castle (to shew my Improvements in the Mathematicks) is all built with my own Hands*' (p. 231).

Swift may have remembered the following sentence in Vaughan's *Anima Magica Abscondita*, p. 14: 'I would faine know *who taught* the *spider* his *Mathematicks*? how comes he to *lodge* in the *Center* of his *Web*, that he may *sally* upon all *Occasions* to any part of the *Circumference*?'

INDEX

PRINTED IN
GREAT BRITAIN
AT THE
UNIVERSITY PRESS
OXFORD
BY
CHARLES BATEY
PRINTER
TO THE
UNIVERSITY